C

Sudarsana Rao

D1090721

PROCEEDINGS OF A SYMPOSIUM IN APPLIED MATHEMATICS OF THE AMERICAN MATHEMATICAL SOCIETY

Held in New York City
April 30–May 2, 1963

COSPONSORED BY
THE SOCIETY FOR INDUSTRIAL AND APPLIED MATHEMATICS

Richard Bellman
EDITOR

PROCEEDINGS OF
SYMPOSIA IN APPLIED MATHEMATICS

VOLUME XVI

STOCHASTIC PROCESSES IN MATHEMATICAL PHYSICS AND ENGINEERING

AMERICAN MATHEMATICAL SOCIETY
190 HOPE STREET, PROVIDENCE, RHODE ISLAND

1964

Prepared by the American Mathematical Society under Grant No. AF-AFOSR-66-63 with the United States Air Force Office of Scientific Research and Contract No. DA-31-124-ARO(D)-81 with the U.S. Army Research Office (Durham).

Library of Congress Catalog Number 64-18128

Copyright © 1964 by the American Mathematical Society
Printed in the United States of America

All rights reserved except those granted to the United States Government. Otherwise, this book, or parts thereof, may not be reproduced in any form without permission of the publishers.

CONTENTS

INTRODUCTION

In the study of the classification and recognition of mathematical processes, dichotomies can be introduced in several different fashions. Two of the most useful have been "deterministic vs. stochastic" and "descriptive vs. variational." In recent years, we have seen greater and greater emphasis laid upon stochastic and decision processes, and even a blending of the two in the form of modern control theory.

The gradual shift of interest from the classical deterministic descriptive process has been largely a consequence of the continuing challenges to the mathematician to explain phenomena, produce numbers, and guide research in such fields as physics, engineering, economics, biology, medicine and operations research. Combinations of complexity and uncertainty have forced a more frequent use of probabilistic concepts.

In this volume, the emphasis is upon stochastic processes, divided a bit unevenly between descriptive and decision aspects. In dealing with random effects, we can use deterministic or stochastic equations, just as in dealing with deterministic effects we can employ stochastic or deterministic equations or in treating descriptive processes, we can use either descriptive or variational equations. The choice of a particular analytic formulation is a tribute to the existing analytic techniques and the computational resources available, as well as a reflection of the underlying physical process and the prevalent scientific philosophy.

The papers by Adomian, Bharucha-Reid, Hoffman, Keller, Richardson, and Twersky deal with various and overlapping aspects of the general theory of stochastic equations, principally ordinary and partial differential equations. Much of this work is motivated by particular equations arising in wave propagation and scattering theory, as the papers by Hoffman, Keller, and Twersky indicate. The objective of obtaining specific analytic results leads to the development of perturbation techniques and the consideration of questions of closure, as, for example, in Richardson's paper.

The paper by Bellman deals with stochastic iteration, a topic which arises from the consideration of stochastic differential equations in very much the same way as classical iteration theory arises from deterministic differential equations. A particularly important type of stochastic iteration arises in the theory of stochastic approximation. This approach is used by Gray to study a design problem arising from circuits with random components. In their papers, Blackwell and Derman use dynamic programming, the first to obtain estimates in probability theory by identification with a stochastic decision process, and the second to treat an interesting class of sequential decision processes of Markovian type.

Classical estimation and identification problems arising from stochastic processes are treated by Parzen and Root using new and powerful approaches.

Finally, the papers by Montroll, Rota, and Wong consider deterministic equations associated respectively with random walk, turbulence, and diffusion theory.

Looking over the papers in this volume, we see many new, fascinating, and difficult classes of problems, ideal areas for the young analyst to test his talents, develop his techniques, and plant his flag.

RICHARD BELLMAN
Santa Monica, California
1964

STOCHASTIC GREEN'S FUNCTIONS

BY

G. ADOMIAN

1. **Introduction.** The purpose of this paper is a brief introduction to an approach [**1**] to the theory of random equations which appears fruitful. Such equations arise in many connections. Physical constants for equations representing dynamical systems are usually the mean value of a set of experimental observations so in reality are not constants at all but random variables whose values are subject to a probability distribution. Often it may be that the random equation actually is more likely to bring theory and experiment into agreement but the problem has been simplified to avoid the complication of randomness. In many-body problems it may be desirable to consider a stochastic Hamiltonian operator to represent the effects of many other bodies on the body of interest trading the complexity of $3n$ coordinates for 3 coordinates but with randomness in the operator. In wave propagation problems with random media and in optimization problems with complex systems involving random parameters, and in many other connections, such random equations arise. In the work to follow, we intend to be more concerned with vigor than rigor although a rigorous reformulation more in line with the work of the Prague probabilists [**2**; **3**] and methods of probabilistic functional analysis will hopefully follow.

The remainder of this paper is divided into three sections. In §2 we present a basic summary of necessary ideas and definitions sufficient for the level of presentation in the remainder of this paper. The paper of Bharucha-Reid in this volume will present on a rigorous level the definitions and theorems. §§3 and 4 respectively are devoted to a treatment of two types of physical problems. In §3, a linear transformation or operator theory is developed which allows the operators as well as the operand to be stochastic. Statistical measures and distributions are found for the transformed function under general conditions. The effects of a propagation medium, or of a physical observation or measuring process, or of some control system with statistically varying parameters can be represented in terms of such stochastic operators where instead of a Green's function for the kernel of the operator inverting the differential operator, one is interested in a stochastic Green's function which maps a desired statistical measure from the space of the original random function to the space of the transformed function. §4 is devoted to a consideration of the far more difficult problem of the stochastic differential operator. We are interested in relating this problem to the operator formulation to give statistical measures for the dependent variable.

Some early applications appear in [1], and more extensive treatments are to be published elsewhere. Other applications are readily suggested by the papers of Keller [4] and Hoffman [5]. We will begin by reviewing fundamentals without worrying about rigorous aspects.

2. A summary of the basic ideas.

2.1. THE NATURE OF STOCHASTIC PROCESSES. Certain phenomena in nature are characterized by unpredictable changes in time; they exhibit variations from one observation to the next which no amount of effort or control can remove. They will be called random or stochastic processes and are represented by random functions. If these processes were completely unpredictable in every sense, no theory at all could be formulated. However, they often show regularities or stabilized properties as the number of observations increases. These regularities are called statistical properties and our theories will apply to these. Since the theory of probability is the mathematical theory for statistical properties, our methods will be based on such concepts. Obviously these methods will be appropriate to physical systems whose individual initial states and transition laws cannot be specified in such a way as to yield unique descriptions of final states, but whose behavior in the large (or statistical behavior) is predictable. To summarize, a physical phenomenon is interpreted as a stochastic process if the future cannot be determined from the present except in a statistical way using probability theory. In other words, whenever a process develops in time in a manner controlled by probabilistic rather than deterministic laws, we have a stochastic process. Examples are provided by the path of a particle in Brownian motion, growth of a bacterial population, fluctuating numbers of electrons in a cosmic ray shower, etc. Some interesting examples have been discussed by Kac [6].

2.2. JOINT DISTRIBUTION FUNCTIONS. In order to form some intuitive notions before attacking the general problem, let us refer briefly to an excellent treatment by Lawson and Uhlenbeck [7], of the mathematical description of noise output of receivers. When no signal is present, the output is not always zero but fluctuates randomly around some average value. These fluctuations are called noise and are of great concern because they often prevent detection of weak signals. Observation of the output $y(t)$ of a single receiver over a period of time does not make it possible to predict the output for any later time or to predict the output as a function of time for another receiver identical with the first. If we imagine now a great number of macroscopically identical receivers (an "ensemble" of receivers) all turned on simultaneously, we can observe the noise outputs $y_1(t), y_2(t), \cdots$. All these functions are different. At a definite time t, it can be observed for what fraction of the total number of cases y occurs in a given interval between y and $y + \Delta y$. This fraction now depends on y and t and is proportional to Δy when Δy is small. It is written $F_1(y, t)\,dy$. Next can be considered all the pairs of values of y occurring at two given times t_1 and t_2. The fraction of the total number of pairs in which y occurs in the range $(y_1, y_1 + \Delta y_1)$ at t_1 and in the range $(y_2, y_2 + \Delta y_2)$ at t_2 is written $F_2(y_1, t_1; y_2, t_2)\,dy_1\,dy_2$. We can continue in this manner determining all the triples of values of y at three given times to arrive at F_3, etc. The joint probability (density) F_n is called the nth probability distribution for the random process.

The general theory of stochastic processes is of great interest in many other areas than noise theory alone. Applications exist in many branches of physics, astronomy, engineering, biology, economics, and in mathematics itself. Therefore, let us rephrase what we have said in somewhat more general terms **[8]**.

To define a stochastic process $u(P)$ where P is a variable point in a given set, we specify the joint probability distributions $F_n(u_1, u_2, \cdots, u_n; P_1, P_2, \cdots, P_n)$, where $u_i = u(P_i)$. These distributions F_n with increasing n describe the stochastic process in increasing detail. Some relations immediately follow.

1. $F_n \geqq 0$ (since the F_n are probability densities).

2. F_n is a symmetric function of its arguments (u_k, P_k) since F_n is a joint probability distribution.

3.
$$F_m(u_1, \cdots, u_m; P_1, \cdots, P_m)$$
$$= \int_{u_{m+1}} \cdots \int_{u_n} F_n(u_1, \cdots, u_n; P_1, \cdots, P_n)\, du_{m+1} \cdots du_n$$

and

$$\int_{u_1} \cdots \int_{u_n} F_n\, du_1 \cdots du_n = 1.$$

(Therefore each function F_n must imply all the previous F_m with $m < n$.) In the noise theory example the expression for F_m in (3) would be

$$\int \cdots \int F_n(y_1, \cdots, y_n; t_1, \cdots, t_n)\, dy_{m+1} \cdots dy_n$$

and it is clear that any one of the F_m with $m < n$ can be determined from F_n.

Wang and Uhlenbeck **[9]** have classified stochastic processes by the order of n required for a complete description. In general, joint probability distributions of unbounded order are required to describe general processes. It is of interest to consider some special, or simple, stochastic processes in which only first or second probability distribution functions are sufficient to determine the process. Among these are:

a. *Purely random or independent process.* In this case the successive values of u are statistically independent. Hence the first probability distribution function is sufficient to determine all probability distribution functions, i.e., for $(P_i \neq P_j)$

$$F_n(u_1, \cdots, u_n; P_1, \cdots, P_n) = \prod_{j=1}^{n} F_1(u_j; P_j).$$

b. *Simple Markov process.* This is determined by the second probability distribution function. The simple Markov process is defined by the equation

$$p_n(u_n, P_n | u_1, \cdots, u_{n-1}; P_1, \cdots, P_{n-1}) = p_2(u_n, P_n | u_{n-1}, P_{n-1})$$

(assuming $P_1 < P_2 < \cdots$) where $p(a|b)$ means the conditional probability of a where b is given **[10]**. (We may describe this intuitively as a short memory situation in which only the preceding value matters.)

Processes are also classified according to the type of their distribution functions, i.e., the probability law involved. For example we speak of a Gaussian process, a Poisson process, etc. The probability density function for the Gaussian process, which is of particular significance because of the Central Limit Theorem **[11]** is

$$F_n \, du_1 \cdots du_n = (2\pi)^{-n/2} B^{-1/2} \exp\left\{-(2B)^{-1} \sum_{j,k}^{n} B_{jk} u_j u_k\right\} du_1 \cdots du_n$$

where B is the determinant of B_{jk}. Thus in our noise example we have

$$F_n = F(y_1, y_2, \cdots, y_n)$$

obtained from the above by substituting y's for the u's, assuming $\langle y_i \rangle = 0$. The matrix is symmetric and positive definite. B_{jk} is the cofactor of the matrix element b_{jk} defined by the quadratic average or "moment"

$$b_{jk} = \langle y_j y_k \rangle = \int_{-\infty}^{\infty} \cdots \int_{-\infty}^{\infty} y_j y_k F(y_1, \cdots, y_n) \, dy_1 \cdots dy_n.$$

The one-dimensional form is more familiar and often occurs in applications

$$F(y) = [1/\sigma(2\pi)^{1/2}] \exp\{-(y - \bar{y})^2/2\sigma^2\}$$

where the average value is $\langle y \rangle$ or $\bar{y}$ and the variance $\sigma^2 = \langle (y - \bar{y})^2 \rangle$.

2.3. STATIONARITY AND ERGODICITY. We classify linear and nonlinear processes with customary definitions. Further, a stochastic process is called a statistically nonhomogeneous or nonstationary process if its distribution functions depend on the points $P_1, P_2, \cdots, P_n$ as we have so far written. If the distribution functions depend only on differences $P_i - P_j$ with $(i, j = 1, 2, \cdots, n)$ for $i \neq j$, the process is said to be statistically homogeneous or stationary.

Consider again our noise example of an ensemble of receivers. One could object that an observation on the ensemble could not be made in this example. (In other areas, e.g., statistical mechanics or thermodynamics, this is the only type of observation which can be made; we cannot follow the motion of a single system.) When all transients have damped out so that the receiver is in a "stationary state" all the statistics are obtainable from a sufficiently long record of the output of a single receiver.[1] If this record is cut into pieces of duration T where T is long compared to any periodicities in the process, each piece can be considered part of an ensemble of observations from which the distributions can be determined. We note immediately that the distributions are simpler now. The first example $F_1(y, t)$ is now $F_1(y)$, i.e., the probability of finding y between y and $y + \Delta y$ no longer depends upon t. The second distribution F_2 depends only on the time difference $t_2 - t_1$ so we write $F_2(y_1, y_2, t)$. Continuing, $F_3(y_1, y_2, y_3, t_1, t_2) \, dy_1 \, dy_2 \, dy_3$ is

[1] Implicitly assumes the ergodic property to be discussed later.

the joint probability of finding a triple of values of y in the ranges dy_1, dy_2, dy_3 where dy_1 and dy_2 are the time interval t_1 apart and dy_2 and dy_3 are the time interval t_2 apart, etc. This is an example of stationarity. For a stochastic process $x(t)$, it clearly means an invariance of the distribution functions to a translation of the time origin. (This is sometimes called stationarity in the strict sense to distinguish it from stationarity in the wide sense, to be defined later. Processes which are stationary in the strict sense are also stationary in the wide sense.)

A property implicitly assumed in the discussion so far of the stationary random process involved in the noise example is the ergodic property. Thus we stated the sequence of samples drawn from a single function (the pieces of length T of the record of the output of a single receiver) can be taken as an ensemble. We implicitly used the ergodic hypothesis [**12**] in saying this latter ensemble possesses the same statistical characteristics as the original ensemble. An equivalent statement of the ergodic property is that all statistical averages of any random variable are equal to the time averages of every member of the ensemble. Thus for a stationary random process $x(t)$, the ergodic property holds if for any random variable $V(x)$ such as $x^2(t)$, $x(t_1)x(t_2)$, etc., the expectation value $\langle V\{x(t)\}\rangle$ is equal to

$$\lim_{T\to\infty} \frac{1}{2T}\int_{-T}^{T} V\{x(t+\tau)\}\,d\tau$$

except for a set of measure zero.

If the process is ergodic, statistical averages across the ensemble are equal to the time averages of the individual sample functions. Again in an intuitive way, the essence of the ergodicity condition is that each sample function must eventually take on all the modes of behavior of every other sample function in order for the process to be ergodic, i.e., for time averages to equal statistical or ensemble averages. Ergodicity implies stationarity, i.e., the invariance of the statistics (across the ensemble) to time translation, but the converse need not be true. (See *Ergodic theorem* of Birkhoff [**12**].) Finally if a process is stationary, a statistical average will be time-independent. If it is ergodic as well, a time average of a member of the ensemble will be the same as for any other member of the ensemble. Thus the two ways of averaging give the same result. Whether ergodicity holds or not, time averaging an already statistically averaged process gives the same result as the operations in inverse order.

2.4. Random variables and random processes. Some more general mathematical concepts are often valuable in the treatment of random functions. Thus we may understand the randomness of a stochastic function by considering $u(P)$ to be a function of a random point in the sample space, or event, ω, as well as the deterministic point P. We write $u = u(P; \omega)$ assuming ω ranges over a sample space (or probability space) or a set of elementary events, Ω. For each ω a probability is defined. To be more precise, we would say u is a p-measurable function of ω, and the p-measure, or probability measure, is defined on the Borel field generated by subsets of Ω. This notation conveniently gives an ordinary function for a fixed value of ω, say ω_1, which represents an experiment or event. Thus $u(P; \omega_1) = u(P)$ is a realization or realized value or sample function of u. For a fixed value of P, on the other hand, we have $u(P_1; \omega) = u(\omega)$ as a random variable on the probability space Ω.

An example of such a random variable is the outcome of a particular random experiment E which may be repeated under similar conditions a large number of times. Let the result of this experiment on each trial be given by a single real quantity ω. (In tossing a die, ω represents the numbers 1 to 6 which can come up.) Thus we introduce a variable point ω in a probability, or measure, or sample space S representing the possible outcomes. (In the case of the die, S is a set of 6 discrete points.) When ω has a particular outcome we say ω has the value associated with a sample point in S. We associate a measure or probability with each sample point and we speak of the probability that ω has a particular value.

A random (or stochastic) process is an ensemble of functions in time together with a probability measure by which we can determine probabilities of observable properties. Thus at each sample point we now have a time function $u(t)$, or $u(P)$ in general. The ensemble of such functions over the space is the random process and could be symbolized by $\{u(P)\}$ although we frequently omit the brackets when the meaning is clear. We can also look upon a stochastic process as a family of random variables involving t as a parameter, i.e., for each value of t we get an observed value of the random variable. Each realization of the process is the result of an observation on the process. If we fix the parameter t we get an ordinary random variable. The family of such variables arising from considering t as a parameter can be regarded as the process.

The member functions of the random process $u(t)$ may be defined for discrete instants of time only as well as for a continuum in t in which case we speak of a random series. Depending then on whether the member functions are a continuum or a discrete set, we then speak of a continuous or discrete random series. An important physical example of a continuous random series is the classical problem of the random walk where the steps or displacements at any one move may take a value $y^{(j)}(t_k)$ from a continuum $(a < y < b)$ but these moves are made only at discrete instants $t_1, t_2, \cdots, t_k, \cdots$. An example of a discrete random series is provided by a sequence of tossed coins. The t_k represent the times at which the coin is tossed; the two possible values $y^{(1)}(t_k)$ and $y^{(2)}(t_k)$ correspond to "heads" and "tails" respectively. Finally we have discrete random processes where t represents a continuum but y can only take discrete values as in counters for nuclear particles. The general case is a continuous random process and a Dirac δ formalism can be used for special cases. Finally we may remark that all representations of an ensemble need not be entirely random but may exhibit periodicities. In fact, sets of functions exhibiting no random behavior are included. These are ensembles of a single unit where all members are identical. Thus there is a definite functional dependence upon time and the future behavior of any representative is completely known by a measurement. This is a deterministic process.

2.5. AVERAGE VALUES AND COVARIANCE FUNCTIONS. The stochastic process $u(P)$ is taken now as $u(t)$ and the probability distributions are

$$F_n(u_1, u_2, \cdots, u_n;\ t_1, t_2, \cdots, t_n)$$

where $u_i = u(t_i)$. From the first distribution $F_1(u, t)$, the average value

$$\langle u \rangle = \int u F_1(u, t)\, du$$

can be determined. It clearly depends in general on the time t, unless stationarity holds. This is a statistical or ensemble average and can be regarded as the average at a time t of the ensemble of functions represented by u. On the other hand, the time average

$$[u]_{\text{av}} = \lim \frac{1}{2T} \int_{-T}^{T} dt\, u(t) \qquad (T \to \infty)$$

is independent of time but, in general, different for each member of the ensemble of u. For an ergodic process the two ways of averaging give the same result. Then $\langle u \rangle$ is independent of time and $[u]_{\text{av}}$ is the same for each member of the ensemble.

We can now define the moments

$$m_n = E\{u^n\} = \langle u^n \rangle = \int u^n F_1(u)\, du$$

and the fluctuation, or variance, or dispersion

$$\sigma^2 = \langle (u - m_1)^2 \rangle = \int (u - m_1)^2 F_1(u)\, du.$$

An often useful concept called the characteristic function is defined by

$$\phi_1(\lambda) = \langle e^{i\lambda u} \rangle = \int e^{i\lambda u} F_1(u)\, du$$

and if all the moments are finite, we can write[2]

$$\phi_1 = \sum_{n=0}^{\infty} \frac{(i\lambda)^n}{n!} \langle u^n \rangle = \sum_{n=0}^{\infty} \frac{(i\lambda)^n}{n!} m_n$$

where

$$F_1(u) = \frac{1}{2\pi} \int_{-\infty}^{\infty} d\lambda\, e^{-i\lambda u}\, \phi_1(\lambda)$$

so that the probability distribution is determined uniquely[3] by the characteristic function.

---

[2] Assuming convergence.

[3] In most cases. See Loève, *Probability theory* **[15]**.

From the second distribution $F_2(u_1, u_2; t_1, t_2)$ an important average is $\langle u_1 u_2 \rangle$ or $E\{u_1 u_2\}$ defined by

$$\langle u_1 u_2 \rangle = \iint u_1 u_2 F_2(u_1, u_2; t_1, t_2)\, du_1\, du_2$$

in general, a function of t_1 and t_2. Letting $t_2 = t_1 + \tau$ and time-averaging over t_1 we have

$$R(\tau) = \lim_{T\to\infty} \frac{1}{2T} \int_{-T}^{T} \langle u_1(t_1) u_2(t_1 + \tau) \rangle\, dt_1 = [\langle u_1 u_2 \rangle]_{\text{av}}.$$

If we take

$$[u(t_1)u(t_1 + \tau)]_{\text{av}} = \lim_{T\to\infty} \frac{1}{2T} \int_{-T}^{T} u(t_1)u(t_1 + \tau)\, dt_1$$

and now average over the ensemble, clearly, we get $R(\tau)$ again. However, if the process is ergodic either $\langle u_1 u_2 \rangle$ or $[u(t_1)u(t_1 + \tau)]_{\text{av}}$ gives the same result. $R(\tau)$ is a measure of the correlation between successive values of u and is therefore called the correlation function.

The conditional probability distribution $P_2(u_2, t_2 | u_1, t_1)$ gives the probability of finding u between u_2 and $u_2 + du_2$ at time t_2 given that $u = u_1$ at t_1. Clearly,

$$F_2(u_1, t_1; u_2, t_2) = F_1(u_1, t_1) P_2(u_2, t_2 | u_1, t_1);$$

also

$$\int P_2(u_2, t_2 | u_1, t_1)\, du_2 = 1,$$

$$\int F_1(u_1, t_1) P_2(u_2, t_2 | u_1, t_1)\, du_1 = F_1(u_2, t_2),$$

since

$$\int F_2\, du_2 = F_1(u_1, t_1),$$

$$\int F_2\, du_1 = F_1(u_2, t_2).$$

The notion of the characteristic function is easily extended to multivariate characteristic functions. Thus the bivariate characteristic function of the random variables u_1 and u_2 is

$$\begin{aligned}\phi_2(\lambda_1, \lambda_2) &= \langle e^{i(\lambda_1 u_1 + \lambda_2 u_2)} \rangle \\ &= \iint e^{i(\lambda_1 u_1 + \lambda_2 u_2)} F_2(u_1, u_2)\, du_1\, du_2 \\ &= \sum_{j=0}^{\infty} \sum_{k=0}^{\infty} \frac{(i\lambda_1)^j}{j!} \frac{(i\lambda_2)^k}{k!} \langle u_1^j u_2^k \rangle.\end{aligned}$$

The quantity $\langle u_1^j u_2^k \rangle$ is a joint moment analogous to m_n in the expression for $\phi_1(\lambda)$. F_2 is found from ϕ_2 by a two-dimensional Fourier transform. Finally the n-dimensional general case gives

$$\phi_n(\lambda) = \int_{-\infty}^{\infty} \cdots \int_{-\infty}^{\infty} \exp\left[i \sum_{j=1}^{n} \lambda_j u_j\right] F_n(u_1; t_1, u_2; t_2, \cdots, u_n; t_n)\, du_1 \cdots du_n$$

and the multivariate density function

$$F_n(u_1; t_1, u_2; t_2, \cdots, u_n; t_n) = \frac{1}{(2\pi)^n} \int_{-\infty}^{\infty} \cdots \int_{-\infty}^{\infty} \exp\left[-i \sum \lambda_j u_j\right] \phi_n\, du_1 \cdots du_n.$$

If the functions ϕ_n can be determined for the output the problem is solved by taking the inverse Fourier transform.

There are several methods for doing this in very special cases. The Kac–Siegert approach **[16]** exists for cases in which the input to a deterministic linear system is a squared Gaussian process and the Fortet–Siegert **[17–20]** approach assumes the input is either a Markov process or one component of a multidimensional Markov process. Samuels **[21]** shows ϕ_n can also be derived from knowledge of the correlation function as we suspect by looking at ϕ_1 and ϕ_2 and the generalized expression. We will return to this point in a moment.

Return now to our expression $\langle u_1 u_2 \rangle$ also written as $E\{u_1 u_2\}$ and examine it more closely. $u(t)$ is a random process. u_1 and u_2 are a pair of random variables referring to possible values which can be assumed at the given instants t_1 and t_2, respectively, by the sample functions of the process $u(t)$. However, the joint probability distribution of u_1 and u_2 may change as t_1 and t_2 change, in general. Therefore, the average denoted by $\langle u_1 u_2 \rangle$ may well depend upon both time instants.[4] In general then we write the correlation function as $R_u(t_1, t_2)$ and call it the autocorrelation because it involves only the u process. Similarly we could consider random variables $u(t)$ and $v(t)$ and define $\langle uv \rangle$ as a cross-correlation. Also used is the covariance function defined by $\langle (u - \bar{u})(v - \bar{v}) \rangle$ for random variables u and v. Thus in the joint moments $\langle u_1^j u_2^k \rangle$ already defined, the case $j = k = 1$ or second order joint moment is the correlation function for u_1 and u_2 (autocorrelation if u_1 and u_2 are derived from u and cross-correlation if they are different random variables). If $\bar{u}_1 = \bar{u}_2 = 0$ the second order joint moment is also the covariance function. In generalizing to nth order correlations, knowledge of all the correlations implies knowledge of all the joint-moments since some of the time variables in the correlation functions can be made equal to obtain all the joint moments.

The various joint moments can be obtained from their joint characteristic function by successive differentiations **[22]**; or a series expansion of the joint characteristic function in terms of the various joint moments is easily obtained as in the cases of ϕ_1 and ϕ_2.

If a given random process u is stationary, the joint probability distribution for u_1 and u_2 depends only on the time difference $\tau = t_2 - t_1$ and not on the

[4] If the process is complex, $R_u = \langle u_1 u_2^* \rangle$.

particular values of t_1 and t_2. Then $R_u(t_1, t_2)$ can be written $R_u(\tau)$ for any t. Sometimes a process is not stationary in the strict sense defined earlier, i.e., the probability distributions are not invariant under time translation, yet the autocorrelation can be written as $R_u(\tau)$ and the various means are constant functions of time. It is then said to be stationary in the wide sense. Obviously, processes stationary in the strict sense are also stationary in the wide sense.[5] This implies an obvious idealization. No physical process can start at $-\infty$ or continue till ∞ without changes in the underlying mechanism. One always deals in actuality with finite samples, and what is of importance is the correlation time relative to the sample length.

We now consider a random field **[23]** $v(x, t)$ where x represents the three space coordinates and t is the time. Following previous definitions we define the nth order correlation R_n by the natural generalization

$$\int \cdots \int v_1 v_2 \cdots v_n F_n(v_1, v_2, \cdots, v_n; t_1, \cdots, t_n, x_1, \cdots, x_n)\, dv_1 \cdots dv_n$$

$$= \langle v_1 v_2 \cdots v_n \rangle = E\{v(x_1, t_1; \omega) v(x_2, t_2; \omega) \cdots v(x_n, t_n; \omega)\}$$

$$= R_n(x_1, x_2, \cdots, x_n; t_1, t_2, \cdots, t_n),$$

the integral being over the domain of the random variables $v_1, v_2, \cdots, v_n$ and the x_j and t_j being ordered. (E is sometimes called the expectation operator.) We note knowledge of all the R_n implies knowledge of all the joint moments.

We can now define the n-dimensional characteristic function

$$\phi_n(\lambda; t, x) = \int e^{i\lambda \cdot v} F_n(v; t, x)\, dv$$

where λ, v, x are n-dimensional vectors and the integration is over the domain of v.

Now since F_n and ϕ_n are n-dimensional Fourier transform pairs, F_n can be determined from ϕ_n (see Levy's inversion theorem) **[24]**. Knowledge of all the F_n for the output process gives us complete knowledge, i.e., solves the problem. Now ϕ_n can be written as a series involving all the correlation functions as is clear in principle from what has been said so far. Writing out ϕ_n in this form as given by Samuels and Eringen,

$$\phi_n(\lambda) = 1 + \sum_{k=1}^{\infty} \frac{(i)^k}{k!} \left\{ \sum_{m_j} R_k(x_1^{(m_1)}, x_2^{(m_2)}, \cdots; t_1^{(m_1)}, \cdots, t_n^{(m_n)})(\lambda_1^{m_1} \cdots \lambda_n^{m_n}) \right\},$$

where the summation over m_j means the sum of such expressions for all values of the individual m's subject to $\sum_{j=1}^{n} m_j = k$. Now, e.g., ϕ_1 becomes

$$\phi_1(\lambda) = 1 + \sum_{k=1}^{\infty} \frac{(i\lambda)^k}{k!} R_k(x^{(k)}; t^{(k)}),$$

---

[5] The converse is not true except for Gaussian processes where knowledge of the covariance and the mean functions completely determines the process.

the R_k clearly representing all the moments so we get the same expression as given earlier. Similarly,

$$\phi_2(\lambda_1, \lambda_2) = 1 + \sum_{k=1}^{\infty} \frac{(i)^k}{k!} \left\{ \sum_{m_j} R_k(x_1^{(m_1)}, x_2^{(m_2)}; t_1^{(m_1)}, t_2^{(m_2)}) \lambda_1^{m_1} \lambda_2^{m_2} \right\}$$

where $m_1 + m_2 = k$.

The value of this expression as Samuels and Eringen point out is the fact that in linear deterministic systems, the correlation functions of the output are simply related to those of the input if Green's functions can be found. Thus knowledge of the correlation functions of the input allows writing those for the output from which ϕ_n and finally F_n can be determined.

However, we can go even further. For linear stochastic systems we can write output autocorrelations in terms of input autocorrelations by using appropriate stochastic Green's functions. In principle at least, then we can similarly write all the correlations of the output (i.e., any order correlation) in terms of those of the input. The stochastic kernels are by no means the same; however, they are determinable in the same manner. Thus we have outlined a method in principle for the determination of all the distribution functions of the output knowing those for the input and, therefore, in this sense a solution of the most general statistical problem for a linear system.

2.6. SPECTRAL DENSITY. We wish now to define a function called the power spectral density or simply spectral density (alternatively, spectrum or power spectrum) which gives the distribution in frequency of the power of a signal or noise and is closely related to the autocorrelation.

Suppose $u(t)$ is any function and assume that $u(t)$ is zero outside the time interval $[-T, T]$. The function can now be developed in a Fourier integral

$$u(t) = \int_{-\infty}^{\infty} df\, A(f)\, e^{2\pi i f t},$$

i.e., $u(t)$ and $A(f)$ are a Fourier transform pair. $A(f) = A^*(-f)$ if $u(t)$ is real. By the Parseval theorem

$$\int_{-\infty}^{\infty} u^2(t)\, dt = \int_{-T}^{T} u^2(t)\, dt = \int_{-\infty}^{\infty} |A(f)|^2\, df$$

assuming the last integral is not unbounded (Plancherel's theorem). We note that $|A(f)|^2$ is an even function, and letting $T \to \infty$,

$$[u^2]_{av} = \lim_{T\to\infty} \frac{1}{2T} \int_{-T}^{T} u^2(t)\, dt = \int_0^{\infty} G(f)\, df$$

where[6]

$$G(f) = \lim_{T\to\infty} \frac{|A(f)|^2}{T}$$

[6] This definition requires care in use. Integration before limiting processes avoids difficulties because the means converge. See Davenport and Root [22] for a discussion of this point.

is called the spectral density or power spectrum of the function $u(t)$ whenever the limit exists. Now instead of $[u(t)u(t)]_{av}$ take $[u(t)u(t+\tau)]_{av}$

$$[u(t)u(t+\tau)]_{av} = \lim_{T\to\infty} \frac{1}{2T}\int_{-T}^{T} u(t)u(t+\tau)\,dt.$$

Developing $u(t)$ and $u(t+\tau)$ in Fourier integrals as before

$$[u(t)u(t+\tau)]_{av} = \int_{-\infty}^{\infty} e^{-2\pi i f\tau}\,G(f)\,df.$$

Assume now $u(t)$ is actually a random process so the above functions u are members of the ensemble of the process u, i.e., sample functions or representatives. Then each of these representatives has a corresponding $G(f)$ which we can now average over the ensemble. The resulting $\langle G(f)\rangle$ or $\Phi(f)$ is the spectral density or power spectrum of the random process. We saw earlier that $\langle [u(t)u(t+\tau)]_{av}\rangle$ is the correlation function $R(\tau)$ for the process, so we have

$$R(\tau) = \int_{-\infty}^{\infty} e^{-2\pi i f\tau}\,\Phi(f)\,df.$$

We defined $G(f)$ as a time spectrum (the spectrum corresponding to a time function), and then averaged over the ensemble of such functions to get $\Phi(f)$. Thus $\langle G(f)\rangle = \Phi(f)$. We note $G(f)$ is the Fourier transform of the correlation function $\mathscr{R}(\tau)$ where $\mathscr{R}(\tau) = [u(t)u(t+\tau)]_{av}$ and $\Phi(f)$ is the Fourier transform of $R(\tau)$ where $R(\tau) = \langle \mathscr{R}(\tau)\rangle$.

The time autocorrelation $\mathscr{R}(\tau)$ (i.e., the autocorrelation of a sample function of the random process) is equal to the statistical autocorrelation $R(\tau)$ if the process is ergodic (with probability one).

Finally for nonstationary processes, the (statistical) autocorrelation must be written $R(t, \tau)$ and its Fourier transform $\Phi(t, f)$ might be considered a power spectrum for a limited interval. If the limit exists as $T \to \infty$ of the quantity $(2T)^{-1} \int_{-T}^{T} \Phi(t, f)\,dt$, and this average is equal to nearly all the measurements of $\Phi(t, f)$ for all values of t, it can be inferred the process is stationary.

3. Stochastic operations on random processes: operator formulation.

3.1. CONCEPT OF A STOCHASTIC OPERATOR AND STOCHASTIC GREEN'S FUNCTIONS. In many physical problems of interest, we are concerned with the properties of a function obtained by transformation of a given function by a known operator. In others, the inverse problem arises, where the quantity of interest is the dependent variable in a differential equation. Often the real physical problem involves randomness which has been ignored to make equations tractable. Unavoidable random effects are present or a lack of definite knowledge exists. These problems can be considered by generalizing the above operators to be linear *stochastic* operators which reduce to ordinary operators as randomness vanishes and parameters become deterministic. Analogous to the usual representation of operators by matrices, stochastic operators will be represented by stochastic matrices or matrices whose elements have a distribution. Thinking of a given deterministic operator as a realization of a stochastic operator, or of a stochastic operator as an ensemble of such deterministic operators, one immediately thinks of stochastic mappings between generalized spaces in mathematics; of quantum theory and many-body problems, statistical mechanics, or wave propagation in random media in the area of physics; or of randomly time-varying systems, communication theory, or control system theory in the area of engineering.

In applications, stochastic operators arise in the processing of an input quantity (which may itself be a random process) by a linear system, observation, or measurement, in which certain parameters are random or stochastic variables. Problems involving random inputs to fixed linear systems (i.e., where all the a_ν are constants and only x is stochastic) are well understood. A great deal of attention has been devoted also to deterministic time variations in linear systems (linear differential equations with time-varying coefficients). When random variations of system parameters (or of the a_ν in the differential equation example) occur, the analysis is more subtle. The output now for either a deterministic or a random input is a stochastic process. A complete description of the output would involve the determination of all multivariate probability distributions of the output from similar knowledge of the input. Such a complete description is usually neither possible nor necessary.

It is instructive to consider a subclass of stochastic differential operators given by

$$L = \sum_{\nu=0}^{n} a_\nu(t) \frac{d^\nu}{dt^\nu}$$

and differential equations of the form $Ly = x$, where the nonhomogeneous term $x(t)$, called the input or forcing function, and the operator L, by virtue of the coefficients $a_\nu(t)$, are, in general, stochastic quantities. The converse problem involving the conceptual inversion of the matrix for the random differential operator L is especially interesting. For appropriate operators, we think of y as the result of operating on the input by a stochastic operator symbolically denoted by H or by L^{-1} and otherwise undefined except to say it would include the action of any accompanying boundary conditions. We wish to keep the differential equation formulation in mind in the analysis, although in this section we are primarily interested in general operators H acting on a process x with as little restriction as possible.

Suppose that $x(t)$ is a known input process or the operand. We wish to determine the result of an operation on x by the stochastic operator H. Thus, x might be a communication signal into the proverbial black box which then represents the operator H. The box may be a circuit, filter, servo, observation, experiment, or measurement, or a transmission medium which has random properties. All real media are inhomogeneous, i.e., the mean physical properties vary from one point to another. When, in addition, there is a variance from the mean at each point, the medium is a random inhomogeneous medium. When the properties or parameters of the medium are constants and $x(t)$ is nonstochastic, the output $y = L^{-1}x$ is often found without difficulty (depending on the nature of the operator). When the x is stochastic, and certainly when the properties of the medium vary randomly with time, we can only hope to obtain various statistical measures or estimates of y in terms of similar measures of x. If the inverse H of the stochastic matrix L exists, we have the general problem again given by $y = Hx$ (where we emphasize the product is not multiplicative but denotes the action of the stochastic operator H on the process x) and the differential equation could be solved as well as the general problem Hx. However, the inversion of a stochastic matrix is clearly to be avoided. Since we are asking only for an appropriate statistical measure of y rather than y itself, we may be able to solve the differential equation at the same time as the general problem without the inversion. A well-known and convenient statistical measure is the power spectral density or power spectrum, or by the Wiener–Khinchin theorem, the autocorrelation function [7]. Thus, if $\Phi_x(f)$ is the power spectrum of the input and $\Phi_y(f)$ is the power spectrum of the output, we would like to obtain Φ_y in terms of Φ_x. Such an expression can be obtained as an integral equation whose kernel K_H involves the random parameters of the operator H. We will then clarify the interpretation of the stochastic kernel K_H and show its derivation from the L as well, providing certain restrictions on L are met. The constant-parameter system is handled easily in terms of Green's functions (weighting functions in control system theory) or frequency response functions and transfer functions, respectively, the Fourier and Laplace transforms of the system Green's function. We will (in the stochastic case) obtain a stochastic Green's function that depends on the statistical measure chosen for a solution and which reduces to the ordinary expressions when the parameters are constants or nonstochastic.

3.2. Examples of stochastic operators. In many cases of physical interest (2) can be determined directly from the nature of the process. Thus we have an input $x(t)$ and a "stochastically filtered" or processed output $F_{\alpha,\beta,\ldots}\{x(t)\}$ where the stochastic operator $F_{\alpha,\beta,\ldots}$ depends on the distributions of its parameters $\alpha, \beta, \cdots$. For example, (a) a function $x(t)$ is translated by amounts α_n at intervals of time τ so $F\{x(t)\} = x(t - \alpha_n)$ for $n\tau < t < (n + 1)\tau$, (b) $x(t)$ is multiplied by β_n over intervals of length τ. Thus $F\{x(t)\} = \beta_n x(t)$ for $n\tau < t < (n + 1)\tau$. These are linear processes and the random variables in question are the α_n and the β_n. The distribution functions of these parameters determine the statistical properties of the process. An example (c), of greater interest arising in an application to be considered is the operation $S\{x(t)\} = x(t_n)$ for $t_n < t < t_{n+1}$ for all n where the intervals $l_n = t_{n+1} - t_n$ are random variables with a distribution $P(l)\,dl$. Thus S might be called a "random sampling operator" (where the last sample value is held until another is taken). The S operator gives the correct results for the much-used case of regular sampling as randomness vanishes. A closely related example (d) is $P\{x(t)\}$ which samples randomly as before but inverts alternate samples. Thus $P\{x(t)\} = (-1)^n x(t_n)$ for $t_n < t < t_{n+1}$ where the intervals $l_n = t_{n+1} - t_n$ are specified by $P(l)\,dl$.

The Green's functions for these latter processes ((c) and (d)) can be written by inspection

$$s_i(t, \tau) = \sum_k \Delta(t_k, l_k; t)\delta(\tau - t_k),$$

$$p_i(t, \tau) = \sum_k (-1)^k \Delta(t_k, l_k; t)\delta(\tau - t_k),$$

where

$$\Delta(t_k, l_k; t) = \begin{cases} 1 & \text{if } t_k < t < t_k + l_k, \\ 0 & \text{otherwise.} \end{cases}$$

The spectral densities for the results of operations on x by S or P are considered in the referenced dissertation in connection with a generalized random-walk problem, first studied jointly with DuBois. We state the results here as examples.

$$\Phi_{Sx}(f) = \text{Re}\left\{\frac{1 - z(f)}{2\pi^2 f^2 \bar{l}} \int_{-\infty}^{\infty} ds \Phi_x(s - f)[1 - z(s - f)] \sum_0^{\infty} z^n(s)\right\},$$

$$\Phi_{Px}(f) = \text{Re}\left\{\frac{1 - z(f)}{2\pi^2 f^2 \bar{l}} \int_{-\infty}^{\infty} ds\, \Phi_x(s - f)[1 + z(s - f)] \sum_0^{\infty} (-1)^n z^n(s)\right\}$$

where $z(f)$ is the characteristic function of the distribution for the sampling intervals $P(l)$, i.e.,

$$z(f) = \int_0^{\infty} dl\, P(l)\, e^{-2\pi i f l},$$

$$\bar{l} = \int_0^{\infty} lP(l)\, dl = -\frac{1}{2\pi i} z'(0),$$

relations which are clearly of the same form as (3) with rather complicated kernels dependent on the probability laws in this case just $P(l)$ for the parameters which are random. Evaluation of the kernel in terms of distributions of the random parameters is obtained directly from the nature of the process on the input, i.e., from Hx.

3.3. Development of a stochastic Green's function. Now consider a linear operation $H_{\alpha,\beta,\cdots}$, or H for brevity, on an input process x for which the spectral density Φ_x is known. The operation represents a medium or processing system with parameters $\alpha(t)$, $\beta(t)$, $\cdots$, one or more of which are random. Thus H is determined only by the probability distributions of its parameters, i.e., in the sense of an ensemble of possible operations H_i which have a distribution determined by the parameters. Each of the H_i corresponds to an ordinary nonstochastic matrix. Each member H_i of the ensemble H has associated with it a Green's function $h_i(t, \tau)$ which represents the response at time t of the system H_i to a unit impulse $\delta(t - \tau)$ applied at time τ. More specifically, h_i should be written $h_i(\alpha, \beta, \cdots, t; \tau)$ where α, β, $\cdots$ are the parameters of H subject to probability laws. The response of the H_i system to the input $x(t)$, thinking of x as a defined continuous member of the x process for the moment, can now be given in terms of the Green's function by

$$H_i x(t) = \int_{-\infty}^{\infty} h_i(\alpha, \beta, \cdots, t; \tau) x(\tau)\, d\tau,$$

or for brevity, where parameter dependence is not used,

$$H_i x(t) = \int_{-\infty}^{\infty} h_i(t; \tau) x(\tau)\, d\tau, \tag{1}$$

where for causal (physically realizable) systems, $h_i(t, \tau)$ is zero for $t < \tau$. The upper limit can also be written t without change. The implication of the lower limit is that all past values are significant. We can write the spectral density of $H_i x(t)$ by first developing this function in a Fourier integral. Thus assuming stationarity and supposing $H_i x$ to be zero outside some interval $[-T, T]$ then taking the limit at $T \to \infty$

$$H_i x(t) = \int_{-\infty}^{\infty} df A_i(f)\, e^{2\pi i f t}$$

$$\Phi_{H_i}(f) = \lim_{T\to\infty} \frac{1}{T} |A_i(f)|^2.$$

Our stationarity assumption can be modified somewhat in that the $A_i(f)$ can depend on T, thus $A_i^T(f)$, as long as the limit exists. The above expression holds for all $H_i x$ which are members of the ensemble Hx. Each $H_i x$ is developed in a Fourier integral as we have shown. The corresponding spectra Φ_{H_i} are averaged over the ensemble. The result which could have been written immediately is $\Phi_{Hx}(f)$, the spectral density of the output. Thus,

$$\Phi_{Hx}(f) = \lim_{T\to\infty} \frac{1}{T} \left\langle \left| \int_{-T}^{T} dt\, H_i\{x(t)\}\, e^{-2\pi i f t} \right|^2 \right\rangle,$$

where the average is over the ensembles of H and of x.

$$\Phi_{Hx}(f) = \lim_{T\to\infty} \frac{1}{T} \int_{-T}^{T} \int_{-T}^{T} dt_1\, dt_2 \langle H_i\{x(t_1)\} H_i^*\{x(t_2)\}\rangle\, e^{-2\pi i f(t_1 - t_2)}.$$

The quantity in brackets is evidently an autocorrelation function. Let us define the autocorrelation of the Hx as

$$R_{Hx}(\tau) = \langle Hx(t) H^* x(t + \tau)\rangle,$$

where the random process may be complex and we have limited ourselves to stationary input $x(t)$, though it is possible the operator H may be nonstationary. On using (1), this equation becomes

$$R_{Hx}(\tau) = \iint_{-\infty}^{\infty} d\tau_1\, d\tau_2 \langle h(t; \tau_1) h^*(t + \tau; \tau_2) x(\tau_1) x(\tau_2)\rangle.$$

We note the h's correspond to different times t_1 and t_2 (or t and $t + \tau$). Thus we have $h(\alpha_1, \beta_1, \cdots, t_1; \tau_1)$ and $h^*(\alpha_2, \beta_2, \cdots, t_2; \tau_2)$ so all parameters are different.

In many cases of physical interest, the $x(t)$ and the $a_\nu(t)$ are independent. In other words, the input process and the "filtering" process are independent. Transmission of a signal through a randomly varying medium (*a stochastic filter*) is such a case. The result of the action of the medium on x is the stochastically filtered signal Hx. The term in brackets in the expression for $R_{Hx}(\tau)$ can now be factored. Indicating the autocorrelation for x alone by R_x

$$R_x(\tau_2 - \tau_1) = \langle x(\tau_1)x^*(\tau_2)\rangle,$$

with averaging obviously over the ensemble of x, we now have

$$R_{Hx}(\tau) = \int d\tau_1 \int d\tau_2\, R_x(\tau_2 - \tau_1)\langle h(t; \tau_1)h^*(t + \tau; \tau_2)\rangle.$$

The corresponding spectral density is

$$\begin{aligned}\Phi_{Hx}(f) &= \int d\tau\, e^{2\pi i f\tau} R_{Hx}(\tau) \\ &= \int d\tau_1 \int d\tau_2 \int d\tau\, e^{2\pi i f\tau} R_x(\tau_2 - \tau_1)\langle h(t; \tau_1)h^*(t + \tau; \tau_2)\rangle \\ &= \int d\tau_1 \int d\tau_2 \int d\tau \int ds\, e^{2\pi i \tau f}\, e^{-2\pi i(\tau_2 - \tau_1)s}\langle h(t; \tau_1)h^*(t + \tau; \tau_2)\rangle\Phi_x(s),\end{aligned}$$

where $\Phi_x(s)$ is the (power) spectral density of $x(t)$. The last equation is now rewritten in the convenient form

$$\Phi_{Hx}(f) = \int_{-\infty}^{\infty} ds\, K_H(s, f)\Phi_x(s), \tag{2}$$

where the integral kernel or "stochastic kernel"

$$K_H(s, f) = \int_{-\infty}^{\infty} d\tau_1 \int_{-\infty}^{\infty} d\tau_2 \int_{-\infty}^{\infty} d\tau\, e^{2\pi i \tau f}\, e^{-2\pi i(\tau_2 - \tau_1)s}\langle h(t; \tau_1)h^*(t + \tau; \tau_2)\rangle \tag{3}$$

is a "stochastic Green's function." The form of the kernel or stochastic Green's function depends on the statistical measure chosen for the solution. In solving $Ly = x(t)$, we can express y in terms of x by the use of a Green's function $G(t, \tau)$. However, we are now solving not for y but Φ_y in terms of Φ_x and a "Green's function" appropriate to such measures. This is our kernel K_H or what we call a stochastic Green's function. Since it depends upon the statistical measure, we should properly identify the kernel K_H as a stochastic Green's function for power spectral density measures or a spectral density Green's function.

Whereas H and the above results are quite general, the L in the differential equation was very special, for convenience, though still an important form. No difficulty in principle would be expected in generalizing to systems of differential equations with many dependent variables (multiple inputs and outputs) or to random fields $V(x, t)$.

To the spectral density derived for the "output" we should add any contributions due to a mean value since the derivation tacitly assumed a zero-mean random process x. When the time average of the process is nonzero, there are singular peaks of the well-known Dirac δ-function type in the spectral density. Thus, to the $\Phi_x(f)$, which represents only the spectrum of what we could call the a.c. part in electrical language, we should add a term $2\bar{x}^2\delta(f)$. Equivalently, to $\Phi_y(f)$ we add a term $2\bar{x}^2K_H(0, f)$.

3.4. General statistical problem. Now, in principle at least, we can express all the correlations of the output by similar expressions involving correlations of the input for general linear stochastic operations on arbitrary random inputs. But the n-dimensional multivariate characteristic function ϕ_n of the "output" or transformed process can be given in terms of all the correlations of the output, and by the above reasoning can now be given in terms of all the correlations of the input. These, in turn, are clearly determinable from knowledge of all the joint distribution functions of the input process or operand. Finally the n-dimensional joint distribution function for the output is obtained by Fourier inversion of ϕ_n. Thus we have suggested a method, at least in principle, for solving the most general statistical problem for a linear system.

3.5. Linear properties. Equation (2) shows that the power spectrum (or autocorrelation function by use of the Wiener–Khinchin theorem) of the output can be given as a transform of the corresponding measure of the input and a kernel which, as we shall see, involves the probability laws for the parameters. Thus the spectral density of the output is related to the spectral density of the input by a linear operation. The solution of any problem of this type involves finding the appropriate kernel. We write (2) symbolically as

$$\Phi_{Hx} = K_H \cdot \Phi_x$$

understanding K_H to be the appropriate integral operator. We note some properties which would reasonably be expected.

If $x = ax_1 + bx_2 + \cdots$, where the x_i are mutually independent, then $Hx = aHx_1 + bHx_2 + \cdots$ and $\Phi_{Hx} = K_H \cdot \Phi_x = a^2K_H \cdot \Phi_{x1} + b^2K_H \cdot \Phi_{x2} + \cdots$. Also if $H = H_1 + H_2$, then $\Phi_{Hx} = (K_{H_1} + K_{H_2}) \cdot \Phi_x$.

3.6. Interpretation of the kernel in special cases. Consider first a special case of (2) corresponding to a constant-parameter medium. For such a case (differential equations with constant coefficients and random forcing function), the Green's function depends only on the time interval between application of the impulse and observation of the output. The averaging is obviously unnecessary now, so that (3) can be rewritten

$$K_H(s, f) = \int_{-\infty}^{\infty} d\tau_1 \int_{-\infty}^{\infty} d\tau_2 \int_{-\infty}^{\infty} d\tau \, e^{2\pi i\tau f} \, e^{-2\pi i(\tau_2 - \tau_1)s} h(t - \tau_1)h(t + \tau - \tau_2),$$

which with appropriate changes of variables becomes

$$K_H(s, f) = \int_{-\infty}^{\infty} d\tau\, e^{-2\pi i(f-s)\tau} \int_0^{\infty} d\tau_2\, e^{2\pi i\tau_2 s} h(\tau_2) \int_0^{\infty} d\tau_1\, e^{-2\pi i\tau_1 s} h(\tau_1)$$

$$= |\, Y(s)|^2 \delta(f - s),$$

where

$$Y(s) \doteq \int_0^{\infty} d\tau\, e^{-2\pi i\tau s} h(\tau),$$

i.e., the Fourier transform of the Green's function. Then (2) becomes

$$\Phi_{Hx}(f) = |\, Y(f)|^2 \Phi_x(f),$$

a well-known result.

Occasionally, the notion of frequency response function is extended to linear time-varying systems by defining:

$$Y(s, t) \doteq \int_0^{\infty} h(t; t - \tau)\, e^{-2\pi i s\tau}\, d\tau.$$

The general kernel $K_H(s, f)$ becomes

$$K_H = \int_{-\infty}^{\infty} d\tau\, e^{2\pi i\tau f} \int_{-\infty}^{\infty} d\tau_2\, e^{-2\pi i\tau_2 s} \int_{-\infty}^{\infty} d\tau_1\, e^{2\pi i\tau_1 s} \langle h(t; \tau_1) h^*(t + \tau; \tau_2)\rangle$$

$$= \int_{-\infty}^{\infty} d\tau\, e^{2\pi i\tau f} \left\langle \int_{-\infty}^{\infty} d\tau_2\, e^{-2\pi i\tau_2 s} h^*(t + \tau; \tau_2) \int_{-\infty}^{\infty} d\tau_1\, e^{2\pi i\tau_1 s} h(t; \tau_1) \right\rangle$$

$$= \int_{-\infty}^{\infty} d\tau\, e^{2\pi i\tau f} \langle Y^*(s, t + \tau)\, e^{-2\pi i s\tau}\, Y(s, t)\rangle$$

$$= \int_{-\infty}^{\infty} d\tau\, e^{2\pi i\tau(f-s)} \langle Y^*(s, t + \tau)\, Y(s, t)\rangle.$$

This is compatible with our definition for the constant-parameter case since the above expression then reduces to

$$\int d\tau\, e^{2\pi i\tau(f-s)} \langle |\, Y(s)|^2\rangle = \delta(f - s) |\, Y(s)|^2.$$

So far, our stochastic kernel has been quite general. The matrix H has elements with any distribution. However, some statistical properties of matrices whose elements have normal, or Gaussian, distributions are well known. We can make further identifications by specializing to the case of such distributions (possibly first determining the eigenvalues of the operator then the Green's functions, and consequently the kernel). To see how the distributions enter, it is noted that the Green's functions involve the random parameters α, β, · · ·, which have distributions $p(\alpha), p(\beta), \cdots$ that must be used in obtaining the average or expectation value involved in the kernel. Thus, for ergodic operators

$$\langle h(\alpha, \beta, \cdots, t; \tau_1)h^*(\alpha, \beta, \cdots, t + \tau; \tau_2)\rangle$$

$$= \lim_{T\to\infty} \frac{1}{2T}\int_{-T}^{T} du \int_0^\infty d\alpha \int_0^\infty d\beta \int \cdots p(\alpha)p(\beta)\cdots$$

$$\times\, h(\alpha, \beta, \cdots, t + u; \tau_1)h^*(\alpha, \beta, \cdots, t + \tau + u; \tau_2)$$

and we can specialize to certain distributions or even to the case where the distribution is given by a δ function and the parameter is not random.

3.7. STATISTICAL (MEASURE) OPERATIONS. A class of operations on random processes including, e.g., the ensemble average of a random process, the autocorrelation, mean squared, or higher means, can be called statistical or measure operations. A statistical operator or measure in this sense indicates a (nonstochastic) deterministic operation on a random process. It is distinguished from ordinary deterministic operations on ordinary functions only in that the operand is now a random process rather than a function, so that the averages are with respect to a random variable. Clearly, any ordinary deterministic operator, e.g., a Laplace (or other) transform should commute with such statistical operators and one could consider a possibility of appropriate (statistical) transforms of random processes since this would just mean the ordinary transform of the result of the statistical operation on the random process, or a transform of a mean.

Stochastic operators present much more difficulty. Let us consider a random function or process $y(t)$. It can be regarded as a generalized vector in an infinite dimensional continuum or a (infinite) continuous (column) matrix, since it consists of an entire ensemble of sample functions or representatives. The elements of the matrix vary according to the distribution to which $y(t)$ is subject. A (stochastic) operator represented by a (stochastic) matrix (with elements subject to an appropriate distribution) now acts on the matrix of the input random process. Clearly, we expect only to find some statistical property of the result. Let us indicate the statistical measure by Γ. Thus, emphasizing the random processes by brackets { },

$$\{y(t)\} = H\{x(t)\},$$

$$\Gamma(y(t)\} = \Gamma H\{x(t)\}.$$

If we choose spectral density as our statistical measure Γ, we have $\Gamma\{y(t)\} = \Phi_y(f)$ and $\Gamma\{x(t)\} = \Phi_x(f)$. Noting that Γ and H do not commute (unless H is deterministic), we have derived Φ_y in terms of Φ_x in the integral relation of equation (2), or

$$\Phi_y = \Gamma H\{x(t)\} = \int K_H(s, f)\Phi_x(s)\, ds.$$

When the stochastic operation H and the random process x are statistically independent, the statistical operator Γ must act separately on each, i.e., providing ΓH is defined (and it should be if H is representable by a matrix) and if neither

ΓH nor Γx is zero (eliminating a zero-mean random process if Hx does not also have a zero mean) then

$$\Gamma Hx = \Gamma H \cdot \Gamma x.$$

This means the appropriate statistical operation over each ensemble, i.e., $\Gamma_H H \cdot \Gamma_x x$. Thus Γx is found by forming $\langle x(t)x^*(t+\tau)\rangle$ then making the transform $\int e^{2\pi i f\tau}\langle\ \rangle\, d\tau$. Similarly ΓH is given by

$$\Gamma H = \int e^{2\pi i f\tau}\langle H(t)H^*(t+\tau)\rangle\, d\tau.$$

Thus we can compute an appropriate autocorrelation and then a transform to get ΓH, or a spectral density of H, if we are given the stochastic matrix of H. Thus we can write

$$\Phi_y = \Phi_H \cdot \Phi_x = \int K_H(s,f)\Phi_x(s)\, ds.$$

If we can find Green's functions, the kernel K_H can be found and Φ_y determined. We can always do this in principle for deterministic operators, as we shall show, and at least for stochastic operators having the ergodicity property, as mentioned earlier. If H is given as a stochastic matrix, K_H and therefore Φ_y correspond to the transform of the autocorrelation of the matrices.

Finally, if H is a deterministic operator $\Gamma Hx = H\Gamma x$ or $\Phi_y = H\Phi_x$. Thus if H is the Laplace transform operator, i.e.,

$$H(\ ) = \int_0^\infty e^{-st}(\ )\, dt,$$

then

$$\Gamma Hx = \Gamma\int_0^\infty e^{-st}x(t)\, dt = \int_0^\infty e^{-st}\Gamma x(t)\, dt = H\Gamma x.$$

This clearly is not $\Gamma X(s)$ where $X(s)$ is the transform. Γ acts only on the random function $x(t)$. Further, even for stationary $x(t)$, Hx or $X(s)$ would not be stationary and $\Gamma X(s)$ would be undefined. But (supposing the statistical measure Γ to be the spectral density) we have

$$H\Gamma x = \int_0^\infty e^{-st}\Gamma x(t)\, dt = \int_0^\infty e^{-st}\Phi_x(s)\, dt,$$

noting the variable of Φ_x should be the same as the transform variable s. Thus

$$H\Gamma x = \Phi_x(s)\int_0^\infty e^{-st}\, dt = \frac{\Phi_x(s)}{s}$$

and we see that a statistical measure Γ (in this case the spectral density) of the (Laplace) transform of a random process $x(t)$ is given by a pole of magnitude Γx (the spectral density of $x(t)$ in the transform plane).

3.8. Stochastic Green's functions for correlation measures of input and output. The stochastic Green's functions or stochastic kernels for other statistical measures of input and output can be found in the same way as carried out for spectral density measures. Some of these kernels, e.g., those for correlation functions, are particularly valuable, both because we frequently want to determine the correlation matrix for a random process and because of our suggestion for determination of the nth joint distribution function, if we can first find all the output correlations in terms of the input correlations.

The kernel for the autocorrelation measure of input and output for the stationary case can be seen from the derivation of K_H in §1. Thus, the relation of the autocorrelations R_{Hx} of the output and R_x of the input for an operation H is

$$R_{Hx}(\beta) = \int_{-\infty}^{\infty} d\sigma G_H(\beta, \sigma) R_x(\sigma),$$

where the kernel G_H is given by

$$G_H(\beta, \sigma) = \int_{-\infty}^{\infty} d\tau \langle h(t, \tau) h^*(t + \beta, \tau + \sigma)\rangle.$$

Transformation of R_{Hx} and R_x to spectral densities again gives the relation involving the spectral density kernel $K_H(s, f)$. Because G_H is simpler than K_H, it is usually desirable to work with correlations although this investigation has emphasized spectra.

3.9. Nonstationary processes.[7] If we had not restricted ourselves to stationary processes in writing $R_{Hx}(\tau)$ (early in §2), we would instead write $R_{Hx}(t_1, t_2)$ or simply $R(t_1, t_2)$ given by

$$R(t_1, t_2) = \iint \langle h_i(t_1, \sigma) x(\sigma) h_i(t_2, \tau) x(\tau)\rangle \, d\sigma \, d\tau$$

$$= \iint R_x(\sigma, \tau) \langle h_i(t_1, \sigma) h_i(t_2, \tau)\rangle \, d\sigma \, d\tau,$$

where $R_x(\sigma, \tau)$ is the correlation of the input. Thus,

$$R(t_1, t_2) = \iint R_x(\sigma, \tau) H(t_1, t_2, \sigma, \tau) \, d\sigma \, d\tau,$$

where $H(t_1, t_2, \sigma, \tau)$ can be considered a kernel for the autocorrelation where the processes need not be stationary. When the processes are stationary, $R_x(\sigma, \tau) = R_x(\sigma - \tau)$, and H becomes $H(t_1 - \sigma, t_2 - \tau)$, a function of two variates as in $K_H(s, f)$.

3.10. Mapping of spaces. If the measure chosen for $x(t)$ and $y(t)$ is the spectrum Φ, we have

$$\Phi_y(f) = \int K(s, f) \Phi_x(s) \, ds.$$

If the measure chosen is the autocorrelation we have

$$R(\beta) = \int G(\beta, \sigma) R_x(\sigma) \, d\sigma.$$

[7] This treatment was suggested by Professor Balakrishnan, of the University of California at Los Angeles.

A mathematically more elegant formulation is to define a general statistical measure μ.[8] Thus the measure of y is $\mu(y)$ and the measure of x is $\mu(x)$. Now $\mu(y)$ may be $\Phi(f)$ or $R(\tau)$, for example. It means a chosen measure defined over the space of the random y. Similarly, $\mu(x)$ is defined over the space of $x(t)$ and may, for example, be the spectrum $\Phi_x(s)$. Now we can define

$$\Phi_x(s)\, ds = d\mu(x)$$

and write (1) as

$$\mu(y) = \int K(y, x)\, d\mu(x).$$

This form is now appropriate to any chosen measure operation. The kernel $K(y, x)$ maps from the space of x to the space of y and depends on the chosen μ.

A stochastic process $X(t)$,[9] can be described in terms of n-dimensional random variables $X(t_1), X(t_2), \cdots, X(t_n)$ by means of their families of distribution functions $F_n(t_1; X_1, t_2; X_2, \cdots, t_n; X_n)$. However, such a law will be meaningless on the quantum level since it implies the observation of a physical phenomenon at an instant determined by a point on a time scale, or generalizing immediately to random fields for precise measurements of position, momentum, or other variables. Such precise or instantaneous observations are inconsistent with basic postulates so a reinterpretation becomes necessary. However, it is not essential to consider random processes as families of random variables depending upon t (or $\mathbf{t}$). Instead, we think of X as an element in a function space. Each realization of the process $X(t)$ becomes one point in the function space. We define a general random element X with values in a space χ in the following way. Let $x(u)$ be a mapping from a measurable space of elementary events U into the space χ. The random element X is the result of the mapping. The elements of χ are the values which X can take. Fortet **[25]** gives some good examples. If X is a random variable, χ is the space R of real numbers. If X is a k-dimensional random variable, then χ is a k-dimensional Euclidean space. If X is a Gaussian random function of t on an interval (t_1, t_2) (with continuous covariance) then χ may be either the Hilbert space of those functions on (t_1, t_2) whose square is integrable or the space of all functions on (t_1, t_2).

Now we can extend the definition of stochastic operators to abstract spaces. Thus, the stochastic operator L acting on the random function X can be defined as the transformation which maps the space χ into a space κ representing values which LX can take. Any operator satisfies the definition so far; now we include linear transformations which themselves require statistical treatment in terms of realizations such as we gave $X(t)$. A single realization of a stochastic operator yields an ordinary operator or nonrandom matrix. It is possible that a formulation of quantum theory using stochastic operators may couple the advantages of the

[8] Called Γ in the section on statistical measure operations.

[9] We can generalize to a random field by writing $X(t, r)$ or simply letting t be a vector, i.e., X can be a function of several variables.

Feynman formulation with calculable expressions and a more natural appearance of probabilities. This work is intended to lay the foundation for later use in this connection. The extension will be of the nature of a general transformation theory involving topological spaces and functional analysis.

3.11. SOME GENERAL MATHEMATICAL PROPERTIES OF KERNELS AND OPERATORS. We note in passing some general mathematical properties of the kernel and its relations to stochastic operations and statistical measure operations. If $y = Hx$, where H is a stochastic operation on the stochastic process or random function x and we take the statistical measure μ of both sides of this equation, we have

$$\mu(y) = \mu(Hx) = \int K(y, x)\, d\mu(x) \doteq K\mu(x)$$

(it being assumed that μ does not assign finite measure to a point). In order that the integral operator K exists, μ must have certain properties with respect to H. From the above equation we can write the operator equation

$$\mu H - K\mu = 0.$$

Let us assume that the quantity $H\mu$ is operationally defined in some sense. We have already seen in the section on measure operations that μ does not commute with stochastic operations, i.e.,

$$\mu H \neq H\mu.$$

Since we have assumed that $H\mu$ is defined, we may define the operator ζ by

$$\mu H = H\mu + \zeta\mu.$$

Substituting this into the equation $\mu H - K\mu = 0$, we have

$$(H + \zeta - K)\mu = 0.$$

Thus, under the assumption that $H\mu$ exists, we have

$$K = H + \zeta + \sigma,$$

where σ is any operator such that

$$\sigma\mu = 0.$$

Conversely, if K exists and $H\mu$ is defined, then the equation $\mu H - K\mu = 0$ is satisfied if and only if there exists an operator ζ such that

$$\mu H = H\mu + \zeta\mu.$$

Combining the above considerations, we obtain the following result:

THEOREM. *If $H\mu$ is defined, there exists an operator K which satisfies the operator equation*

$$\mu H - K\mu = 0$$

if and only if there exists an operator ζ such that

$$\mu H = H\mu + \zeta\mu.$$

If these conditions are satisfied, then K is given by

$$K = H + \zeta + \sigma,$$

where σ is any operator such that $\sigma\mu = 0$.

Now assume that σ is zero so $H + \zeta$ represents K. The procedure is clear in principle. For a given stochastic operation and chosen measure operation, a kernel K exists if $\mu H - K\mu$ is a set of measure zero over the space of x on which H acts. The commutator of μ with H determines ζ. Then $K = H + \zeta$.

If we consider μ and H as operators each with a unique set of eigenvectors and suppose these sets are nonparallel, i.e., μ and H do not commute, then ζ is orthogonal to H, i.e., the eigenvectors of ζ are orthogonal to the eigenvectors of H. We are defining an operator ζ such that the eigenvectors of $H + \zeta$ commute with K. For H and μ such that ζ is sufficiently simple, it is conceivable that one could determine K from $H + \zeta$.

Now consider the inverse problem $Ly = x$ where we are particularly, but not exclusively, interested in the (unbounded) differential operator. Again we suppose that $\mu(x)$ is a well-defined measure given for x and we ask for $\mu(y)$. Write $\mu(Ly) = \mu(x)$. L and y are not statistically independent, so μ does not act separately on L and y as in the case Hx. Again the measure operation μ does not commute with the stochastic operation L. Suppose the commutation relation is

$$\mu L = L\mu + \chi\mu,$$

where again χ may be, and in general is, quite complicated. Now supposing $\mu(y)$ exists,

$$L\mu(y) + \chi\mu(y) = \mu(x)$$

or

$$LK\mu(x) + \chi K\mu(x) = \mu(x),$$

and we can write the operator relation

$$(L + \chi)K = 1.$$

Thus, given the measure operator μ and the stochastic operator L, the operator K is defined and exists when χ exists or when $\mu(y)$ and $\mu(x)$ exist. However this is not a method of calculating K since we do not know how to calculate the inverse of a stochastic matrix. We may also note that even if $\mu(x)$ exists, $\mu(y)$ may not exist. L is an unbounded operator (for the differential operators) which may be nonmeasure-preserving. The space of y must be suitably restricted. If a measure on x space is mapped into the same measure on y space, then it is clear that not all measures will work for an arbitrary L.

This shows $(L + \chi)(H + \zeta) = 1$ or $H + \zeta$ is inverse to $L + \chi$, but we started with the supposition that H was inverse to L by writing $y = Hx$ as the solution for $Ly = x$. This implies that $\chi H + L\zeta + \chi\zeta = 0$ or that χ and ζ are related for a particular L and its inverse H.

We will now generalize our remarks in the following manner. We have seen that we can write

$$\Phi_y(f) = \int ds\, K_H(s,f)\Phi_x(s)$$
$$\doteq W(s,f)\Phi_x(s)$$

defining $W(s,f)$ to mean the integral operator $\int ds K_H(s,f)$. The above expression is equivalent to

$$\Gamma Hx = W(s,f)\Gamma x,$$

where Γ represents the statistical measure operation of forming the spectral density. To keep track of the arguments f or s we use subscripts on the Γ operator. Thus, $\Phi_y(f) = \Gamma_f Hx$ and $\Phi_x(s) = \Gamma_s x$. Now

$$\Gamma_f Hx = W(s,f)\Gamma_s x = \Gamma H \cdot \Gamma_f x$$
$$= \Gamma H\delta(s-f)\Gamma_s x$$

so that

$$W(s,f) = \Gamma H\delta(s-f).$$

Also, knowing ΓH is a noncommuting pair, we write

$$\Gamma_f H = H\Gamma_f + \eta\Gamma_f,$$
$$\eta\Gamma_f = \Gamma_f H - H\Gamma_f$$
$$= \Gamma H\delta(s-f)\Gamma_s - H\delta(s-f)\Gamma_s$$
$$= [W(s,f) - H\delta(s-f)]\Gamma_s.$$

Thus, $\eta\Gamma_f$ is an essentially singular operation. η is related to our kernel operation $W(s,f)$ by an additive Dirac matrix. We have shown that η exists and have shown its specific structure. If Γ were to represent an ordinary averaging operation and H a stochastic operation, then ΓHx is a defined operation. $H\Gamma x$ is undefined, but the Dirac function behavior of η is just such as to eliminate the point in space from which the indeterminism results.

We can now state the following as a theorem:

THEOREM. *There exists a kernel $K(s,f)$ or the integral operator*

$$W(s,f) = \int_{-\infty}^{\infty} ds K_H(s,f)$$

if and only if there exists an η satisfying the commutation relation $\Gamma H - H\Gamma = \eta\Gamma$, such that

$$W(s,f) = \Gamma H\delta(s-f) + \chi,$$

where χ is an arbitrary operator such that $\chi\Gamma x = 0$, i.e., χ annihilates Γ.

We have shown $K(s,f)$ exists under the assumption $\Gamma Hx = \Gamma H \cdot \Gamma x$. Now one could consider all Γ, for example, that result in in $\Gamma Hx = \Gamma H \cdot \Gamma x$ plus some other term and again find a necessary and sufficient condition for existence of a kernel.

3.12. PHYSICAL MEASUREMENTS AND ESTIMATES OF STATISTICS. With a priori knowledge of probability distributions of given random processes we have calculated various statistical measures (moments, characteristic functions, spectral densities, etc.) for these distributions.

In physical measurements of random processes with unknown distributions (where there is no possibility of taking advantage of the Central Limit Theorem), a question of great importance we may ask is whether from a set of measurements we can now determine some of the statistical properties (mean, variance, etc., . . .).

Suppose we have available N measurements of a basic experiment defining a process or N observations or measurements of the value of a sample function of a given random process at N different instants of time. This set of N values is a sample point in an N-dimensional space characterizing the entire experiment. Clearly, this single point will not uniquely determine the statistical property we seek. In this situation the statistician speaks of making an estimate of the particular statistical property by finding a function or statistic of the set of results or values which gives a reasonably close estimate of the statistical property for the process. This is called sampling theory and is discussed by Davenport [**22**], Cramer [**11**, Part III], and others. It is clear from the theory and our own results on the random sampling example, that we can now give more generalized sampling theorems for situations in which it may matter that the N instants of time at which measurements are made may not be regularly spaced but are subject to a distribution.[10] Such a case might occur, for example, if the observations were to be made whenever an incoming particle triggered the observing apparatus.

The application of the theory to the statistical description of mechanical systems of macroscopic dimensions is a clear possibility. We can assume a stochastic process corresponding to the measurement of an n-tuple of macroscopic observables. Then a theory of repeated observations or measurements can be made using stochastic operators, where some parameter of the observation is unknown and can only be given a distribution.

4. The inverse problem: stochastic differential equations.

4.1. DIFFERENTIAL OPERATORS. We have discussed in §3 various statistical measures for the action of a linear stochastic operator on a random process, or equivalently, a linear (stochastic) transformation of a random process. A particular measure of interest, the spectral density measure, involves a stochastic kernel or spectral density Green's function K_H for a stochastic operator H. This formulation is useful in some problems involving the statistical optimization of complex systems and in the synthesis of models for some physical phenomena. In other

[10] Since the term random sampling is already used by statisticians to indicate that the sample is chosen from a general population in a random manner, it might be better to call this stochastic sampling.

physical problems, however, the convenient formulation involves a "stochastic differential equation" rather than a given operator. Generally, linear operators, linear transformation, linear filters, linear networks, and linear control systems are equivalent mathematical systems describable by systems of linear integro-differential equations. The forcing functions are the inputs. The outputs or dependent variables appear as the operands. For simplicity, we consider a single input, single output equation in the form

$$Ly = x$$

where

$$L = \sum_{\nu=0}^{n} a_\nu(t) \frac{d^\nu}{dt^\nu}$$

and both $a_\nu(t)$ and $x(t)$ are stochastic. Samuels **[26]**, Sundstrom **[27]**, and others have pointed out that such problems arise in the study of linear servomechanisms in which several parameters are undergoing noise modulations **[28; 29]** and in certain propagation problems in stochastically varying media **[30–33]** or media with random inhomogeneities.

We now consider the equation $Ly = x$, where L is the previously defined stochastic operator and $x(t)$ is a random function. Defining H as the operator inverse to L, we investigate the possibility of determining the kernel K_H for H by examining L and avoiding the problem of inversion, i.e., not determining H. We assume reasonable restrictions on L.

1. The inverse must exist. Thus L must be nonsingular, i.e., the determinant of the matrix corresponding to L must never become zero as the elements vary according to some distribution.

2. K_H is stationary or, at least, the coefficients in L can be translated, i.e., have stationary properties.

Now, it is possible that differential equations can be solved in this sense, i.e., in terms of a statistical measure, where the coefficients are stochastic as well as where the coefficients can be considered to be chosen from random processes. The previous solution for a statistical measure of y, given H, is the solution to the differential equation if the kernel can be determined from L, i.e., in terms of given statistics of the random coefficients. Our stationarity condition means simply that the probability distributions of the random parameters are such that the stochastic coefficients (time functions) in the differential equation describe stationary processes during a time interval of interest, i.e., the statistical characteristics during the interval are constants. In order to have a full description of the processes, the time interval must be at least so long that the correlation between values at the limit points can be neglected. Actually, widesense stationarity is sufficient for the coefficients.

4.2. Evaluation of stochastic Green's function for a differential operator. A series of papers by Sundstrom **[34]** leads to the following approach for expressing the kernel in terms of the coefficients of the differential equation. Treating x not as a random process but as a defined continuous member of the x

process in the interval $[-T/2, T/2]$, and similarly treating y and a_ν, we define Fourier transforms of the "input" x, the "output" y, and the coefficients a_ν.

$$x(t) = \int_{-\infty}^{\infty} X(f)\, e^{2\pi i f t}\, df,$$

(4) $$y(t) = \int_{-\infty}^{\infty} Y(f)\, e^{2\pi i f t}\, df,$$

$$a_\nu(t) = \int_{-\infty}^{\infty} A_\nu(f)\, e^{2\pi i f t}\, df.$$

Now if $y(t)$ is differentiated ν times, we have

$$y^{(\nu)}(t) = \int_{-\infty}^{\infty} (2\pi i f)^\nu\, Y(f)\, e^{2\pi i f t}\, df.$$

Substituting in the differential equation

$$\sum_{\nu=0}^{n} a_\nu(t) y^{(\nu)}(t) = x(t).$$

Multiplying by $e^{-2\pi i s t}$ and integrating from $-T/2$ to $T/2$, we obtain:

(5) $$\int_{-\infty}^{\infty} df\, \mathscr{A}(f, s)\, Y(f) = X(s)$$

as a formal relation between input and output transforms where:

(6) $$\mathscr{A}(f, s) = \sum_\nu (2\pi i f)^\nu A_\nu(s - f).$$

However, it is clear that we need an expression for $Y(f)$ in terms of $X(s)$, since ensemble averages to be taken later must be separable and, while the x can be statistically independent of the a_ν, the output y cannot, except in a trivial case, and except for one special case of some interest considered by Samuels **[26]**. He analyzes random linear systems containing one or more nonindependent parameters under the restriction that the parameter processes and the solution or output process have very widely separated spectra. He considers an equation of our form $Ly = x$ with the $a_\nu(t)$ and the $x(t)$ as prescribed random functions, supposing as in our treatment that $x(t)$ is statistically independent of any $a_\nu(t)$ while the $a_\nu(t)$ may or may not be correlated with each other. Following his treatment we assume the mathematical expectation[11] $\langle a_\nu(t)\rangle$ of each coefficient a_ν exists and write

$$a_\nu(t) = \langle a_\nu(t)\rangle + \alpha_\nu(t)$$

so that α_ν represents the randomly fluctuating part of $a_\nu(t)$. The differential equation can now be written

$$Hy = \sum_0^n a_\nu(t) \frac{d^\nu y}{dt^\nu} = x(t) - \sum_0^n \alpha_\nu \frac{d^\nu y}{dt^\nu}.$$

[11] Mathematical expectation or statistical average or mean or ensemble average of a continuous random variable $g(x)$ is $E\{g(x)\} = \int_{-\infty}^{\infty} g(x)p(x)\, dx = \langle g(x)\rangle$.

Now the left side can again be viewed as an operator acting on y, but this is now a nonrandom operator H, and a Green's function can immediately be written, say $h(t, \tau)$, for the left side alone. Now the solution is

$$y(t) = \int_{t_0}^{t} h(t, \tau)x(\tau)\, d\tau - \int_{t_0}^{t} h(t, \tau) \sum_{\nu=0}^{n} \frac{d^\nu y(\tau)}{d\tau^\nu} \alpha_\nu(\tau)\, d\tau + \sum_{\nu=1}^{n} c_\nu \varphi(t),$$

where the φ_ν are a fundamental set of independent solutions of the homogeneous nonrandom equation $Hy = 0$ and the c_ν are arbitrary constants. The upper limit can be ∞ for a realizable system. The lower limit is a matter of memory. Using t_0 instead of $-\infty$ implies simply that all earlier values are not significant. Considering infinite limits

$$y(t) = F(t) - \int_{-\infty}^{\infty} K(t, \tau) y(\tau)\, d\tau,$$

where

$$K(t, \tau) = h(t, \tau) \sum_{\nu=0}^{n} \alpha_\nu(\tau) \frac{d^\nu}{d\tau^\nu}$$

$$= \sum_{\nu=0}^{n} (-1)^\nu \frac{\partial^\nu}{\partial \tau^\nu} [\alpha_\nu(\tau) h(t, \tau)],$$

$$F(t) = \int_{-\infty}^{\infty} h(t, \tau)x(\tau)\, d\tau + \sum_{\nu=1}^{n} c_\nu \varphi_\nu(t).$$

Now multiply $y(t_1)$ and $y^*(t_2)$ and average.

$$\langle y(t_1) y^*(t_2) \rangle = \langle F(t_1) F^*(t_2) \rangle - \int_{-\infty}^{\infty} \langle K(t, \tau) F^*(t_2) y(\tau) \rangle\, d\tau$$

$$- \int_{-\infty}^{\infty} \langle K^*(t_2, \tau) F(t_1) y^*(\tau) \rangle\, d\tau$$

$$+ \iint_{-\infty}^{\infty} \langle K(t_1, \tau_1) K^*(t_2, \tau_2) y(\tau_1) y^*(\tau_2) \rangle\, d\tau_1\, d\tau_2.$$

Assume the α_ν are stationary and ergodic and the $\langle a_\nu \rangle$ are constants so $h(t, \tau)$ is $h(t - \tau)$. Then it is true that $y(t)$ and $\alpha_\nu(t) y(t)$, etc., are stationary and ergodic. Also, Samuels states if the $\langle a_\nu(t) \rangle$ approach constants as $t \to \infty$ then the products in question are "almost ergodic" for large t. We then assume both K and y are ergodic. Now we replace ensemble averages by time averages,[12] e.g.,

$$E\{G_1(\xi) G_2(\xi)\} = \lim_{x \to \infty} \frac{1}{2x} \int_{-x}^{x} G_1(\xi) G_2(\xi)\, d\xi = \bar{G}_1 \bar{G}_2$$

[12] Time averages are indicated by a bar over a single letter without exponents. For more complicated expressions we will use the symbol [ ]$_{\text{av}}$.

if the rates at which the functions change are reasonably far apart, e.g., if G_1 is a rapidly changing quantity and G_2 is slowly varying, in which case the plot of the autocorrelation of G_2 is wide and that of G_1 is very narrow, so the spectral densities are well separated narrow peaks. (G_2 close to zero frequency and G_1 farther out.) This is also shown by integrating by parts assuming one rate, say $G_2'(\xi) \simeq 0$. Now we can make the separations

$$\langle K(t, \tau)F^*(t_2)y(\tau)\rangle = \langle K(t, \tau)\rangle\langle F^*(t_2)y(\tau)\rangle,$$
$$\langle K^*(t_2, \tau)F(t_1)y^*(\tau)\rangle = \langle K^*(t_2, \tau)\rangle\langle F(t_1)y^*(\tau)\rangle,$$
$$\langle K(t_1, \tau_1)K^*(t_2, \tau_2)y(\tau_1)y^*(\tau_2)\rangle = \langle K(t_1, \tau_1)K^*(t_2, \tau_2)\rangle\langle y(\tau_1)y^*(\tau_2)\rangle.$$

Substituting and noting $\langle K\rangle = 0$, since $\langle \alpha_\nu\rangle = 0$,

$$\langle y(t_1)y^*(t_2)\rangle = R_y(t_1, t_2),$$
$$\langle F(t_1)F^*(t_2)\rangle = R_F(t_1, t_2),$$

we now have

$$R_y(t_1, t_2) = R_F(t_1, t_2) + \iint_{-\infty}^{\infty} \langle K(t_1, \tau_1)K^*(t_2, \tau_2)\rangle R_y(\tau_1, \tau_2)\, d\tau_1\, d\tau_2.$$

The above kernel is given by

$$\langle K(t_1, \tau_1)K^*(t_2, \tau_2)\rangle = \sum_{j,k=0}^{n} (-1)^{j+k} \frac{\partial^{j+k}}{\partial\tau_1^k \partial\tau_2^j} \{\rho_{kj}(\tau_1, \tau_2)H(t_1, \tau_1)H(t_2, \tau_2)\},$$

which is a convenient form when the various cross correlations ρ_{kj} are given. If the cross-spectral densities are specified and $\langle a_\nu(t)\rangle$ are constants, a more convenient form is obtained by taking a double Fourier transform of $R_y(t_1, t_2)$ thus defining

$$\iint_{-\infty}^{\infty} e^{i(\zeta_1 t_1 + \zeta_2 t_2)} R_y(t_1, t_2)\, dt_1\, dt_2 = \Phi_y(\zeta_1, \zeta_2)$$

with inverse

$$R_y(t_1, t_2) = \frac{1}{4\pi^2} \iint_{-\infty}^{\infty} e^{-i(\zeta_1 t_2 + \zeta_2 t_2)} \Phi_y(\zeta_1, \zeta_2)\, d\zeta_1\, d\zeta_2.$$

We can now write

$$\Phi_y(\zeta_1, \zeta_2) = \Phi_F(\zeta_1, \zeta_2) + \sum_{k,j=0}^{n} \frac{(-1)^{k+j}}{4\pi^2} \iint_{-\infty}^{\infty} \Phi_H(\zeta_1)$$
$$\times\, \Phi_H(\zeta_2)\beta_1^k\beta_2^j\Phi_{\rho_{kj}}(\zeta_1 - \beta_1;\ \zeta_2 - \beta_2)\Phi_y(\beta_1, \beta_2)\, d\beta_1\, d\beta_2,$$

where $\Phi_{\rho_{kj}}$ is the cross-spectral density of the coefficients. If the α_ν are wide-sense stationary,

$$\Phi_{\rho_{kj}}(\zeta_1 - \beta_1; \zeta_2 - \beta_2) = 2\pi\Phi_{\rho_{kj}}(\zeta_2 - \beta_2)\delta(\zeta_1 - \beta_1 + \zeta_2 - \beta_2).$$

Now we have a second-order linear integral equation which can be solved in closed form. Samuels develops a mean square stability theory and considers some special cases, e.g., an RLC circuit with randomly varying capacitance. He applies Kirchoff's laws to get a differential equation, then considers mean-square stability, i.e., regions where

$$\lim_{t\to\infty} \langle y^2(t)\rangle < M$$

where M is a finite constant. Mean-square capacity deviation is plotted against damping of the circuit to show regions of stable operation.

These results, though interesting, are not sufficient for our purpose since they apply to a special case where the ensemble averages can be separated on the basis of rate. Furthermore, we would really like a solution for the output in terms of the input (see §1) and the parameter variation rather than in terms of an integral involving the output again.

At this point, we will first note that some interesting approximation methods are possible for special cases where $a_\nu(t)$ are given by

$$a_\nu(t) = \langle a_\nu(t)\rangle + \alpha_\nu(t) = a_\nu + \alpha_\nu(t)$$

where we suppose the a_ν are constant and the $\alpha_\nu(t)$ are zero-mean random processes such that $\langle\alpha_\nu(t)\rangle = 0$. Thus α_ν represents the randomly fluctuating part of $a_\nu(t)$. Now the differential equation $Ly = x$ becomes

$$Hy = \sum_{\nu=0}^{n} a_\nu \frac{d^\nu y}{dt^\nu} = x(t) - \sum_{\nu=0}^{n} \alpha_\nu \frac{d^\nu y}{dt^\nu}$$

where the left side is again an operator acting on y but a nonrandom operator for which a Green's function $h(t, \tau)$, actually $h(t - \tau)$ if a_ν is a constant as stated, can be written. The solution is

$$y(t) = \int_{-\infty}^{\infty} h(t, \tau)x(\tau)\, d\tau - \int_{-\infty}^{\infty} h(t, \tau) \sum_{\nu=0}^{n} \frac{d^\nu y(\tau)}{d\tau^\nu} \alpha_\nu(\tau)\, d\tau$$

if we neglect the solution of the homogeneous nonrandom equation $Hy = 0$. Let us call the first integral $F(t)$ and rewrite the second as $\int K(t, \tau)y(\tau)\, d\tau$. A Born approximation, or method of successive approximations, is promising now. Thus suppose $y(t)$ can be expanded in a series which is convergent with probability 1. Let

$$y(t) = \sum_{i=0}^{\infty} (-1)^i y_i(t).$$

Then

$$y(t) = F(t) - \int K(t, \tau) \sum_{i=0}^{\infty} (-1)^i y_i(\tau)\, d\tau.$$

If we write $y_0 = F(t) = \int h(t, \tau)x(\tau)\, d\tau$, we see each y_i is given in terms of the preceding one; thus,

$$y_i = \int K(t, \tau)y_{i-1}(\tau)\, d\tau \qquad (i = 1, 2, \cdots).$$

Convergence properties remain to be considered but one notes immediately the separation of the ensemble averages involving the y and the α

$$\langle K(t,\tau)F^*(t_2)y(\tau)\rangle = \langle K(t,\tau)F^*(t_2)[y_0(\tau) - y_1(\tau) + y_2(\tau) - \cdots]\rangle.$$

The first term is

$$\langle K(t,\tau)F^*(t_2)y_0(\tau)\rangle = \langle K(t,\tau)\rangle\langle F^*(t_2)F(\tau)\rangle = 0.$$

The second term

$$\langle K(t,\tau)F^*(t_2)y_1(\tau)\rangle = \int \langle K(t,\tau)K(\tau,\sigma)\rangle F^*(t_2)F(\sigma)\,d\sigma$$

etc. Where $L = \langle L\rangle + \Delta L$ and $\Delta L << \langle L\rangle$ so there is only a small amount of randomness, the problem simplifies considerably. A trivial case shows that $\langle y\rangle$ can be written immediately in terms of x and a kernel depending only on averages of L. A more interesting result is obtained by considering a second order differential equation [35].

$$\frac{d^2y}{dt^2} + 2n\frac{dy}{dt} + [1 + \varepsilon\xi(t)]y = 0 \qquad (n << 1)$$

where $\xi(t)$ is a random function and ε is a small parameter. We assume the correlation function $R(\Delta t) = \langle\xi(t + \Delta t)\xi(t)\rangle$ is known and $\langle\xi(t)\rangle = 0$. By the substitution of variables

$$z = e^{nt}y, \qquad \tau = t\sqrt{(1 + n^2)}$$

this equation is reduced to

$$\frac{d^2z}{d\tau^2} + z = -\varepsilon'\xi(\tau)z \qquad \varepsilon' = \frac{\varepsilon}{1 + n^2}$$

which is now in a form for successive approximations. Thus we see we can handle first order linear equations whose integration can be carried out [36] and second order equations where assumptions can be made of small fluctuations in the parameters. We are interested though in further consideration of the problem of finding the statistical characteristics of solutions directly and in avoiding the restriction to perturbation methods.

Now returning to equation (5), we define a new function $B(\sigma, s)$ by the following orthogonality requirement

(7) $$\int_{-\infty}^{\infty} ds\,\mathscr{A}(f, s)B(\sigma, s) = \delta(f - \sigma).$$

From (5) and (7) we immediately obtain

(8) $$Y(f) = \int_{-\infty}^{\infty} ds\,B(f, s)X(s).$$

The power spectrum (of the representative member of the ensemble we have chosen) is then given by

$$G_y(f) = \lim_{T\to\infty} \frac{2}{T}\iint_{-\infty}^{\infty} d\sigma\, ds\, B(\sigma,f)B^*(s,f)X(\sigma)X^*(s).$$

The spectrum of the process is $\langle G_y(f)\rangle$ or

$$\Phi_y(f) = \lim_{T\to\infty} \frac{2}{T}\iint_{-\infty}^{\infty} \langle B(\sigma,f)B^*(s,f)X(\sigma)X^*(s)\rangle\, d\sigma\, ds.$$

But B depends only on the coefficients a_ν not on the input x so that the parameter processes and the input process are statistically independent. Thus,

$$\Phi_y(f) = \lim_{T\to\infty} \frac{2}{T}\iint_{-\infty}^{\infty} \langle B(\sigma,f)B^*(s,f)\rangle\langle X(\sigma)X^*(s)\rangle\, d\sigma\, ds,$$

$$\Phi_y(f) = \lim_{T\to\infty} \frac{2}{T}\iint_{-\infty}^{\infty} \langle B(\sigma,f)B^*(s,f)\rangle\left\langle \int_{-T/2}^{T/2} x(t)\,e^{-2\pi i\sigma t}dt \int_{-T/2}^{T/2} x^*(t)\,e^{2\pi i s t}dt \right\rangle d\sigma\, ds,$$

$$\Phi_y(f) = \lim_{T\to\infty} \frac{2}{T}\iint_{-\infty}^{\infty}\iint_{-T/2}^{T/2} d\sigma\, ds\, du\, dv\, \langle B(\sigma,f)B^*(s,f)\rangle\langle x(u)x^*(v)\rangle\, e^{2\pi i(sv-\sigma u)}.$$

If the input is stationary ($v = u + \tau$) this becomes

$$\lim_{T\to\infty} \frac{2}{T}\int\cdots\int d\sigma\, ds\, du\, d\tau \langle B(\sigma,f)B^*(s,f)\rangle\langle x(u)x^*(u+\tau)\rangle\, e^{2\pi i(s-\sigma)u}\, e^{2\pi i s\tau}.$$

But, $\langle x(u)x^*(u+\tau)\rangle = R_x(\tau)$ and $\int R_x(\tau)\, e^{2\pi i s\tau}\, d\tau = \Phi_x$ in the limit $T\to\infty$. Thus we can write our earlier result from §2

$$\Phi_y(f) = \int ds K_H(s,f)\Phi_x(s)$$

with K_H now defined by

$$K_H(s,f) = \int_{-\infty}^{\infty} d\sigma \int_{-\infty}^{\infty} du\, \langle B(\sigma,f)B^*(s,f)\rangle\, e^{2\pi i(s-\sigma)u}$$

$$= \int d\sigma \langle B(\sigma,f)B^*(s,f)\rangle \int du\, e^{2\pi i(s-\sigma)u}$$

$$= \int d\sigma\, \delta(s-\sigma)\langle B(\sigma,f)B^*(s,f)\rangle$$

or

(9) $$K_H(s,f) = \langle |B(s,f)|^2\rangle,$$

so that the stochastic kernel has been expressed in terms of the coefficients of the differential equation. While this result establishes the existence of the connection we were seeking in a surprisingly simple relationship, it can only be useful in solving problems or specific equations if we can evaluate it, using the definitions (6) and (7). Now the difficulties become clear, for if $\mathscr{A}$ and B are represented by matrices, these matrices must be orthogonal and the two are obviously not independent so we cannot make separations in any ensemble averaging. Thus, we have not shown a prescription for the solution of differential equations unless a method can be shown for finding the ensemble mean given by (9) in terms of the given statistics of the $a_\nu(t)$.

We return now to our condition defining B in terms of $\mathscr{A}$, i.e.,

$$\int_{-\infty}^{\infty} ds\, \mathscr{A}(f, s)B(\sigma, s) = \delta(f - \sigma).$$

If we write $B(s, \sigma)$ instead of $B(\sigma, s)$ (this was an arbitrary choice) and conceive the function $\mathscr{A}(f, s)$ to be a matrix by imagining the f as representing a continuous row index and s a continuous column index, the left-hand side looks like a matrix product while the right-hand side is similar to the identity matrix except that the Dirac δ in place of a Kronecker δ implies ∞ on the diagonal rather than a series of 1's. By analogy we are justified in applying the term "inverse" to B. More specifically, we call B an inverse functional of $\mathscr{A}$. Now, it is obvious that $\langle \mathscr{A}\mathscr{A}^* \rangle$ can be given explicitly in terms of the correlations R_{a_ν} for the random coefficients $a_\nu(t)$ in $\mathscr{L}$. To see this we use the definition of A_ν and write

$$\langle A_\nu(s - f)A_\nu^*(s - f)\rangle = \iint_{-T/2}^{T/2} \langle a_\nu(u)a_\nu(v)\rangle\, du\, dv.$$

Let $v = u + \tau$, then the above quantity becomes

$$\int_{-T/2}^{T/2} du \int_{-T/2-u}^{T/2-u} d\tau\, R_{a_\nu}(\tau).$$

Finally,

$$\langle \mathscr{A}(f, s)\mathscr{A}^*(f, s)\rangle = \sum_\mu \sum_\nu (-1)^\mu (2\pi i f)^{\mu+\nu} \int_{-T/2}^{T/2} du \int_{-T/2-u}^{T/2-u} d\tau\, R_{a_\nu}(\tau). \tag{10}$$

If we could write B in terms of $\mathscr{A}$, form $\langle BB^* \rangle$ and possibly expand in a series of functions or powers of $\langle \mathscr{A}\mathscr{A}^* \rangle$, we might have a computational method of interest. Of course, we are still suggesting the inversion of a matrix, but a much simpler one than the problem of inversion of the matrix corresponding to $\mathscr{L}$. Our matrices are continuous and infinite here but can be made discrete by originally using series instead of transforms. Consider the case of discrete, ordinary or deterministic matrices and the matrix product $AB = I$, where I is the identity matrix. Now B is called the inverse or reciprocal matrix and is indicated by A^{-1}. To see how A^{-1} is written in terms of A let A be represented by the array of elements:

$$A = \left\| \begin{matrix} a_{11} & a_{12} \cdots a_{1n} \\ a_{21} & a_{22} \cdots \\ \cdot & \\ \cdot & \\ \cdot & \\ a_{n1} & a_{n2} \cdots a_{nn} \end{matrix} \right\|.$$

We know, of course, that the determinant of A, or $|A|$, can be expanded by cofactors as

$$|A| = \sum_j a_{ij}A_{ij} = \sum_i a_{ij}A_{ij},$$

if we define A_{ij} as the cofactor of a_{ij}. We know further that $|A|$ vanishes if any two rows or columns of A are the same. Thus,

$$\sum_j a_{kj}A_{ij} = \sum_j a_{ji}A_{jk} = 0 \qquad i \neq k.$$

Combining these statements

(11) $$\sum_j a_{ij}A_{kj} = \sum_j a_{ji}A_{jk} = |A|\,\delta_{ki},$$

which says simply that expansion by a row or column i in terms of the cofactors of a row or column k vanishes if $i \neq k$ and is equal to $|A|$ when $i = k$.

Now equation (11) looks like a matrix product. Set $\hat{a}_{ij} = A_{ji}$ and (11) becomes

$$\sum_j a_{ij}\hat{a}_{jk} = \sum_j \hat{a}_{kj}a_{ji} = |A|\,\delta_{ki},$$

which can be written in matrix form as

$$A\hat{A} = \hat{A}A = |A|I$$

if

$$\hat{A} = \|\hat{a}_{ij}\| = \left\| \begin{matrix} A_{11} & A_{21} \cdots A_{n1} \\ A_{12} \cdots & \\ \cdot & \\ \cdot & \\ \cdot & \\ A_{1n} \cdots & A_{nn} \end{matrix} \right\|.$$

Now following Hadley [37] we define

(12) $$A^{-1} = (1/|A|)\hat{A}.$$

Then

$$AA^{-1} = A^{-1}A = A\hat{A}/|A| = I.$$

If A is nonsingular, it has an inverse defined by (12) and further, the inverse is unique.

To sum up we say if $AB = I$ then $B = \hat{A}/|A|$ where we write $\hat{A}$ to mean the so-called adjoint matrix of A where this overworked term is not to be confused with the Hermitian adjoint $A^\dagger$ since $\hat{A}$ is found from the transpose of the cofactors of the elements of A not the transpose of the complex conjugates of the elements of A.

Thus, in our own problem with the defined (but discretized) $\mathscr{A}$ and B we write

$$\langle BB^* \rangle = \left\langle \frac{\hat{\mathscr{A}}\hat{\mathscr{A}}^*}{|\mathscr{A}||\mathscr{A}|^*} \right\rangle = \left\langle \frac{\hat{\mathscr{A}}\hat{\mathscr{A}}^*}{|\mathscr{A}\mathscr{A}^\dagger|} \right\rangle,$$

which means precisely the average of the following array

$$\frac{\begin{Vmatrix} A_{11} & A_{21} & \cdots & A_{n1} \\ A_{12} & \cdots & & \\ \cdot & & & \\ \cdot & & & \\ \cdot & & & \\ A_{1n} & \cdots & & A_{nn} \end{Vmatrix} \begin{Vmatrix} A_{11}^* & A_{21}^* & \cdots & A_{n1}^* \\ \cdot & & & \\ \cdot & & & \\ \cdot & & & \\ A_{1n}^* & \cdots & & A_{nn}^* \end{Vmatrix}}{\begin{vmatrix} a_{11} & a_{12} & \cdots & a_{1n} \\ a_{21} & a_{22} & \cdots & \\ \cdot & & & \\ \cdot & & & \\ \cdot & & & \\ a_{n1} & \cdots & & a_{nn} \end{vmatrix} \begin{vmatrix} a_{11}^* & a_{12}^* & \cdots & a_{1n}^* \\ \cdot & & & \\ \cdot & & & \\ \cdot & & & \\ a_{n1}^* & \cdots & & a_{nn}^* \end{vmatrix}},$$

where a_{ij} are the elements of $\mathscr{A}$ and A_{ij} are the cofactors of a_{ij}.

The difficulty in finding $|\mathscr{A}|$ and the above expression is avoided in quantum theory by using approximate representations in which $\mathscr{A}$ is diagonal. The general problem here appears to be enormously difficult even with arbitrary limitations of the number of rows and columns for successive approximations. Since we do know $\langle \mathscr{A}\mathscr{A}^* \rangle$ explicitly it is logical to ask if we can write our expression in some series of powers of $\langle \mathscr{A}\mathscr{A}^* \rangle$ or some function of $\langle \mathscr{A}\mathscr{A}^* \rangle$ which could then be written as a function of R_{a_ν}. It is not clear how the desired expansion is to be made so the problem is not completed. In the referenced dissertation a differential equation with a random Gaussian coefficient is studied at length and a solution is obtained. Perhaps then if the expansion is used for the same problem, we will be able to see how it can be done or if $\langle \mathscr{A}\mathscr{A}^* \rangle$ is already the first term. We know the series terminates in that problem and we can see that the kernel is a function of the correlation of the random coefficient alone which is easily calculable. It seems reasonable to expect that our desired calculation can be made for that same (Gaussian) case.

Whether this general problem can be solved is still a question. However much else can be done and many possibilities exist for approximation and asymptotic methods. Further, we note that for equations where ordinary Green's functions can be found once explicit time dependences are obtained by making Karhunen–Loève expansions of the random coefficients, we can then obtain stochastic Green's functions. Conditions under which this can be done have been discussed in a recent paper [1] and in a dissertation submitted in April 1961. However, much work remains to be done in investigation of the connections between this and the matrix method. Also, it is often true that knowledge of a Green's function for a simple nonrandom problem can be used to generate stochastic Green's functions or approximate stochastic Green's functions for randomized versions of the same problem, i.e., the class of known Green's functions can be thought of as generating stochastic Green's functions for more difficult problems involving random media or properties. Examples have been discussed elsewhere [1] and more extensive treatments in terms of the general matrix problem will appear in a forthcoming book. A rigorous reformulation will be desirable connecting with much recent work in obtaining probabilistic analogues of well-known results in the theory of deterministic operator equations in studying properties of mappings in generalized spaces, existence, uniqueness, convergence, measurability properties, and applications to problems in physics.

References

1. G. Adomian, *Linear stochastic operators*, Rev. Modern Phys. **35** (1963), 185–207.

2. A. Spaček, *Zufallige Gleichungen*, Czechoslovak Math. J. **5** (**80**) (1955), 462–466.

3. O. Hanš, *Random operator equations*, Proc. 4th Berkeley Sympos. on Math. Statist. and Prob., Vol. II, pp. 185–202, Univ. of California Press, Berkeley, Calif., 1961.

4. J. B. Keller, *Propagation through random media*, Proc. Sympos. Appl. Math., Vol. 16, pp. 145–170, Amer. Math. Soc., Providence, R. I., 1964.

5. W. C. Hoffman, *The electromagnetic field in a randomly inhomogeneous medium*, Proc. Sympos. Appl. Math., Vol. 16, pp. 117–144, Amer. Math. Soc., Providence, R. I., 1964.

6. M. Kac, *Lectures in probability and related topics in physical sciences*, Interscience, New York, 1959.

7. J. L. Lawson and G. E. Uhlenbeck, *Threshold signals*, Massachusetts Institute of Technology Radiation Laboratory Series, Vol. 24, McGraw-Hill, New York, 1950.

8. A. Kolmogorov, *Grundbegriffe der Wahrscheinlichkeitsrechnung*, Springer, Berlin, 1933; *Foundations of the theory of probability*, Chelsea, New York, 1948.

9. M. C. Wang and G. E. Uhlenbeck, *On the theory of the brownian motion*. II, Rev. Modern Phys. **17** (1945), 323–342.

10. A. Markoff, *Extension of the law of large numbers to dependent events*, Bull. Soc. Phys. Math. Kazan (USSR) (2) **15** (1906), 135–156.

11. H. Cramer, *Mathematical methods of statistics*, Princeton Univ. Press, Princeton, N. J., 1946.

12. G. D. Birkhoff, *Proof of the ergodic theorem*, Proc. Nat. Acad. Sci. U. S. A. **17** (1931), 650–655, 656–660.

13. A. Ya. Khinchin, *Mathematical foundations of statistical mechanics*, Chapters 2, 3, Dover, New York, 1953.

14. J. L. Doob, *Stochastic processes*, Chapters 10, 11, Wiley, New York, 1953.

15. M. Loève, *Probability theory*, Chapter 9, Van Nostrand, Princeton, N. J., 1955.

16. M. Kac and A. J. F. Siegert, *On the theory of noise in radio receivers with square law detectors*, J. Appl. Phys. **18** (1947), 383–397.

17. A. Blanc-Lapierre and R. Fortet, *Théorie des fonctions aléatoires*, Masson et Cie, Paris, 1953.

18. A. J. F. Siegert and D. A. Darling, *On the distribution of certain functionals of Markov processes*, Rand report P429, 1954.

19. A. J. F. Siegert, *Passage of stationary processes through linear devices*, IRE Trans. **PGIT-3** (1954).

20. D. A. Darling and A. J. F. Siegert, *A systematic approach to a class of problems in the theory of noise and other random phenomena*, IRE Trans. on Information Theory, **3** (1957), no. 1, 32–37; 38–43. March, 1957.

21. J. C. Samuels and A. C. Eringen, *On stochastic linear systems*, Tech. Rep. No. 11, Division of Engineering Sciences, Purdue University, Lafayette, Ind., 1957.

22. W. B. Davenport and W. L. Root, *An introduction to the theory of random signals and noise*, McGraw-Hill, New York, 1958.

23. J. E. Moyal, *Stochastic processes and statistical physics*, J. Roy. Statist. Soc. Ser. B **11** (1949), 150–210.

24. P. Lévy, *Processus stochastiques et mouvement brownien*, Gauthier-Villars, Paris, 1948.

25. R. Fortet, *Recent advances in probability theory*, Some aspects of analysis and probability, pp. 169–240, Wiley, New York, 1958.

26. J. C. Samuels, IRE Trans. Circuit Theory, CT–6 (Special Supplement), 1959.

27. M. Sundstrom, *Some statistical problems in the theory of servomechanisms*, Ark. Mat. **2** (1951), 52.

28. A. Rosenbloom, *Analysis of randomly time-varying linear systems*, Ph.D. thesis, University of California, Los Angeles, Calif., 1954 (unpublished).

29. J. F. Buchan and R. S. Raven, *Gain modulation of servomechanisms*, IRE (Wescon) Convention Record, Part 4, August 1957 (unpublished).

30. P. G. Bergman, *Propagation of radiation in a medium with random inhomogeneities*, Phys. Rev. (2) **70** (1946), 486.

31. D. Mintzer, *Wave propagation in randomly inhomogeneous medium*. III, J. Acoust. Soc. Amer. **26** (1954), 186–190.

32. L. A. Chernov, *Wave propagation in a random medium*, McGraw-Hill, New York, 1960.

33. F. Villars and V. F. Weisskopf, *The scattering of electromagnetic waves by turbulent atmospheric fluctuations*, Phys. Rev. (2) **94** (1954), 232–240.

34. M. Sundstrom, Tech. Notes TN 45–51, Royal Institute of Technology, Stockholm, Sweden (unpublished).

35. B. Chelpanov, *Vibration of a second-order system with a randomly varying parameter*, Appl. Math. Mech. **26** (1962), no. 4, 1145.

36. V. I. Tihonov, *The effect of fluctuation action in the simplest parametric systems*, Automat. Remote Control **19** (1958), 705.

37. G. Hadley, *Linear algebra*, Addison-Wesley, Reading, Mass., 1961.

HUGHES AIRCRAFT COMPANY
CULVER CITY, CALIFORNIA

ON THE THEORY OF RANDOM EQUATIONS

BY

A. T. BHARUCHA-REID[1]

1. **Introduction.** The purpose of this paper is to present a brief survey of the theory of random equations. Random equations arise in virtually every branch of physics and engineering, as well as in other areas of science and technology; and many specific types of random equations have been studied by physicists and engineers. In order to understand how random equations arise, and why they are important, we have only to look at the experimental procedures used to investigate various physical phenomena and the mathematical equations, or models, used to describe these phenomena.

The mathematical equation, or equations, used to describe a given physical phenomenon usually contains one or more coefficients, or parameters, which have some definite physical interpretation. For example, in the theory of diffusion we have the diffusion coefficient, in the theory of wave propagation the propagation coefficient, and in the theory of elasticity the modulus of elasticity. In all of the cases mentioned, the magnitudes of the coefficients are experimentally determined. When solving the appropriate mathematical equation, and in subsequent calculations, it is usually the *mean value* of a set of experimental observations that is used as the value of the coefficient or parameter. In some instances this may provide an adequate description; but in many instances the variance may be sufficiently large to warrant consideration. Hence, when we talk about physical constants we are not, in many instances, talking about constants at all, but random variables whose values are determined by some probability distribution. Therefore a more realistic approach would be to introduce the coefficient or parameter as a random variable, obtain the "random solution" of the mathematical equation, and then study its statistical properties.

Random equations arise in many other ways; for example, in the study of wave propagation in stochastic media, in the study of random vibration problems, in magnetohydrodynamics when the magnetic field is subject to random fluctuations, in electrical circuit theory when, for example, the capacitor is subject to random variation, in the study of differential equations with random initial and/or boundary conditions, and in the study of integral equations with random kernels, or defined over random domains. We could go on, but the above examples should suffice.

[1] Supported by National Science Foundation Grant G-24334 and U. S. Army Research Office (Durham) Grant No. DA-ARO(D)-31-124-G124.

Although random equations arise in many different branches of physics and engineering, and have been studied by many workers, it is only recently that attempts have been made to develop a theory of random equations. The study of random equations, employing the methods of functional analysis, was initiated by the Prague school of probabilists under the direction of the late Antonín Špaček. Their research was motivated by the importance of random equations in applied mathematics, and as a concrete application of results in probabilistic functional analysis.[2]

The remainder of this paper is divided into six sections. In §2 we present some theory of random equations. The main purposes of this section are to give some definitions and theorems from probabilistic functional analysis that are used in the theory of random equations, and to give some basic results concerning random equations and their solutions. §§3–6 are devoted to different classes of random equations, and in these sections we outline some of the results that have been obtained for random algebraic equations, random difference equations, random differential equations, and random integral equations. In §7, the last section, we say a few words about stochastic processes associated with random equations.

We make no attempt in this paper to discuss the numerous applications of random equations. A reasonably complete and unified treatment of random equations and their applications, together with a complete bibliography, will be given in our monograph **[19]**.

2. Some theory of random equations.

2.1. Generalized random variables and random operators. In this subsection we give certain basic definitions and theorems which will be used throughout this section and the remainder of the paper. Let $(\Omega, \mathscr{A}, \mu)$ denote a probability measure space, i.e., Ω is a nonempty abstract set, $\mathscr{A}$ is a σ-algebra of subsets of Ω, and μ is a complete probability measure on $\mathscr{A}$; and let $(\mathscr{X}, \mathscr{B})$ be a measurable space, where $\mathscr{X}$ is a complex, separable Banach space, and $\mathscr{B}$ is the σ-algebra of all Borel subsets of $\mathscr{X}$.

Definition 2.1.[3] *A mapping $x(\omega)$ of Ω into $\mathscr{X}$ is called a generalized random variable (with values in the Banach space $\mathscr{X}$) if $\{\omega: x(\omega) \in B\} \in \mathscr{A}$ for all $B \in \mathscr{B}$.*

Definition 2.2. *A mapping $T(\omega)$ of the Cartesian product space $\Omega \times \mathscr{X}$ into a Banach space $\mathscr{Y}$ is called a random transformation if $T(\omega)[x]$ is for every $x \in \mathscr{X}$ a generalized random variable with values in $\mathscr{Y}$.*

Definition 2.3. *A random transformation $T(\omega)$ is said to be*

(i) *linear, if $T(\omega)[\alpha x_1 + \beta x_2] = \alpha T(\omega)[x_1] + \beta T(\omega)[x_2]$ for every $\omega \in \Omega$, x_1, $x_2 \in \mathscr{X}$ and $\alpha, \beta \in R$;*

[2] Probabilistic functional analysis is concerned with the application, and extension, of the methods of functional analysis in the study of the various concepts, processes, and structures that arise in probability theory and its applications.

[3] In applications where a parameter set Θ, say $\Theta = \{t: t \geqq 0\}$, is introduced, we will say that the mapping $x(\omega, t)$ on $\Omega \times \Theta$ into $\mathscr{X}$ is a generalized random variable if $\{\omega: x(\omega, t) \in B\} \in \mathscr{A}$ for all $B \in \mathscr{B}$ and for every fixed $t \in \Theta$.

(ii) *bounded, if there exists a mapping* $c(\omega)$ *on* Ω *into* R (*i.e.*, $c(\omega)$ *is a real-valued random variable*) *such that for all* $\omega \in \Omega$ *and* $x \in \mathscr{X}$, $\|T(\omega)x\| \leqq c(\omega)\|x\|$.

DEFINITION 2.4. *A random transformation* $T(\omega)$ *on* $\Omega \times \mathscr{X}$ *into* $\mathscr{X}$ *is called a random operator*; *and a bounded linear random operator on* $\Omega \times \mathscr{X}$ *to* $\mathscr{X}$ *is called a random endomorphism of* $\mathscr{X}$.

Several examples might clarify the above definitions.

EXAMPLE 1. The $n \times n$ matrix $A = (a_{ij})$, where the matrix elements $a_{ij} = a_{ij}(\omega)$, $\omega \in \Omega$. $A(\omega)$ is then a random operator on $\Omega \times R_n$ to R_n.

EXAMPLE 2. The ordinary differential operator $Lx = \sum_{i=0}^{n} a_i(t)d^ix/dt^i$, $x \in R$, say, where the coefficients $a_i(t) = a_i(\omega, t)$, $\omega \in \Omega$. $L(\omega)$ is then a random operator on $\Omega \times R$ to R.

EXAMPLE 3. The partial differential operator $Hu = D\partial^2 u/\partial x^2$, $u \in C[-\infty, \infty]$, where the coefficient $D = D(\omega)$, $\omega \in \Omega$. $H(\omega)$ is then a random operator on $\Omega \times C[-\infty, \infty]$ to $C[-\infty, \infty]$.

EXAMPLE 4. The integral operator

$$Tx = \int_a^b K(t, u)x(u)\,du, \qquad x \in C[a, b],$$

where the kernel $K(t, u) = K(\omega, t, u)$, $\omega \in \Omega$. $T(\omega)$ is then a random operator on $\Omega \times C[a, b]$ to $[Ca, b]$.

We will denote by $E(\mathscr{X})$ the Banach algebra of endomorphisms of a Banach space $\mathscr{X}$, and by $\mathscr{C}$ the σ-algebra of all Borel subsets of the space $E(\mathscr{X})$, provided the norm topology is assumed.

DEFINITION 2.5. *The mapping* $S(\omega)$ *is said to be the inverse of the random operator* $T(\omega)$ *if* $\mu\{\omega\colon T(\omega)[S(\omega)x] = x$ *for every* $x \in \mathscr{X}\} = 1$.

DEFINITION 2.6. *Let* $\mathscr{X}^*$ *denote the adjoint space of* $\mathscr{X}$. *The mapping* $T^*(\omega)$ *of the Cartesian product space* $\Omega \times \mathscr{X}^*$ *into* $\mathscr{X}^*$ *is called the random adjoint of* $T(\omega)$ *if, for every* $\omega \in \Omega$, *the equality*

$$y^* = T^*(\omega)[x^*]$$

is equivalent to the equality

$$x^*(T(\omega)[y]) = y^*(y)$$

for every $y \in \mathscr{X}$.

We now state two basic theorems due to O. Hanš [**39**; **42**].

THEOREM 2.1. *If* $x_1(\omega), x_2(\omega), \cdots$ *is a sequence of generalized random variables with values in* $\mathscr{X}$ *converging almost surely to a mapping* $x(\omega)$ *of* Ω *into* $\mathscr{X}$, *then* $x(\omega)$ *is a generalized random variable with values in* $\mathscr{X}$.

THEOREM 2.2. *Let* $x(\omega)$ *be a generalized random variable with values in* $\mathscr{X}$, *and let* $T(\omega)$ *be a continuous random operator on* $\Omega \times \mathscr{X}$ *to* $\mathscr{X}$. *Then the mapping* $y(\omega)$ *of* Ω *into* $\mathscr{X}$ *defined for every* $\omega \in \Omega$ *by* $y(\omega) = T(\omega)[x(\omega)]$ *is a generalized random variable with values in* $\mathscr{X}$.

2.2. RANDOM EQUATIONS. Let us first consider the *deterministic operator equation*

$$T[\xi] = y, \tag{2.1}$$

where ξ, y are elements of a Banach space $\mathscr{X}$, and T is an operator on $\mathscr{X}$. Let S denote the set

$$S = \{x: T[x] = y\}.$$

We will call S the *solution set* of equation (2.1), and say that an element x of S is a *solution* of equation (2.1). If $S = \varnothing$ (the empty set), we say that equation (2.1) does not possess a solution; and if $S \neq \varnothing$ we say that equation (2.1) is solvable. If S has only one element we say that equation (2.1) has a unique solution.

We now consider some stochastic analogues of equation (2.1). Firstly, we might consider $y = y(\omega)$ to be a generalized random variable with values in $\mathscr{X}$. Hence equation (2.1) becomes

$$T[x] = y(\omega). \tag{2.2}$$

In this case, if T^{-1} exists, $x(\omega) = T^{-1}[y(\omega)]$ will also be a generalized random variable with values in $\mathscr{X}$. Secondly, we might take $T = T(\omega)$ to be a random operator on $\Omega \times \mathscr{X}$ to $\mathscr{X}$, and y to be a deterministic element. In this case

$$T(\omega)[x] = y \tag{2.3}$$

will be called a *random operator equation*; and $x(\omega) = T^{-1}(\omega)[y]$ will be, for the set of ω's for which $T^{-1}(\omega)$ exists, a generalized random variable with values in $\mathscr{X}$. Thirdly, we have the most general case of a random operator equation in which $T(\omega)$ is a random operator on $\Omega \times \mathscr{X}$ to $\mathscr{X}$ and $y = y(\omega)$ is a generalized random variable with values in $\mathscr{X}$. Hence equation (2.1) becomes

$$T(\omega)[x] = y(\omega); \tag{2.4}$$

and the solution $x(\omega) = T^{-1}(\omega)[y(\omega)]$ will be a generalized random variable with values in $\mathscr{X}$.

With respect to solutions of equation (2.4), we introduce the following definitions.

DEFINITION 2.7. *Every mapping $x(\omega)$ of Ω into $\mathscr{X}$ satisfying the equality $T(\omega)[x(\omega)] = y(\omega)$ for every $\omega \in \Omega_0$, where $\mu(\Omega_0) = 1$, is said to be a wide sense solution of equation* (2.4).

If, in addition, the wide sense solution is measurable, we have

DEFINITION 2.8. *Every generalized random variable $x(\omega)$ with values in $\mathscr{X}$ satisfying the condition*

$$\mu\{\omega: T(\omega)[x(\omega)] = y(\omega)\} = 1 \tag{2.5}$$

is said to be a random solution of the random operator equation (2.4).

The following is an example of a wide sense solution which is not a random solution (cf. [**42**]). Let $\mathscr{X} = R$ (the space of all real numbers), E a nonmeasurable subset of Ω, and let $T(\omega)$ be a random operator on $\Omega \times R$ into R, defined for every $\omega \in \Omega$ and $x \in R$ by $T(\omega)[x] = x^2 - 1$. Then the mapping $\xi(\omega)$ of Ω into R defined by

$$\xi(\omega) = \begin{cases} 1, & \text{for } \omega \in E, \\ -1, & \text{for } \omega \in \Omega - E \end{cases}$$

is a wide sense solution, but not a random solution of the homogeneous random operator equation $T(\cdot)[x(\cdot)] = 0$.

2.3. Existence, uniqueness, and measurability of the random solution of random operator equations. In order to study the existence, uniqueness, and measurability of the random solutions of random operator equations we will use probabilistic analogues of some well-known results in the theory of deterministic operator equations. It is well known that the principle of contraction mappings and fixed point theorems play a very important role in connection with the existence and uniqueness theory of linear (and nonlinear) operator equations **[68]**. Let $\mathfrak{X}$ be an arbitrary metric space with distance function $d(x_1, x_2)$. A mapping T of $\mathfrak{X}$ into itself is said to be a *contraction mapping* if there exists a number $c < 1$ such that $d(Tx_1, Tx_2) \leqq cd(x_1, x_2)$ for any two elements $x_1, x_2 \in \mathfrak{X}$. The *Principle of Contraction Mappings* can be stated as follows: *Every contraction mapping defined on a complete metric space $\mathfrak{X}$ has one and only one fixed point; that is, if T is a contraction on $\mathfrak{X}$, the equation $T[x] = x$ has one and only one solution.*

Early in the development of the theory of random equations workers in probabilistic functional analysis realized the importance of obtaining stochastic analogues of classical fixed point theorems; and in this connection O. Hanš **[38; 40]** and A. Špaček **[84]** initiated a theory of random contraction operators, and obtained a stochastic generalization of the Banach–Cacciopoli fixed point theorem. It would also be of interest to obtain a stochastic analogue of the Schauder fixed point theorem **[80]**, which can be stated as follows:[4] *Let T be a completely continuous operator which transforms a bounded, closed, convex set E of a Banach space $\mathfrak{X}$ into a subset of E. Then there exists at least one point $x \in E$ such that $T[x] = x$.*

Definition 2.9. *A random operator $T(\omega)$ on $\Omega \times \mathfrak{X}$ to $\mathfrak{X}$ is said to be a random contraction operator if there exists a real-valued random variable $c(\omega)$ such that $c(\omega) < 1$ for all $\omega \in \Omega$, and such that*

$$\|T(\omega)[x_1] - T(\omega)[x_2]\| \leqq c(\omega)\|x_1 - x_2\| \tag{2.6}$$

for every $\omega \in \Omega$ and for every pair of generalized random variables $x_1, x_2 \in \mathfrak{X}$. If $c(\omega) = c$ (a constant) for all $\omega \in \Omega$, we say that $T(\omega)$ is a uniform random contraction operator.

The stochastic analogue of the Banach–Cacciopoli theorem can be stated as follows.

[4] For applications of Schauder's theorem in the theory of integral equations we refer to **[69]**.

THEOREM 2.3. *Let $T(\omega)$ be a random contraction operator on $\Omega \times \mathscr{X}$ to $\mathscr{X}$. Then there exists a generalized random variable $\xi(\omega)$ with values in $\mathscr{X}$ such that*

$$\mu\{\omega: T(\omega)[\xi(\omega)] = \xi(\omega)\} = 1. \tag{2.7}$$

The generalized random variable $\xi(\omega)$ is unique in the sense that if $\psi(\omega)$ is another generalized random variable satisfying (2.7), then $\mu\{\omega: \xi(\omega) = \psi(\omega)\} = 1$. Further, the random fixed point $\xi(\omega)$ can be obtained by successive approximations starting from an arbitrary generalized random variable $x_0(\omega) \in \mathscr{X}$.

Theorem 2.3 has been widely used in the theory of random equations; for if conditions can be found such that a given random operator is a contraction, then Theorem 2.3 can be employed to give the existence, uniqueness, and measurability of the solution, and the theorem also asserts that this solution can be obtained by the method of successive approximations.

Finally, we state a random fixed point theorem, also due to O. Hanš **[40]**, which involves a sequence of random operators.

THEOREM 2.4. *Let $T_0(\omega), T_1(\omega), T_2(\omega), \cdots$ be a sequence of continuous random operators on $\Omega \times \mathscr{X}$ to $\mathscr{X}$ satisfying the following conditions:*

(i) *there exists a mapping $c(\omega)$ on Ω to R with $0 \leqq c(\omega) < 1$ for every $\omega \in \Omega$ and a generalized random variable $\xi(\omega)$ such that for every $x \in \mathscr{X}$*

$$\mu\{\omega: d(T_0(\omega)[x], \xi(\omega)) \leqq c(\omega)\, d(x, \xi(\omega))\} = 1;$$

(ii) *the sequence $T_1(\omega), T_2(\omega), \cdots$ converges uniformly (with respect to $\mathscr{X}$) almost surely to $T_0(\omega)$.*

Let $y_0(\omega)$ be an arbitrary generalized random variable with values in $\mathscr{X}$, and define for every $n = 0, 1, \cdots$ the mapping $y_{n+1}(\omega)$ of Ω into $\mathscr{X}$ for every $\omega \in \Omega$ as follows:

$$y_{n+1}(\omega) = T_n(\omega)[y_n(\omega)]. \tag{2.8}$$

Then $y_1(\omega), y_2(\omega), \cdots$ is a sequence of generalized random variables which converges almost surely to the generalized random variable $\xi(\omega)$.

Theorem 2.4 asserts that if an arbitrary sequence of continuous random operators converges uniformly almost surely to a random operator which is a contraction at its fixed point, then the sequence of generalized random variables defined by (2.8) converges almost surely to a generalized random variable which is the fixed point of the limit random contraction operator. As we shall point out later, Theorem 2.4 and analogous theorems are required for the study of approximate solutions of random operator equations.

For other random fixed point theorems we refer to O. Hanš **[40]**, and O. Hanš and A. Špaček **[43]**.

2.4. RESOLVENT AND SPECTRUM OF A RANDOM OPERATOR. Let U be a bounded closed subset in finite dimensional Euclidean space, and let $x(u)$ be a Lebesgue measurable function defined on U. A large number of operator equations can be written in the form

$$(T - \lambda I)x(u) = y(u), \tag{2.9}$$

where x and y are elements of a concrete Banach space $\mathscr{X}$, T is a linear, not necessarily bounded, operator with domain and range in $\mathscr{X}$, I the identity operator, and λ a scalar.

In this section we consider the stochastic analogue of equation (2.9), namely the random operator equation

$$(T(\omega) - \lambda I)x(\omega, u) = y(\omega, u). \tag{2.10}$$

The main problem we wish to consider is that of the existence and measurability of the random resolvent operator associated with the random linear operator $T(\omega)$. Let

$$T_\lambda(\omega) = T(\omega) = \lambda I, \tag{2.11}$$

and let $(\Lambda, \mathscr{F})$ be a Borel space.[5]

DEFINITION 2.10. *Consider the Borel space $(\Lambda, \mathscr{F})$ where Λ is the complex plane, and $\mathscr{F}$ is the σ-algebra of all Borel sets of complex numbers. The set of those pairs $(\omega, \lambda) \in \Omega \times \Lambda$ for which $T_\lambda(\omega)$ has a linear bounded inverse, say $R(\lambda; T(\omega))$, with domain dense in $\mathscr{X}$, is called the resolvent set $\rho(T(\omega))$ of $T(\omega)$. The operator*

$$R(\lambda; T(\omega)) = T_\lambda^{-1}(\omega) = (T(\omega) - \lambda I)^{-1} \tag{2.12}$$

will be called the resolvent of $T(\omega)$. The set of pairs (ω, λ) for which no inverse of $T_\lambda(\omega)$ exists is called the point spectrum $P\sigma(T(\omega))$ of $T(\omega)$. The set of pairs (ω, λ) for which $T_\lambda(\omega)$ has an unbounded inverse with domain in $\mathscr{X}$ is called the continuous spectrum $C\sigma(T(\omega))$ of $T(\omega)$; and the set of pairs (ω, λ) for which $T_\lambda(\omega)$ has an inverse whose domain is not dense in $\mathscr{X}$ is called the residual spectrum $R\sigma(T(\omega))$ of $T(\omega)$.

We now state two theorems due to C. Ryll-Nardzewski [75].

THEOREM 2.5. *Let Z be a measurable[6] subset of $\Omega \times \Lambda$, and let Z_λ and Z_ω denote the sets $\{\lambda: (\omega, \lambda) \in Z\}$ and $\{\omega: (\omega, \lambda) \in Z\}$, respectively. If the sets Z_ω are countable for almost all $\omega \in \Omega$ (in the sense of the measure μ, where μ is σ-finite), then $\mu(Z_\lambda) = 0$ for all $\lambda \in \Lambda$ with the exception of a countable number of λ's; that is, the cardinality of the set $\{\lambda: \mu(Z_\lambda) > 0\} \leqq \aleph_0$.*

Theorem 2.5, which is of independent interest, has been used to prove the following theorem, which gives sufficient conditions that the point spectrum of a random operator be countable.

[5] A *Borel space* is an abstract set Λ for which there exists a 1-1 point transformation φ on a Borel set E (lying in a complex metric space), and the class $\mathscr{F}$ of subsets of Λ is mapped by φ on the class of all Borel subsets of E.

[6] Here measurability is with respect to the product σ-algebra $\mathscr{A} \times \mathscr{F}$; that is, the smallest σ-algebra containing all rectangles $A \times F$, where $A \in \mathscr{A}$ and $F \in \mathscr{F}$.

THEOREM 2.6. *Let $T(\omega)$ be a random operator on $\Omega \times \mathscr{X}$ to $\mathscr{X}$. If* (1) *the operator-function $\{T(\omega)\}$ is weakly measurable (i.e., the function $x^*(T(\omega)[x])$, as a function of ω is measurable for all $x^* \in \mathscr{X}^*$ and $x \in \mathscr{X}$), and* (2) *for almost every $\omega \in \Omega$, the set of complex numbers for which a bounded inverse of $T_\lambda(\omega)$ does not exist is countable, then the set of λ's for which a bounded inverse $T_\lambda^{-1}(\omega)$ on any set of ω's of positive measure does not exist is also countable.*

The next theorem, due to O. Hanš, describes the resolvent set $\rho(T(\omega))$ of a random endomorphism $T(\omega)$.

THEOREM 2.7. *Let $T(\omega)$ be a random endomorphism of $\mathscr{X}$, $E(\mathscr{X})$ the Banach algebra of endomorphisms of $\mathscr{X}$, $\mathscr{C}$ the σ-algebra of Borel subsets of $E(\mathscr{X})$, and Λ the complex plane. If $T(\omega)$ is such that $\{\omega: T(\omega) \in C\} \in \mathscr{A}$ for every $C \in \mathscr{C}$, then for every $\lambda \in \Lambda$, $\{\omega: (\omega, \lambda) \in \rho(T(\omega))\} \in \mathscr{A}$.*

The spectral properties of some concrete random operators, in particular, random matrices have been studied by several workers. We refer to the papers of F. Dyson [**26**], R. Engleman [**28**], U. Grenander [**34**], M. L. Mehta and M. Gaudin [**63**], and E. Wigner [**92**].

The existence and measurability of the random resolvent operator $R(\lambda; T(\omega))$ is given by the following theorem (cf. [**14**; **42**]).

THEOREM 2.8. *Let $T(\omega)$ be a random endomorphism on $\Omega \times \mathscr{X}$ to $\mathscr{X}$; and let the random operator $T_\lambda(\omega)$ be invertible for each ω separately in the set*

$$\Omega_0(\lambda) = \{\omega: \|T(\omega)\| < |\lambda|, \lambda \neq 0\}.$$

Then the resolvent operator $R(\lambda; T(\omega))$ exists for every $\omega \in \Omega_0(\lambda)$, and $R(\lambda; T(\omega))$ is measurable with respect to the reduced σ-algebra $\Omega_0(\lambda) \cap \mathscr{A}$.

The above theorem can now be used to obtain the existence, uniqueness and measurability of the solution of equation (2.10). We have

THEOREM 2.9. *For every $\omega \in \Omega_0(\lambda)$ the solution $x(\omega, u)$ of equation* (2.10) *is, for every generalized random variable $y(\omega, u)$ with values in $\mathscr{X}$, given by*

$$x(\omega, u) = R(\lambda; T(\omega))[y(\omega, u)]; \tag{2.13}$$

and $x(\omega, u)$ is, for every fixed $u \in U$, measurable with respect to the σ-algebra $\Omega_0(\lambda) \cap \mathscr{A}$.

2.5. EXPECTED SOLUTIONS OF RANDOM EQUATIONS. In applications of the theory of random equations it is often of interest to determine the moments (in particular, the mean and variance) of the solution of a given random equation. With regard to the expectation (or mean), variance and higher moments of a generalized random variable, we introduce the following definitions.

DEFINITION 2.11. *The expectation $\bar{x}$ of a generalized random variable $x(\omega)$ is given by the Bochner integral*

$$\bar{x} = \mathscr{E}\{x(\omega)\} = \int_\Omega x(\omega)\, d\mu(\omega), \tag{2.14}$$

provided the integral exists. The variance of $x(\omega)$ is given, if it exists, by the integral

$$\mathscr{D}^2\{x(\omega)\} = \int_\Omega \|x(\omega) - \bar{x}\|^2\, d\mu(\omega). \tag{2.15}$$

Similarly, higher moments of order k of $x(\omega)$ are given, if they exist, by the integral

$$\mathscr{D}^k\{x(\omega)\} = \int_\Omega \|x(\omega) - \bar{x}\|^k\, d\mu(\omega). \tag{2.16}$$

We also give the definition of the conditional expectation of a generalized random variable.

DEFINITION 2.12. *Let $x(\omega)$ be a generalized random variable, the expectation (2.14) of which exists. Let $\mathscr{A}_0$ and $\mathscr{A}_0'$ be σ-algebras of subsets of Ω, where $\mathscr{A}_0'$ is either in $\mathscr{A}_0$ or differs from $\mathscr{A}_0$ by a set of measure zero. Then the conditional expectation of $x(\omega)$ relative to the σ-algebra $\mathscr{A}_0$, written $\mathscr{E}\{x(\omega)|\mathscr{A}_0\}$, is defined as a $\mathscr{A}_0'$-measurable, Bochner integrable function which satisfies the equation*

$$\int_A \mathscr{E}\{x(\omega)|\mathscr{A}_0\}\, d\mu(\omega) = \int_A x(\omega)\, d\mu(\omega), \tag{2.17}$$

for every $A \in \mathscr{A}_0$.

In §2.2 we introduced three types of random equations and indicated their formal solutions. For the expected solution of equation (2.2), we have, from (2.14)

$$\bar{x} = T^{-1}\int_\Omega y(\omega)\, d\mu(\omega) = T^{-1}[\bar{y}]. \tag{2.18}$$

For the expected solution of equation (2.3) we have

$$\bar{x} = \int_\Omega T^{-1}(\omega)[y]\, d\mu(\omega) = \overline{T^{-1}[y]}. \tag{2.19}$$

Similarly, we have for the expected solution of equation (2.4)

$$\bar{x} = \int_\Omega T^{-1}(\omega)[y(\omega)]\, d\mu(\omega) = \overline{T^{-1}[y]}. \tag{2.20}$$

While (2.19) and (2.20) are formally the same, in concrete situations they would most likely be different. The integral in (2.19) can only be defined over that subset of Ω for which $T^{-1}(\omega)$ exists and for which $T^{-1}(\omega)[y]$ defines a generalized random variable with values in $\mathscr{X}$. Similarly, the integral in (2.20) can only be defined for that subset of Ω for which $T^{-1}(\omega)$ exists and for which $T^{-1}(\omega)[y(\omega)]$ is a generalized random variable.

In §2.4 we considered the random operator equation $(T(\omega) - \lambda I)x(\omega, u) = y(\omega, u)$. In this case the expected solution $\bar{x}(u)$ is given by

$$\bar{x}(u) = \int_{\Omega_0(\lambda)} R(\lambda; T(\omega))[y(\omega, u)]\, d\mu(\omega). \tag{2.21}$$

So much for formalities. Many workers in a number of studies, too numerous to mention here, have investigated the mean and variance, and in some cases higher moments, of the solutions of some concrete random equations of the first three types considered above. In most of these studies the probability measure μ was assumed to be Gaussian; however, other assumptions have also been introduced. In the general case the problem of determining the moments of random solution seems to be rather difficult, and much more work needs to be done in this area.

In connection with random operator equations an important question arises, namely: What is the relationship between the expected solution, if it exists, of a given random operator equation and the solution of the associated deterministic operator equation? To make clear what we mean by the deterministic operator equation we give the definition of the expectation of a random operator. If $T(\omega)$ is a random operator, we have from Definitions 2.2 and 2.11 that $\mathscr{E}\{T(\omega)\} = \bar{T}$ is given by

$$\bar{T}[x] = \int_{\Omega} T(\omega)[x]\, d\mu(x), \tag{2.22}$$

where the Bochner integral is assumed to exist for all $x \in \mathscr{X}$. The above question can now be stated as follows: If $T(\omega)[x(\omega)] = y(\omega)$ is a random equation, and if ξ is the solution of the deterministic (mean) operator equation $\bar{T}[x] = \bar{y}$, under what conditions will

$$\mathscr{E}\{x(\omega)\} = \bar{x} = \xi? \tag{2.23}$$

It is clear that in general the above relation will not obtain. However, we can give examples for which (2.23) does hold. The most trivial one is to consider a random equation with the probability measure μ Dirac measure; that is, $\mu(\{\omega_0\}) = 1$ and $\mu(\Omega - \{\omega_0\}) = 0$. If (2.23) did obtain in all cases we would conclude that the random solution simply takes into consideration the random fluctuations about the deterministic solution ξ, which, in view of (2.23), is identical with the expected solution of the random equation.

To date very little progress has been made toward the resolution of the general problem posed above. However, we would like to refer to the theory of Reynolds operators and suggest that this theory may have some connection with our problem. The notion of a Reynolds operator had its origin in connection with the problem of solving the Navier–Stokes equation. In 1895 O. Reynolds introduced a simplified method for studying the solutions of the Navier–Stokes equations. His method involved taking expected values of the (presumed) solutions of the Navier–Stokes equations, and determining the partial differential equations (the Reynolds equations) satisfied by these expected values.

In our terminology, his method involved regarding the expected solution $\bar{x}$ of the Reynolds equations as the result of a transformation of the random solution $x(\omega)$ of the Navier–Stokes equations (cf. [**73**]). The operator effecting the passage from the Navier–Stokes equations to the Reynolds equations is called a *Reynolds operator*. For a discussion of the characterization and properties of Reynolds operators we refer to [**74**]. We feel that the theory of Reynolds operators is of importance in the general theory of random equations and that their role in connection with the general problem posed above should be investigated.

For other studies concerning the solutions of deterministic operator equations and their relation to the solutions of random operator equations we refer to [**14**; **24**; **42**].

2.6. APPROXIMATE SOLUTIONS OF RANDOM OPERATOR EQUATIONS. In recent years numerical analysts have been utilizing the methods of functional analysis to obtain approximate solutions of linear, and nonlinear, functional and operator equations. For discussions of numerical analysis and functional analysis we refer to [**4**; **5**; **53**]. The iteration procedure developed in various areas of applied mathematics are, in the main, applications of the Banach–Cacciopoli fixed point theorem on successive approximations, or similar fixed point theorems. Because of the importance of iteration procedures for obtaining solutions of many deterministic operator equations, it is to be expected that analogous iteration procedures be considered for random operator equations in applied mathematics.

In [**16**] we considered the stochastic analogue of the Newton–Kantorovitch iteration procedure for the operator equation $y = T[x] = 0$ in a Banach space $\mathscr{X}$. The Newton–Kantorovitch sequence of approximate solutions $\{x_n\}$ is defined by

$$x_{n+1} = x_n - (T'[x_0])^{-1}T[x_n], \qquad n \geqq 0, \tag{2.24}$$

where T' is the Fréchet differential of T, and $x_0 \in \mathscr{X}$ is the initial approach to the solution. In the case of a random operator equation $T(\omega)[x(\omega)] = 0$ in a separable Banach space of generalized random variables, we consider a sequence of generalized random variables defined by

$$x_{n+1}(\omega) = x_n(\omega) - (T'(\omega)[x_0(\omega)])^{-1}T[x_n], \qquad n \geqq 0, \tag{2.25}$$

where the Fréchet differential of $T(\omega)$ is a random endomorphism of $\mathscr{X}$, and $x_0(\omega)$ is an arbitrary generalized random variable with values in $\mathscr{X}$. We can rewrite (2.25) as

$$x_{n+1}(\omega) = S_0(\omega)[x_n(\omega)], \tag{2.26}$$

where

$$S_0(\omega)[x(\omega)] = x(\omega) - (T'(\omega)[x_0(\omega)])^{-1}T(\omega)[x(\omega)].$$

Under appropriate assumptions, and using random fixed point theorems due to Hanš [**40**], we showed that the sequence $\{x_n(\omega)\}$ converges almost surely to a generalized random variable $\xi(\omega)$ which is a solution of $T(\omega)[x(\omega)] = 0$. Problems of uniqueness and rate of convergence were also considered.

For other studies involving the use of stochastic methods in numerical analysis, we refer to the papers of W. Uhlmann [**87**; **88**] who developed a stochastic approach to the Newton–Cotes scheme, and utilized this method in studying the Poisson differential equation.

3. **Random algebraic equations.** Many applied problems lead to the study of algebraic equations whose coefficients are random variables. Algebraic equations with random coefficients will arise, for example, if the coefficients are subject to random error. This might occur when the coefficients result from experimental data, or when numerical procedures require that the coefficients be rounded off to a specified number of decimal places.

Consider the algebraic equation

$$F_n(x) = \xi_0 + \xi_1 x + \cdots + \xi_n x^n = 0, \tag{3.1}$$

where the coefficients $\xi_i = \xi_i(\omega)$, $i = 0, 1, \cdots, n$, and $\omega \in \Omega$, are real- (or complex-) valued random variables. We shall call $F_n(x) = F_n(\omega, x) = 0$ a *random algebraic equation of degree n.*

Within the past 25 years several papers appeared which were devoted to the study of equation (3.1). In this section we shall give a very brief survey of the studies concerned with random algebraic equations.

In [**58**; **59**] J. E. Littlewood and A. C. Offord studied equation (3.1) under the assumption that the coefficients $\xi_i(\omega)$ are independent and identically distributed real-valued random variables. They considered the following three cases:

(i) The coefficients are normally distributed.

(ii) The coefficients are uniformly distributed in $(-1, 1)$.

(iii) The coefficients assume the values $+1$ and -1 with equal probabilities.

Let $N_n = N_n(\xi_0, \xi_1, \cdots, \xi_n)$ denote the number of real roots of equation (3.1). The results of Littlewood and Offord are as follows.

THEOREM 3.1.[7] *In each of the three cases listed above, and for $n \geqq n_0$, the probability that equation* (3.1) *has more than* $25(\log n)^2$ *real roots is at most* $(12 \log n)/n$.

COROLLARY. *For $n \geqq n_0$, $\mathscr{E}\{N_n\} \leqq 25(\log n)^2 + 12 \log n$.*

THEOREM 3.2. *In each of the three cases listed above, the probability that equation* (3.1) *has less than $\alpha\{\log n/(\log \log n)^2\}$ real roots is less than $A/\log n$, where α and A are absolute constants.*

The results of Littlewood and Offord established lower and upper bounds for N_n, as well as an upper bound for $\mathscr{E}\{N_n\}$, in each of the three cases listed.

M. Kac [**47**; **48**; **49**] improved the results of Littlewood and Offord by showing that in the case of a random algebraic equation of degree $n - 1$ with normally distributed coefficients

$$\mathscr{E}\{N_n\} = \frac{4}{\pi} \int_0^1 \frac{(1 - \Phi_n^2)^{1/2}}{1 - x^2}\, dx, \tag{3.2}$$

[7] In particular, the theorem is true for $n_0 = 2{,}000$.

where

$$\Phi_n = nx^{n-1}\left(\frac{1-x^2}{1-x^{2n}}\right). \tag{3.3}$$

He also obtained the asymptotic result

$$\mathscr{E}\{N_n\} \sim \frac{2}{\pi}\log n, \tag{3.4}$$

and the estimate

$$\mathscr{E}\{N_n\} \leqq \frac{2}{\pi}\log n + \frac{14}{\pi}, \quad \text{for } n \geqq 2 \tag{3.5}$$

and showed that (3.4) also holds when the coefficients are uniformly distributed in $(-1, 1)$.

P. Erdös and A. C. Offord [29] have studied the equations

$$F_n(\omega, x) = 1 + \xi_1(\omega)x + \xi_2(\omega)x^2 + \cdots + \xi_n(\omega)x^n = 0 \tag{3.6}$$

in which each coefficient $\xi_i(\omega)$, $i = 1, 2, \cdots, n$ is $+1$ or -1 with equal probability. In this case they proved the following:

THEOREM 3.3. *The number of real roots of most of the equations* (3.6) *is* $(2/\pi)\log n + o\{(\log n)^{2/3}\log(\log n)\}$; *and the exceptional set does not exceed a proportion* $o\{(\log\log n)^{-1/3}\}$ *of the total number of equations.*

More recently, G. Samal [76] has studied equation (3.1) under the following conditions: the coefficients $\xi_i(\omega)$ are independent and identically distributed real-valued random variables with expectations zero, and whose variances and third absolute moments are finite and nonzero. His results can be summarized as follows:

THEOREM 3.4. *The number of real roots of most of equations* (3.1) *satisfies the inequality*

$$\varepsilon_n \log n \leqq N_n \leqq \alpha(\log n)^2, \tag{3.7}$$

where α *is a positive absolute constant, and* $\{\varepsilon_n\}$ *is a sequence of numbers tending to zero but such that* $\varepsilon_n \log n$ *tends to infinity. The measure of the exceptional set tends to zero as n tends to infinity.*

In an important paper [37], J. Hammersley gives a complete formal solution to the problem of determining the distribution of the roots of equation (3.1) in the case where the coefficients $\xi_i(\omega)$ are complex-valued random variables with a given joint distribution. The main tool in his investigation is the *condensed distribution of the roots.* This can be described as the measure which assigns to a Borel subset S of the complex plane $1/n$ times the expected number of roots of equation (3.1) falling in S. Explicit formulae for the condensed distribution of roots are given for several cases; in particular, when the coefficients $\xi_i(\omega)$ are normally distributed real-valued random variables, a generalization of the result of Kac (cf. (3.2)) is obtained. Hammersley's formula contains more information than the formula of Kac in that it not only gives $\mathscr{E}\{N_n\}$, but it also shows how the roots are distributed along the real axis.

The most recent study concerning random algebraic equations is that of D. I. Šparo and M. G. Šur **[85]**. They considered the equation

$$F_n(\omega, z) = \xi_0 + \xi_1(\omega)z + \cdots + \xi_n(\omega)z^n = 0, \tag{3.8}$$

where z is a complex variable, and the coefficients $\xi_i(\omega)$ are independent and identically distributed complex-valued random variables. Their results can be summarized as follows:

THEOREM 3.5. *Let α and β be arbitrary numbers such that $0 \leqq \alpha < \beta < 2\pi$; and let $N_n(\alpha, \beta)$ and $R_n(\delta)$, $\delta > 0$, denote the number of roots of equation* (3.8) *in the sector $\alpha < \arg z < \beta$, and the ring $1 - \delta \leqq |z| \leqq 1 + \delta$, respectively. Then, as $n \to \infty$, $N_n(\alpha, \beta)/n$ tends to $(\beta - \alpha)/2\pi$ in probability, and $R_n(\delta)/n$ tends to* 1 *in probability.*

In closing this section we remark that random algebraic equations are also encountered in the study of random determinants, and in the study of random Fredholm integral equations with separable kernels.

4. **Random difference equations.** A linear difference equation of order n with constant coefficients has the form

$$a_0x(t + n) + a_1x(t + n - 1) + \cdots + a_nx(t) = y(t), \tag{4.1}$$

or

$$T[x(t)] = y(t), \tag{4.2}$$

where the linear operator T is defined by

$$T = a_0\tau^n + a_1\tau^{n-1} + \cdots + a_n\tau^0. \tag{4.3}$$

In (4.3) τ denotes the translation operator, that is, $\tau^n[x(t)] = x(t + n)$, $n = 0, 1, 2, \cdots$.

Linear random difference equations, which are analogous of equation (4.1), are of three types; these types being special cases of equations (2.2), (2.3), and (2.4). In the first we have

$$T[x(t)] = y(\omega, t), \tag{4.4}$$

where T is defined by (4.3). In the second case, which arises when the coefficients are randomly variables (i.e., $a_i = a_i(\omega)$), we have

$$T(\omega)[x(t)] = y(t). \tag{4.5}$$

Finally, in the third case, we have

$$T(\omega)[x(t)] = y(\omega, t). \tag{4.6}$$

Equations of the form (4.4) have been studied rather extensively in mathematical economics and econometrics [**54**; **94**], and in connection with stationary time series [**33**; **93**]. A stochastic process $\{x(\omega, t),\ t = 0, \pm 1, \pm 2, \cdots\}$ satisfying equation (4.4) is called an *autoregressive process*. To obtain the solution of equation (4.4) we can proceed as follows. Let us assume that the $y(\omega, t)$ have mean zero, variance σ^2, and are uncorrelated. If the process $\{y(\omega, t)\}$ is weakly stationary it admits the representation

$$y(\omega, t) = \int_{-\pi}^{\pi} e^{i\lambda t}\, dz_y(\omega, \lambda), \tag{4.7}$$

where $z_y(\omega, \lambda)$ is an orthogonal set function defined on the Borel sets of the interval $(-\pi, \pi)$. Since

$$\mathscr{E}\{y(\omega, t_1)\overline{y(\omega, t_2)}\} = \sigma^2 r(t_1, t_2) = \frac{\sigma^2}{2\pi} \int_{-\pi}^{\pi} e^{i\lambda(t_1 - t_2)}\, d\lambda \tag{4.8}$$

the process $\{y(\omega, t)\}$ has an absolutely continuous spectrum with (constant) spectral density $f(\lambda) = \sigma^2/2\pi$. Hence $\{y(\omega, t)\}$ is a so-called *white noise process*.

If $x(\omega, t)$ is a stationary solution of equation (4.4), we can write

$$x(\omega, t) = \int_{-\pi}^{\pi} e^{i\lambda t}\, dz_x(\omega, \lambda), \tag{4.9}$$

and

$$\mathscr{E}\{x(\omega, t_1)\overline{x(\omega, t_2)}\} = \int_{-\pi}^{\pi} e^{i\lambda(t_1 - t_2)}\, dF_x(\omega, \lambda), \tag{4.10}$$

where $F_x(\omega, \lambda)$ is the spectral decomposition of the process $\{x(\omega, t)\}$. From (4.4), (4.7), and (4.9) we have

$$\begin{aligned} T[x(\omega, t)] &= \int_{-\pi}^{\pi} \sum_{k=0}^{n} a_k\, e^{i\lambda(n-k)}\, e^{i\lambda t}\, dz_x(\omega, \lambda) \\ &= \int_{-\pi}^{\pi} e^{i\lambda t}\, dz_y(\omega, \lambda). \end{aligned} \tag{4.11}$$

The unique stationary solution of equation (4.4) can then be shown to be (cf. [**33**])

$$x(\omega, t) = \int_{-\pi}^{\pi} e^{i\lambda t}[\varphi(e^{i\lambda})]^{-1}\, dz_y(\omega, \lambda), \tag{4.12}$$

where

$$\varphi(r) = \sum_{k=0}^{n} a_k r^{(n-k)}. \tag{4.13}$$

Random difference equations arise in mathematical physics and engineering in connection with differential equations whose coefficients are random but are piecewise constant in the independent variable. The random difference equations which arise are of the form

$$x_k = \Phi_k x_{k-1}, \qquad k = 1, 2, \cdots, \tag{4.14}$$

where x_k is an n-vector, and Φ_k is an $n \times n$ random matrix. Equations of the form (4.14) have been studied in connection with randomly sampled linear systems (cf. [**50**]); and in quantum mechanics in connection with energy levels in random lattices. Equation (4.14) will be considered in §5, when we discuss random differential equations.

5. **Random differential equations.** The literature on random equations contains more studies on random differential equations than any other type of random equation. This is not at all surprising, for mathematical models formulated as nonrandom differential equations have long played a prominent role in mathematical physics and engineering. And, as workers attempted to make their models more realistic and take into account the random nature of many of the systems and media they study, it is only natural that models formulated as random differential equations would play an increasingly active role. For a discussion of random differential equations and their role in physics, engineering, and technology we refer to the paper of I. Babuška [**6**].

The remainder of this section is divided into two parts, which are devoted to random ordinary and partial differential equations, respectively. Random differential equations have attracted the attention of probabilists for quite some time, the work of S. Bernstein [**8**] being the first in this area. Since the work of Bernstein, other workers have continued in the same tradition; we refer, in particular, to the studies of I. I. Gihman, and G. Maruyama. These studies will not be discussed here, since we restrict our attention, in the main, to the random equations of mathematical physics and engineering. We refer to [**19**] for a discussion of their work. Throughout this section we restrict our attention to linear differential equations.

5.1. Random ordinary differential equations. We will restrict our attention to only two types of random ordinary differential equations which have been studied. Brief reference will be made to some studies of particular random equations in mathematical physics. For a general discussion of random ordinary differential equations and their applications in engineering, we refer to the books of V. L. Lebedev [**57**] and V. S. Pugachev [**71**].

The first type of equation we consider is the random analogue of a linear differential equation of order n. This equation is of the form

$$(5.1) \quad T(\omega)x(t) = a_n(\omega, t)\frac{d^n x}{dt^n} + a_{n-1}(\omega, t)\frac{d^{n-1}x}{dt^{n-1}} + \cdots + a_0(\omega, t)x = y(\omega, t),$$

where $a_i(\omega, t)$, $i = 0, 1, \cdots, n$, $y(\omega, t)$ are given random functions. Hence equation (5.1) is a random operator equation of the form $T(\omega)[x] = y(\omega)$. We assume that $y(\omega, t)$ is independent of any of the coefficients $a_i(\omega, t)$; however, the coefficients may be correlated with each other. Equation (5.1) has been studied by a number of workers; we refer, in particular, to the papers of J. C. Samuels [**77**; **78**], and J. C. Samuels and A. C. Eringen [**79**] (cf. also, U. Grenander [**34**]).

The method used by Samuels and Eringen to solve equation (5.1) can be described as follows: We write the coefficients $a_i(\omega, t)$ in the form

$$a_i(\omega, t) = \alpha_i(t) + \varepsilon\beta_i(\omega, t), \qquad i = 0, 1, \cdots, n, \tag{5.2}$$

where $\alpha_i(t) = \mathscr{E}\{a_i(\omega, t)\}$, and the $\beta_i(\omega, t)$ are random variables with $\mathscr{E}\{\beta_i(\omega, t)\} = 0$. With the coefficients as defined by (5.2), a solution of equation (5.1) is sought in the form

$$x(\omega, t) = \sum_{i=0}^{\infty} \varepsilon^i x_i(\omega, t). \tag{5.3}$$

If we now substitute (5.3) in equation (5.1) and equate the coefficients of ε^i, we obtain a system of operator equations

$$\begin{cases} T_\alpha x_0 = y, & \\ T_\alpha x_i = -T_\beta x_{i-1}, & i = 1, 2, \cdots, \end{cases} \tag{5.4}$$

where the differential operators T_α and T_β denote the operator T with the coefficients $a_i(\omega, t)$ replaced by $\alpha_i(t)$ and $\beta_i(\omega, t)$, respectively. Hence T_α is a nonrandom operator and T_β is a random operator. The formal solution of (5.4) is

$$\begin{cases} x_0(\omega, t) = \sum_{i=1}^{n} c_i \xi_i(t) + \int_0^t G(t, \tau) y(\omega, \tau)\, d\tau, & \\ x_i(\omega, t) = -\int_0^t G(t, \tau) T_\beta(\omega) x_{i-1}(\omega, \tau)\, d\tau, & i = 1, 2, \cdots, \end{cases} \tag{5.5}$$

where $\{\xi_i(t)\}$ is a set of fundamental solutions of the operator equation $T_\alpha \xi = 0$, the c_i are constants to be determined by the initial conditions, and $G(t, \tau)$ is the one-sided Green's function associated with the operator T_α. While (5.5) constitutes a solution to equation (5.1) of the form (5.4), it is highly desirable that other methods be developed for solving equations of the form (5.1). For an approach to the study of random ordinary differential equations utilizing stochastic Green's functions, we refer to the studies of G. Adomian [**1**; **2**; **3**]. For some concrete applications of equation (5.1) we refer to [**79**] and related papers.

A problem of great theoretical and practical importance is that of the stability of linear systems described by equations of the form (5.1). This problem is, however, too involved to go into here; hence we will not attempt to summarize the results that have been obtained concerning the stability of random linear systems. For definitions of the various types of stability that have been introduced and studied, and for some concrete applications of stability criteria, we refer to [**9**; **10**; **67**; **72**; **77**; **78**; **79**; **81**].

The next type of equation we consider is the system of random differential equations with piecewise constant coefficients:

$$\frac{dx(\omega, t)}{dt} = A_k x(\omega, t), \quad t \in [t_{k-1}, t_k), k = 1, 2, \cdots, \tag{5.6}$$

where $x(\omega, t)$ is a random n-vector, and A_k is a constant $n \times n$ matrix. Our discussion here is based on the thesis of B. H. Bharucha [**10**]. Given the initial vector $x(\omega, t_0) = x_0(\omega)$ the solution of equation (5.6) in the interval $[t_0, t_1)$ is

$$x(\omega, t) = e^{A_1(t-t_0)}x_0(\omega). \tag{5.7}$$

Proceeding in this way, we obtain

$$x(\omega, t) = e^{A_k(t-t_{k-1})}\, e^{A_{k-1}(t_{k-1}-t_{k-2})} \cdots e^{A_1(t_1-t_0)}x_0(\omega), \tag{5.8}$$

for $t \in [t_{k-1}, t_k)$, $k = 1, 2, \cdots$. The solution $x(\omega, t)$ given by (5.8) satisfies the initial condition $x(\omega, t_0) = x_0(\omega)$, and satisfies equation (5.6) for all values of t except $t = t_1, t_2, \cdots$. It is clear that the behavior of the solution is completely determined by the random sequence $\{A_k(t_k - t_{k-1})\}$.

Let

$$\Phi_k = e^{A_k(t_k-t_{k-1})}; \tag{5.9}$$

then the solution (5.8) can be written as

$$x(\omega, t) = e^{A_k(t-t_{k-1})}\Phi_{k-1}\Phi_{k-2} \cdots \Phi_1 x_0(\omega), \tag{5.10}$$

for $t \in [t_{k-1}, t_k)$, $k = 1, 2, \cdots$. If we restrict our attention to the solution at times $t = t_k$ only, (5.10) becomes

$$x(\omega, t_k) = x_k(\omega) = \Phi_k\Phi_{k-1} \cdots \Phi_1 x_0(\omega). \tag{5.11}$$

Hence the $x_k(\omega)$ satisfy the random difference equation (first mentioned in §4)

$$x_k(\omega) = \Phi_k x_{k-1}(\omega). \tag{5.12}$$

From (5.9) it is clear that the behavior of $x_k(\omega)$ is determined by the sequence of random matrices Φ_k. We remark that from the continuity, with respect to $x_0(\omega)$, of solutions of equation (5.6) it follows that stability of the (trivial) solution of equation (5.6) can be determined by studying the properties of the sequence $\{x_k(\omega)\}$, provided the Φ_k are bounded. In [**10**] this approach to stability is utilized, and stability is studied in the following cases: (i) the Φ_k are independent, identically distributed random matrices, and (ii) the Φ_k form a Markov chain.

In closing this subsection we refer to some other studies on random ordinary differential equations which are of interest in mathematical physics and engineering. S. K. Srinivasan [**86**] has studied equations of the form

$$\frac{dx(\omega, t)}{dt} + Ax(\omega, t) = y(\omega, t), \tag{5.13}$$

where $x(\omega, t)$ and $y(\omega, t)$ are random n-vectors, and A is an $n \times n$ matrix. He investigates the solution of equation (5.13) under the assumption that the components y_i of $y(\omega, t)$ are independent random processes. The theory developed is applied to the Langevin equation, and to some first, second, and third order equations arising in various physical and engineering applications.

D. A. Edwards and J. E. Moyal [**27**], and J. E. Moyal [**66**], have studied several random equations in mathematical physics, in particular, the Langevin equation for simple Brownian motion and the equation for the Brownian oscillator. The random differential equation for the amplitude of a random linear oscillator has been considered by R. H. Kraichnan [**55**]. K. Urbanik [**90**] in his studies on generalized stochastic processes as distributions in the sense of Mikusiński has studied the Langevin equation

$$\frac{dv(\omega, t)}{dt} + \alpha v(\omega, t) = \Phi(\omega, t), \tag{5.14}$$

where $v(\omega, t)$ is the velocity of a Brownian particle, α is a constant, and $\Phi(\omega, t)$ is the generalized derivative of a Gaussian process.

Differential equations with random coefficients and their applications have been studied by D. Maravall Casesnoves [**61**; **62**]; in particular, he has studied the random equation associated with a "stochastic" pendulum.

5.2. Random partial differential equations. The study of random solutions of partial differential equations was initiated by J. Kampé de Fériet ([**51**] and earlier papers). In particular, he has studied random solutions of the heat equation for an infinite rod when the initial temperature at the point x on the rod is a random function $f(\omega, x)$. Let $u(\omega, t, x)$ denote the random solution of the equation

$$\begin{cases} \dfrac{\partial u}{\partial t} = \dfrac{\partial^2 u}{\partial x^2}, & -\infty < x < \infty, \\ u(\omega, t, x) = f(\omega, x). \end{cases} \tag{5.15}$$

Kampé de Fériet showed that the solution of (5.15) is

$$u(\omega, t, x) = \int_{-\infty}^{\infty} K(x - \xi, t) f(\omega, \xi)\, d\xi, \tag{5.16}$$

where $K(x, t) = (4\pi t)\ -\tfrac{1}{2}\ e^{-x^2/4t}$.

The problem investigated by Kampé de Fériet is a special case of what can be called a stochastic boundary value problem. The notion of a stochastic boundary problem is due to Kampé de Fériet; and it was introduced in order to provide a framework within which to study boundary value problems for which the boundary conditions cannot be expressed by a single well-determined or known function $\gamma(u)$, say. In these cases one introduces a set Γ of realizable boundary conditions which is the range of a random variable. Hence an event consists of the choice of an element $\omega_0 \in \Omega$, which in turn specifies the boundary condition $\gamma(\omega_0, u) \in \Gamma$ that is to be imposed.

We would now like to discuss, in some detail, an interesting paper by I. Babuška [**7**] which studies the Dirichlet and Poisson problems for Laplace's equation with random boundary conditions and random right-hand side, respectively. Here we restrict our attention to the random Dirichlet problem.

Let E_n, $n = 1, 2, \cdots$, be Euclidean n-space, K the open unit parallelepiped in E_n, and $\bar{K}$ its closure in E_n. As before, let $(\Omega, \mathscr{A}, \mu)$ denote a probability space, where the elements ω are real-valued functions defined on $\bar{K}$. Functions defined on Ω we denote by f, g, etc., and for $x \in \bar{K}$, $f_x(\omega) = \omega(x)$ will be the function defined on $\Omega \times \bar{K}$. We assume that for every $x \in \bar{K}$ the function $f_x(\omega)$ is μ-measurable, and that

$$\int_\Omega f_x^2(\omega)\, d\mu \leqq M^2 < \infty \tag{5.17}$$

(M independent of x); and also that

$$\lim_{x \to y} \int_\Omega (f_x(\omega) - f_y(\omega))^2\, d\mu = 0. \tag{5.18}$$

Now, let L^{**} denote the set of all functions $f_x(\omega)$ defined on Ω for every $x \in \bar{K}$, together with the function $z_0(\omega) = 1$. L^* denotes the linear module over L^{**} with the reals as coefficient domain. We now define a scalar product and norm in L^* by

$$(g_1, g_2) = \int_\Omega g_1(\omega) g_2(\omega)\, d\mu, \qquad g_1, g_2 \in L^*,$$

$$\|g\| = (g_1, g_2)^{1/2}.$$

Finally, we denote by L the completion, with respect to the norm just defined, of the linear space L^*.

To formulate the stochastic boundary value problem we proceed as follows. Let γ be a continuous function defined on $\bar{K}$, and let U denote a region, with $\bar{U} \subset K$. Denote by $W(\gamma, x)$ the function defined on $\bar{K}$ as follows:

(i) $W(\gamma, x) = \gamma(x)$ for $x \notin U$,

(ii) for $x \in U$, $W(\gamma, x)$ is the generalized (Wiener) solution[8] of the Dirichlet problem for Laplace's equation on U, with the boundary condition defined by $\gamma(x)$ on the boundary of U. The function $W(\gamma, x)$ will be called the solution of the Dirichlet's problem for the boundary function $\gamma(x)$.

We remark that $W(\gamma, x)$ is dependent only on the values which γ assumes on $\tilde{U}$, the boundary of U.

We now introduce the following definition.

Definition 5.1. *A random function $w(\omega, x)$ defined on $\Omega \times \bar{K}$ will be called a random Wiener solution of the Dirichlet problem on U, with boundary condition defined by $f_x(\omega)$, if $w(\omega, x) \in L$ for every $x \in K$ and, for every $z \in L$,*

$$(z, w) = W((z, f_x(\omega)), x). \tag{5.19}$$

Babuška's first result can be stated as follows.

[8] Cf. [21].

THEOREM 5.1. *There is precisely one random solution* (*in the sense of Definition* 5.1) *of the Dirichlet problem.*

We now define the *covariance function* $\rho(x, y)$ as follows: $\rho(x, y) = (f_x(\omega), f_y(\omega))$. From (5.18) it follows that $\rho(x, y)$ is a continuous function if x and y on $\bar{K} \times \bar{K}$. Since, by Theorem 5.1, there is only one random solution of the Dirichlet problem, we will denote this solution by $w(\omega, x)$. For every x, $w(\omega, x) \in L$; hence we can introduce the function

$$R(x, y) = (w(\omega, x), w(\omega, y)). \tag{5.20}$$

$R(x, y)$ will be called the *covariance function of the random solution of the Dirichlet problem on U.*

The next theorem gives an expression for $R(x, y)$ in terms of the solution W.

THEOREM 5.2. *Let* $h_x(x, y) = W(\rho(x, y), x)$, *and* $h_y(x, y) = W(\rho(x, y), y)$. *Then* $R(x, y) = W(h_x(x, y), y) = W(h_y(x, y), x)$.

Finally, we consider the expectation of the random solution $w(\omega, x)$. From (2.14) we have

$$\bar{w}(x) = \mathscr{E}\{w(\omega, x)\} = \int_\Omega w(\omega, x)\, d\mu. \tag{5.21}$$

The function $\bar{f}(x) = \int_\Omega f_x(\omega)\, d\mu$ will be called the *expected value of the random boundary condition.* The following theorem is true.

THEOREM 5.3. *Let* $w(\omega, x)$ *be the random solution* (*in the sense of Definition* 5.1) *of the Dirichlet problem. Then*

$$\bar{w}(x) = W(\bar{f}(x), x). \tag{5.22}$$

This result, which is germane to our discussion in §2.5, states that (deterministic) calculations starting with expected values determine the expected value of random solutions.

We next mention some applications of random equations in quantum mechanics. R. H. Kraichnan **[55]** has studied random solutions of the Schrödinger equation for a particle in a random potential. Similarly, H. L. Frisch and S. P. Lloyd **[31]**, and J. A. Morrison **[64]**, in connection with their studies on electron levels in one-dimensional random lattices, have considered the Schrödinger equation with random potential function

$$V(\omega, x) = V_0 \sum_{i=-\infty}^{\infty} \delta(x - x_i(\omega)), \qquad -\infty < x < \infty, \tag{5.23}$$

where $V_0 < 0$ and $\{x_i(\omega)\}$ is a sequence of real-valued random variables with a Poisson distribution. Let $\psi(x)$ denote the solution of the Schrödinger equation. In **[31]** it was shown that the random variables

$$z_i = \frac{\psi'(x_i - 0)}{\psi(x_i)}, \qquad -\infty < i < \infty$$

form a stationary Markov process.

In another interesting paper, H. Primas **[70]** has considered quantum mechanical systems with random Hamiltonians of the form $H(\omega, t) = H_0(t) + \lambda V(\omega, t)$, where H_0 and V are Hermitean operators, with H_0 being a nonrandom operator, and λ is a real number. In particular, he considers solutions of the random equation

$$\frac{\partial \rho(\omega, t)}{\partial t} = -i[H(\omega, t), \rho(\omega, t)], \tag{5.24}$$

where $\rho(\omega, t)$ is the ordinary density matrix. The theory developed is used to outline a new foundation for F. Bloch's relaxation theory.

In order to study random solutions of partial differential equations using semi-group theory, we have initiated the study of semigroups of random operators, and formulated the stochastic analogue of the abstract Cauchy problem[9] **[18]**. This theory, when developed, should enable us to solve partial differential equations when the differential operator (infinitesimal generator of the semigroup) is a random operator.

In closing, we mention two other interesting studies. W. E. Boyce **[20]** in his studies on random vibration problems has considered what might be called a random Sturm–Liouville problem. In this case the coefficients multiplying the dependent variable and its derivatives are random variables. M. Ullrich **[89]** has developed a theory of random Mikusinski operators, and has used this theory to study random partial differential equations with constant coefficients.

6. **Random integral equations.** Studies on random integral equations have, in the main, proceeded along two different, but we do not think independent, lines. We have the work of K. Ito ([**45**; **46**]; cf. also [**23**]) devoted to the study of random integral equations associated with Markov processes; and we have the studies of O. Hanš **[42]** and the author [**13**; **14**; **15**; **17**] which consider solutions of some classical integral equations with random kernels, or defined over random domains. Random integral equations also arise in connection with certain problems in control theory. The random integral equations of control theory will be treated in **[19]**.

6.1. THE ITO RANDOM INTEGRAL EQUATION. The random integral equation referred to as the *Ito equation* is of the form

$$x(\omega, t) = x(\omega, t_0) + \int_{t_0}^{t} m(\tau, x(\omega, \tau))\, d\tau + \int_{t_0}^{t} \sigma(\tau, x(\omega, \tau))\, dw(\omega, \tau), \tag{6.1}$$

where $x(\omega, t) \in R$, $m(t, x)$, and $\sigma(t, x)$ are real functions continuous in x, uniformly in t, and $w(\omega, t)$ is a Wiener process. Equation (6.1) arises in the following way. Let $w(\omega, t)$ be a process corresponding to the differential operator $d^2/d\xi^2$, and let $x(\omega, t)$ be a process corresponding to the operator $\frac{1}{2}\sigma(\xi)\, d^2/d\xi^2 + m(\xi)\, d/d\xi$. Ito showed that the two processes can be so chosen that the relationship between them

[9] We refer to E. Hille and R. S. Phillips **[44]** for a discussion of the abstract Cauchy problem.

is given by equation (6.1). Equation (6.1) can also be written in the form of the random differential equation

$$dx(\omega, t) = m(t, x)\,dt + \sigma(t, x)\,dw(\omega, t). \tag{6.2}$$

The Ito approach enables us to replace the study of the partial differential equations for the transition probabilities of a Markov process by the study of the random ordinary differential equation of its realizations. Equation (6.2) can be reduced to equation (6.1), and the solution of equation (6.1) can be obtained using the method of successive approximations.

In this paper we will not give a detailed discussion of the Ito equation. The interested reader will find a complete treatment of the Ito equation and its applications in [**19**]. It is, however, of interest to refer to the following recent theoretical studies and applications of the Ito equation: (1) K. Z. Dambis ([**22**]; cf. also [**25**]) has studied random integral equations in Hilbert space; (2) I. V. Girsanov [**32**] has discussed the uniqueness of solutions of the Ito equation; (3) A. V. Skorohod [**82**] has utilized the Ito equation in the study of diffusion processes; (4) M. I. Freĭdlin [**30**] has employed the Ito equation in the study of elliptic differential equations; and (5) T. Nagai [**67**] has investigated the stability of a random linear system of first order using an Ito equation.

6.2. Random solutions of some classical integral equations. The studies of Hanš and the author on random solutions of some classical integral equations were motivated by: (1) the widespread occurrence of integral equations in mathematical physics and other branches of applied mathematics, (2) the existence of a well-developed theory, and (3) the relationship between integral equations and differential equations, systems of linear algebraic equations, boundary value problems, etc. In our studies we have considered the random solutions to be elements of an Orlicz space (generalized Lebesgue space) since much of the recent work in the theory of integral equation (cf. [**56**; **95**]) has been carried out in these spaces.[10]

Let U be a bounded or unbounded interval in k-dimensional Euclidean space R_k (hence we can have $U \equiv R_k$), and let m be Lebesgue measure on U. Let $(\Omega, \mathscr{A}, \mu)$ be a probability space, and let $(L_\Phi, \mathscr{B})$ be a measurable space, where L_Φ is the Orlicz space $L_\Phi(U, m)$ and $\mathscr{B}$ is the σ-algebra of all Borel subsets of L_Φ.

The random version of the nonhomogeneous Fredholm integral equation of second kind, i.e.,

$$\int_U K(t, u)x(u)\,dm(u) - \lambda x(t) = y(t), \tag{6.3}$$

when random boundary conditions are imposed, can be written as

$$\int_{D_\omega} K(t, u)x(\omega, u)\,dm(u) - \lambda x(\omega, t) = y(\omega, t). \tag{6.4}$$

[10] For a detailed discussion of Orlicz spaces and their properties we refer to [**56**; **95**]; we refer to [**11**] for a discussion of generalized random variables with values in an Orlicz space.

In equation (6.4) the unknown function $x(\omega, t)$ and the known function $y(\omega, t)$ are generalized random variables with values in the separable[11] Orlicz space L_Φ. We shall assume that $y(\omega, t) = y(t)$ for all $\omega \in \Omega$, and that the kernel, which is deterministic (i.e., it does not depend on ω) is an $m \times m$-measurable function in $U \times U$. The parameter λ is an arbitrary complex number.

When considering random boundary value problems for Fredholm integral equations, the choice of an element $\omega \in \Omega$ specifies an interval $D_\omega \subseteq U$ which is the fundamental domain over which the integral is defined. Hence D_ω is a *random set*, and m is now random Lebesgue measure with $0 < m(D_\omega) \leq m(U)$. We assume that the integral in (6.4) exists in the sense of Lebesgue for almost all $\omega \in \Omega$.

It is also possible to consider equation (6.3) when the kernel is a function of ω. In our case we have

$$\int_U K(\omega, t, u)x(\omega, u)\, dm(u) - \lambda x(\omega, t) = y(t), \tag{6.5}$$

where

$$K(\omega, t, u) = \begin{cases} K(t, u), & \text{for } u \in D, \\ 0, & \text{for } u \in U - D. \end{cases} \tag{6.6}$$

In operator form equation (6.4) becomes

$$(T(\omega) - \lambda I)x = y, \tag{6.7}$$

where I is the identity operator, and

$$T(\omega)x = \int_{D_\omega} K(t, u)x(u)\, dm(u) \tag{6.8}$$

is an operator on the Orlicz space $L_\Phi(D_\omega, m(D_\omega))$.

We now discuss some properties of the operator $T(\omega)$ defined by (6.8). In particular, we want to know if $T(\omega)$ is a random transformation; that is, $T(\omega)$, as a function of ω, is measurable.

Let us rewrite (6.8) in the form

$$\int_U K(t, u)h(\omega, u)\, dm(u), \tag{6.9}$$

where

$$h(\omega, u) = \begin{cases} x(\omega, u), & \text{for } u \in D, \\ 0, & \text{for } u \in U - D_\omega. \end{cases} \tag{6.10}$$

The function $h(\omega, u)$ can also be written as

$$h(\omega, u) = \mathscr{X}_{D_\omega}(u)x(\omega, u), \tag{6.11}$$

[11] The Orlicz space under consideration will always be separable, since we shall assume that the convex function $\Phi(r)$ defining the Orlicz space satisfies the Δ_2-condition, and the measure m is Lebesgue measure.

where $\mathscr{X}_{D_\omega}(u)$ is the indicator, or characteristic function, of the random set D_ω. Now, since $K(t, u)$ is a continuous function of $t, u \in D_\omega$, and is by hypothesis an $m(D_\omega) \times m(D_\omega)$-measurable function on $D_\omega \times D_\omega$, and if we assume that $x(\omega, u)$ is measurable (in the sense of Theorem 2.9), we see that the following proposition is true: *A sufficient condition for $h(\omega, u)$, and consequently $T(\omega)$, to be measurable is that $\mathscr{X}_{D_\omega}(u)$ be measurable,*[12] *and also the random solution $x(\omega, u)$.*

The results given in **[14]** concerning the Fredholm operator can be summarized as follows: *The Fredholm operator, defined by* (6.8), *on the Orlicz space $L_\Phi(D_\omega, m(D_\omega))$ will be a random endomorphism (i.e., a measurable linear bounded operator) of L_Φ if* (i) *the kernel $K(t, u)$ has the property that*

$$r(\omega, t) = \int_{D_\omega} |K(t, u)x(\omega, u)| \, dm(u)$$

is a generalized random variable with values in L_Φ, and (ii) *the solution $x(\omega, t)$ and the indicator of the random set D_ω are measurable with respect to the same σ-algebra of Borel subsets of Ω.*

In **[42]** Hanš, by introducing a random kernel, establishes the measurability of the Fredholm operator without requiring that the solution of the integral equation be measurable.

Finally, application of Theorems 2.2 and 2.9, and the classical theory, shows that the solution of (6.4) is

$$x(\omega, t) = R(\lambda; T(\omega))[y(t)] \in L_\Phi(D_\omega, m(D_\omega)), \tag{6.12}$$

and that the solution is unique. The theory of random contraction operators can be used to prove the following

THEOREM 6.1. *Consider the random Fredholm integral equation* (6.4) *in the Orlicz space $L_\Phi(D_\omega, m(D_\omega))$, where the kernel $K(t, u)$ is measurable on $D_\omega \times D_\omega$, with $|K(t, u)| < M$, and for all $\omega \in \Omega$ the function $y(t) \in L_\Phi$ is known. If $|\lambda| > m(D_\omega)M$, where $m(D_\omega)$ is the Lebesgue measure of D_ω, then for every fixed $u \in D_\omega$ there exists a mapping $\xi_\lambda(\omega)$ from Ω into L_Φ which is a generalized random variable, and the solution of equation* (6.4).

We remark that the solution of equation (6.4) can be found by the method of successive approximations, the nth approximation being given by

$$x_n(\omega, t) = \frac{1}{\lambda}\left\{\int_{D_\omega} K(t, u)x_{n-1}(\omega, u) \, dm(u) - y(t)\right\}, \tag{6.13}$$

where $x_0(\omega, u)$ is an arbitrary generalized random variable with values in L_Φ.

Similar results can be obtained for the random Volterra integral equations, and for systems of random integral equations. For a discussion of these results we refer to **[14; 42]**. In **[15]** we have considered the random Fredholm integral

[12] $\mathscr{X}_{D_\omega}(u)$ will be measurable if D_ω is measurable.

equations with separable (degenerate, or finite-rank) kernels; that is, we consider equation (6.4) with[13]

$$K(t, u) = \sum_{i=1}^{n} \alpha_i(t)\beta_i(u). \tag{6.14}$$

In this case we obtain the following analogue of a classical result in the theory of Fredholm integral equations: *The solution of a random Fredholm integral equation with separable kernel of rank n is equivalent to the solution of a system of n random linear algebraic equations in n unknowns.* The theory of random contraction operators was used to establish the existence and uniqueness of the system of algebraic equations, and as a consequence the solution of the integral equation.

In **[17]** random solutions of some nonlinear integral equations are considered. In particular, the random Hammerstein equation

$$\int_{D\omega} K(t, u)q[u, x(\omega, u)]\, dm(u) - \lambda x(t) = y(t) \tag{6.15}$$

is studied. While the analysis is a little more involved than in the case of random linear integral equations, fixed point methods are applicable, and were used to establish the existence and uniqueness of solutions.

7. Stochastic processes associated with random equations. In most applied situations we are primarily interested in obtaining the solution of a given random equation and studying its statistical properties. However, from the point of view of the theory of stochastic processes, an interesting problem is to study the stochastic processes generated by solutions of random equations. For example, in the case of equation (2.2), we can ask the following question: If the input $y(\omega, t)$ is a given stochastic process and T is a nonrandom operator, what type of stochastic process $\{x(\omega, t), t \geqq 0\}$ is generated by the solution $x(\omega, t) = T^{-1}[y(\omega, t)]$? This is clearly the simplest case; and many results have been obtained in this case.

We can ask similar questions for the solutions of equations (2.3) and (2.4). However, the analysis of the stochastic processes in these cases can be more involved. In the case of random equations of the form $T(\omega)[x] = y$, some results are available. For example, B. H. Bharucha **[10]** has considered the stochastic process associated with the random difference equation (4.14) when the matrices Φ_k are independent, identically distributed random operators. In this case the process $\{x_k\}$ is an infinite Markov chain. Studies on ordinary differential equations with random coefficients have, in the main, been concerned with the stability (in some sense) of the random solution when the coefficients are, say white noise processes, and not with the stochastic processes generated by the solutions. In the case of random partial differential equations very little is known. We have the

[13] It is also possible to consider equation (6.4) defined on the domain U with a random separable kernel $K(\omega, t, u) = \sum_{i=1}^{n} \alpha_i(t)\beta_i(\omega, u)$, where $\beta_i(\omega, u) = \beta_i(u)$ for $u \in D_\omega$, and zero otherwise.

result of J. Kampé de Fériet [**51**] who showed that when the random initial temperature $f(\omega, x)$ is a stationary (wide sense) process, then the solution $u(\omega, t, x)$ of the heat equation, as a function of x is a stationary (wide sense) process, and as a function of t is exponentially convex.

For random integral equations, we have already pointed out that the solution of the Ito equation is a Markov process; however, nothing is known about the processes associated with the random solutions of the classical integral equations considered in §6.2. In control theory we encounter random integral equations of the form

$$x(\omega, t) = x_0 + \int_{t_0}^{t} K(x, u, \xi)\, d\xi, \tag{7.1}$$

where $x(\omega, t)$ is the state variable and $u(\omega, t)$ is random disturbance. The initial state x_0 may also be a random variable. It is known that if $u(\omega, t)$ is a white noise process, then the solution of equation (7.1) is a Markov process.

In the case of random solutions of the form $x(\omega, t) = R(\lambda; T(\omega))[y(\omega, t)]$ (cf. (2.13)), we feel that a problem of interest is the study of the stochastic processes $\{x(\omega, t)\}$ generated by the process $\{y(\omega, t)\}$ and the random operator $T(\omega)$; in particular, the relationship between the process $\{x(\omega, t)\}$ and the spectral properties of the random operator $T(\omega)$.

Bibliography

1. G. Adomian, *Linear stochastic operators*, Rev. Modern Phys. **35** (1963), 185–207.

2. ———, *Stochastic Green's functions*, Proc. Sympos. Appl. Math. Vol. 16, pp. 1–39, Amer. Math. Soc., Providence, R. I., 1964.

3. ———, *Linear stochastic operators*, Academic Press, New York (to appear).

4. M. Altman, *Lectures on approximation methods in functional analysis*, California Institute of Technology, Pasadena, Calif., 1959 (unpublished).

5. H. A. Antosiewicz and W. C. Rheinboldt, *Numerical analysis and functional analysis*, Survey of Numerical Analysis, pp. 485–517, McGraw-Hill, New York, 1962.

6. I. Babuška, *Random differential equations*, Apl. Mat. **4** (1959), 227–232. (Czech)

7. ———, *On randomized solutions of Laplace's equations*, Časopis Pěst. Mat. **86** (1961), 269–279.

8. S. Bernstein, *Equations différentielles stochastique*, Actualités Sci. Ind., No. 738, Hermann, Paris, 1938, 5–31.

9. J. E. Bertram and P. E. Sarachik, *Stability of circuits with random time-varying parameters*, IRE Trans. **PGIT-5** (1959), Special suppl. 260–270.

10. B. H. Bharucha, *On the stability of randomly varying systems*, Ph.D. thesis, Univ. of California, Berkeley, Calif., 1961.

11. A. T. Bharucha-Reid, *On random elements in Orlicz spaces*, Bull. Acad. Polon. Sci. Cl. III **4** (1956), 655–657.

12. ———, *On random operator equations in Banach spaces*, Bull. Acad. Polon. Sci. Ser. Sci. Math. Astronom. Phys. **7** (1959), 561–564.

13. ———, *On random solutions of Fredholm integral equations*, Bull. Amer. Math. Soc. **66** (1960), 104–109.

14. ———, *On random solutions of integral equations in Banach space*, Trans. 2nd Prague Conf. Information Theory, pp. 27–48, Publ. House Czechoslovak Acad. Sci., Prague, 1960.

15. ———, *Sur les équations intégrales aléatoires de Fredholm à noyaux séparables*, C. R. Acad. Sci. Paris **250** (1960), 454–456, 657–658.

16. ———, *Approximate solutions of random operator equations*, Notices Amer. Math. Soc. **7** (1960), 361.

17. ———, *Random solutions of nonlinear integral equations* (to appear).

18. ———, *Semigroups of random operators* (to appear).

19. ———, *Random equations*, Academic Press, New York (to appear).

20. W. E. Boyce, *Random vibration of elastic strings and bars*, Proc. 4th U. S. Nat. Congr. Appl. Mech. (Univ. of California, Berkeley, Calif., 1962), Vol. 1, pp. 77–85, Amer. Soc. Mech. Engrs., New York, 1962.

21. R. Courant, *Methods of mathematical physics*, Vol. II, Interscience, New York, 1962.

22. K. Z. Dambis, *Stochastic integral equations in Hilbert space*, Diploma thesis, Moscow State University, Moscow, 1959. (Russian)

23. J. L. Doob, *Stochastic processes*, Wiley, New York, 1953.

24. M. Driml and O. Hanš, *On experience theory problems*, Trans. 2nd Prague Conf. Information Theory, pp. 93–111, Publ. House Czechoslovak Acad. Sci., Prague, 1960.

25. E. B. Dynkin, *Markov processes and analysis problems connected with them*, Uspehi Mat. Nauk **15** (1960), no. 2 (92), 3–24. (Russian)

26. F. J. Dyson, *A Brownian-motion model for the eigenvalues of a random matrix*, J. Mathematical Phys. **3** (1962), 1191–1198.

27. D. A. Edwards and J. E. Moyal, *Stochastic differential equations*, Proc. Cambridge Philos. Soc. **51** (1955), 663–677.

28. R. Engleman, *The eigenvalues of a randomly distributed matrix*, Nuovo Cimento (10) **10** (1958), 615–621.

29. P. Erdös and A. C. Offord, *On the number of real roots of a random algebraic equation*, Proc. London Math. Soc. (3) **6** (1956), 139–160.

30. M. I. Freĭdlin, *Mixed boundary value problem for elliptic differential equations of second order with small parameter*, Dokl. Akad. Nauk SSSR **143** (1962), 1300–1303. (Russian)

31. H. L. Frisch and S. P. Lloyd, *Electron levels in a one-dimensional random lattice*, Phys. Rev. (2) **120** (1960), 1175–1189.

32. I. V. Girsanov, *Ein Beispiel der uneindeutlichkeit der Lösung der stochastischen Integralgleichung von K. Ito*, Teor. Verojatnost. i Primenen. **7** (1962), 336–342. (Russian)

33. U. Grenander and M. Rosenblatt, *Statistical analysis of stationary time series*, Wiley, New York, 1957.

34. U. Grenander, *Some non linear problems in probability theory*, Probability and statistics, pp. 108–129, Wiley, New York, 1959.

35. ———, *Stochastic groups*, Ark. Mat. **4** (1960), 163–183.

36. ———, *Stochastic groups and related structures*, Proc. 4th Berkeley Sympos. Math. Statist. and Prob. (1960), Vol. II, pp. 171–184, Univ. of California Press, Berkeley, Calif., 1961.

37. J. Hammersley, *The zeros of a random polynomial*, Proc. 3rd Berkeley Sympos. Math. Statist. and Prob. (1955), Vol. II, pp. 89–111, Univ. of California Press, Berkeley, Calif., 1956.

38. O. Hanš, *Reduzierende zufällige Transformationen*, Czechoslovak Math. J. **7** (1957), 154–158.

39. ———, *Generalized random variables*, Trans. 1st Prague Conference on Information Theory, Statistical Decision Functions, and Random Processes (1956), pp. 61–103, Czech. Acad. Sci., Prague, 1957.

40. ———, *Random fixed point theorems*, ibid., pp. 105–125.

41. ———, *Inverse and adjoint transforms of linear bounded random transforms*, ibid., pp. 127–133.

42. ———, *Random operator equations*, Proc. 4th Berkeley Sympos. Math. Statist. and Prob. (1960), Vol. II, pp. 185–202, Univ. of California Press, Berkeley, Calif., 1961.

43. O. Hanš, and A. Špaček, *Random fixed point approximations by differentiable trajectories*, Trans. 2nd Prague Conference on Information Theory, pp. 203–213, Publ. House Czechoslovak Acad. Sci., Prague, 1960.

44. E. Hille and R. S. Phillips, *Functional analysis and semi-groups*, Amer. Math. Soc. Colloq. Publ. Vol. 31, Amer. Math. Soc., Providence, R. I., 1957.

45. K. Ito, *On a stochastic integral equation*, Proc. Japan Acad. **22** (1946), 32–35.

46. ———, *On stochastic differential equations*, Mem. Amer. Math. Soc. No. 4 (1951), 51 pp.

47. M. Kac, *On the average number of real roots of a random algebraic equation*, Bull. Amer. Math. Soc. **49** (1943), 314–320, 938.

48. ———, *On the average number of real roots of a random algebraic equation*. II, Proc. London Math. Soc. (2) **50** (1948), 390–408.

49. ———, *Probability and related topics in physical sciences*, Interscience, New York, 1959.

50. R. E. Kalman, *Control of randomly varying linear dynamical systems*, Proc. Sympos. Appl. Math. Vol. 13, pp. 287–298, Amer. Math. Soc., Providence, R. I., 1962.

51. J. Kampé de Fériet, *Random solutions of partial differential equations*, Proc. 3rd Berkeley Sympos. Math. Statist. and Prob. (1955), Vol. III, pp. 199–208, Univ. of California Press, Berkeley, Calif., 1956.

52. ———, *Statistical mechanics of continuous media*, Proc. Sympos. Appl. Math. Vol. 13, pp. 165–198, Amer. Math. Soc., Providence, R. I., 1962.

53. L. V. Kantorovič, *Functional analysis and applied mathematics*, Uspehi Mat. Nauk **3** (1948), no. 6 (28), 89–185. (Russian)

54. T. Koopmans, *Statistical inference in dynamic economic models*, Cowles Commission for Research in Economics, Monograph No. 10, Wiley, New York, 1950.

55. R. H. Kraichnan, *Dynamics of nonlinear stochastic systems*, J. Mathematical Phys. **2** (1961), 124–148.

56. M. A. Krasnosel′skiĭ and Ya. B. Rutickiĭ, *Convex functions and Orlicz spaces*, Gosudarstv. Izdat. Fiz.-Mat. Lit, Moscow, 1958. (Russian)

57. V. L. Lebedev, *Random processes in electrical and mechanical systems*, Gosudarstv. Izdat. Fiz.-Mat. Lit., Moscow, 1958. (Russian)

58. J. E. Littlewood and A. C. Offord, *On the number of real roots of a random algebraic equation*, J. London Math. Soc. **13** (1938), 288–295.

59. ———, *On the number of real roots of a random algebraic equation*. II, Proc. Cambridge Philos. Soc. **35** (1939), 133–148.

60. J. L. Lumley, *An approach to the Eulerian-Lagrange problem*, J. Mathematical Phys. **3** (1962), 309–312.

61. D. Maravell Casenoves, *Algunos nuevos procesos estocásticos y sus aplicaciones*, Rev. Acad. Ci. Madrid **53** (1959), 435–489, 659, 726.

62. ———, *Ingenieria de las oscilaciones*, Dossat, Madrid, 1959.

63. M. L. Mehta and M. Gaudin, *On the density of eigenvalues of a random matrix*, Nuclear Phys. **18** (1960), 420–427.

64. J. A. Morrison, *On the number of electron levels in a one-dimensional random lattice*, J. Math. Phys. **3** (1962), 1023–1027.

65. E. Mourier, *Eléments aléatoires dans un espace de Banach*, Ann. Inst. H. Poincaré **13** (1953), 161–244.

66. J. E. Moyal, *Stochastic processes and statistical physics*, J. Roy. Statist. Soc. Ser. **B 11** (1949), 150–210.

67. T. Nagai, *Stability problem of random linear system of the first order*, Mem. Fac. Sci. Kyushu Univ. Ser. A **16** (1962), 47–59.

68. V. V. Nemytskiĭ, *The method of fixed points in analysis*, Uspehi Mat. Nauk **1** (1936), 141–174. (Russian)

69. W. Pogorzelski, *Integral equations and their applications*, Vols. I and II, Pánstwowe Wydawnictwo Naukowe, Warsaw, 1953, 1958. (Polish)

70. H. Primas, *Über quantenmechanische Systeme mit einem stochastischen Hamiltonoperator*, Helv. Phys. Acta **34** (1961), 36–57.

71. V. S. Pugachev, *Theory of random functions and its application to problems of automatic control*, Gosudarstv. Izdat. Tekh.-Teor. Lit., Moscow, 1957. (Russian)

72. A. Rosenbloom, *Analysis of random time-varying linear systems*, Ph.D. thesis, Univ. of California, Los Angeles, Calif., 1954.

73. G.-C. Rota, *On the passage from the Navier–Stokes equations to the Reynolds equations*, Proc. Internat. Conf. on Partial Differential Equations and Continuum Mechanics, pp. 374–376, Univ. of Wisconsin Press, Madison, Wis., 1961.

74. ———, *Linear operators satisfying algebraic identities*, Proc. Sympos. Appl. Math. Vol. 16, pp. 70–83, Amer. Math. Soc., Providence, R. I., 1964.

75. C. Ryll-Nardzewski, *An analogue of Fubini's theorem and its application to random linear equations*, Bull. Acad. Polon. Sci. Ser. Sci. Math. Astronom. Phys. **8** (1960), 511–513.

76. G. Samal, *On the number of real roots of a random algebraic equation*, Proc. Cambridge Philos. Soc. **58** (1962), 433–442.

77. J. C. Samuels, *On the mean square stability of random linear equations*, IRE Trans. **PGIT-5** (1959), Special suppl., 248–259.

78. ———, *On the stability of random systems and the stabilization of deterministic systems with random noise*, J. Acoust. Soc. Amer. **32** (1960), 594–601.

79. J. C. Samuels and A. C. Eringen, *On stochastic linear systems*, J. Math. and Phys. **38** (1959), 83–103.

80. J. Schauder, *Der Fixpunktsatz in Funktionalräumen*, Studia Math. **2** (1930), 171–180.

81. O. Šefl, *On stability of a randomized linear system*, Sci. Sinica **7** (1958), 1027–1034.

82. A. V. Skorohod, *Stochastic equations for diffusion processes in a bounded region*, Teor. Verojatnost. i Primenen **6** (1961), 287–298. (Russian)

83. ———, *On the existence and uniqueness of solutions of stochastic differential equations*, Sibirsk Mat. Ž. **2** (1961), 129–137.

84. A. Špaček, *Zufällige Gleichungen*, Czechoslovak Math. J. **5 (80)** (1955), 462–466.

85. D. I. Šparo and M. G. Šur, *On the distribution of roots of random polynomials*, Vestnik Moskov. Univ. Ser. I Mat. Meh. **1962**, 40–43. (Russian)

86. S. K. Srinivasan, *On a class of stochastic differential equations*, Z. Angew. Math. Mech. **43** (1963), 259–265.

87. W. Uhlmann, *Eine Wahrscheinlichkeitstheorestische Begründung der Integrationsformeln von Newton-Cotes*, Z. Angew. Math. Phys. **10** (1959), 189–207.

88. ———, *Über harmonische und isotrope stochastische Prozesse mit Fehterschätzung für ein Differenzenverfahren*, Z. Angew. Math. Mech. **41** (1961), 428–447.

89. M. Ullrich, *Random Mikusiński operators*, Trans. 2nd Prague Conf. Information Theory, pp. 639–659, Publ. House Czechoslovak Acad. Sci., Prague, 1960.

90. K. Urbanik, *Generalized stochastic processes*, Studia Math. **16** (1958), 268–334.

91. G. A. van Lear, Jr. and G. E. Uhlenbeck, *The Brownian motion of strings and elastic rods*, Phys. Rev. (2) **38** (1931), 1583–1598.

92. E. P. Wigner, *On the distribution of the roots of certain symmetric matrices*, Ann. of Math. (2) **67** (1958) 325–327.

93. H. Wold, *A study in the analysis of stationary time series*, Almquist and Wiksells, Stockholm, 1950.

94. H. Wold and L. Juréen, *Demand analysis*, Wiley, New York, 1952.

95. A. C. Zaanen, *Linear analysis*, Interscience, New York, 1953.

WAYNE STATE UNIVERSITY,
DETROIT, MICHIGAN

REYNOLDS OPERATORS

BY

GIAN-CARLO ROTA[1]

DEDICATED TO PROFESSOR JOSEPH KAMPÉ DE FÉRIET ON THE OCCASION OF HIS RETIREMENT

1. **Introduction.** Let A be an algebra over a field of characteristic not equal to 2. A *Reynolds operator* (or Reynolds endomorphism) is a linear map of A into A which satisfies the following identity, for any f and g in A:

$$R(fg) = RfRg + R((f - Rf)(g - Rg)).$$

We call this identity the *Reynolds identity*. It occurs for the first time in a famous paper of Osborne Reynolds[2] on turbulence theory.

A related identity, introduced almost contemporarily by Kolmogorov and Kampé de Fériet and studied by Garrett Birkhoff, is the *averaging identity*

$$A(fAg) = (Af)(Ag).$$

A linear operator A satisfying the averaging identity is usually called an *averaging operator*. In this paper we discuss the relationship between averaging operators and Reynolds operators, and we give a representation of a Reynolds operator when A is an algebra of bounded measurable functions, provided the operator satisfies a certain mild continuity restriction.

There is an extensive literature on averaging operators, motivated largely by the fact that they characterize and generalize the operation of conditional expectation in probability theory. It is easy to see that

PROPOSITION 1. *If the algebra* A *has an identity* 1 *and* A *is an averaging operator such that* $A1 = 1$, *then* A *is a Reynolds operator.*

The proof is immediate: setting $f = 1$ in the averaging identity, we get $A^2 = A$.

Expanding the Reynolds identity, we get the equivalent identity

$$R(fRg + gRf) = RfRg + R(RfRg), \tag{1}$$

from which it is clear that if A is an averaging operator such that $A^2 = A$, then $A = R$ is a Reynolds operator.

The converse of Proposition 1 is not true, and we shall see that there is an interesting variety of Reynolds operators other than conditional expectation. In fact, our first question is the following:

---

[1] This work was begun under contract NSF-GP-149, continued under Contract with the Office of Naval Research, and concluded while the author was a Fellow of the Sloan Foundation.

[2] Authors' names refer to the bibliography at the end.

QUESTION 1. Under what conditions is a Reynolds operator an averaging operator?

The answer (Theorem 1) is found, unexpectedly, to depend on whether or not the range of R is a closed subspace, in a suitable topology. Of course there are Reynolds operators without a closed range.

We shall be concerned with Reynolds operators on the algebra $L_\infty(S, \Sigma, m)$ of bounded measurable functions on a measure space (S, Σ, m). This choice is motivated in part by the idea of applying the results to probability and ergodic theory, in part by the fact that this algebra has a particularly simple structure. We shall not assume the measure space to be finite; it suffices to assume enough so that the Radon-Nikodym theorem is applicable; to avoid verbal detours, we shall simply assume that the measure space is σ-finite.

The choice of a topology in $L_\infty(S, \Sigma, m)$ is an old and thorny question, which we shall resolve in the easiest way. Norm-convergence in $L_\infty(S, \Sigma, m)$ bears notoriously little relation to the measure-theoretic structure. On the other hand, there is a topology which is the natural one for L_∞, namely, the topology of L_1-convergence, and *this is the topology we shall use*. Thus, all Reynolds operators are assumed continuous in this topology, as well as, of course, everywhere defined in $L_\infty(S, \Sigma, m)$. With this proviso, an answer to Question 1 is the following:

THEOREM 1. *A Reynolds operator in $L_\infty(S, \Sigma, m)$ is an averaging operator if and only if its range is closed in the L_1-topology.*

Of course the continuity restriction on R can be relaxed, but only at the cost of introducing pathological cases, even for operators acting on the sequence space l_∞, and even in the case of "conditional expectation."

It seems unexpected at first that the answer to a question which appears to be purely algebraic should depend upon a topological condition, but we hope that the proof below shows the "reason" for this phenomenon.

The second question we shall attack is the following:

QUESTION 2. Find an analytic representation for Reynolds operators.

To answer this question, we drop the assumption of continuity in the L_1-topology, but in exchange make a more stringent assumption on R, namely the following:

$$\int_S |Rf|^2\, dm \leqq \int_S |f|^2\, dm \tag{2}$$

for any f in L_∞. Such an assumption could be justified on "physical grounds" (Reynolds operators should not "increase the energy"); mathematically, it enables us to use the machinery of spectral theory in Hilbert space. At any rate, assumption (2) is more innocuous than the assumption of positivity of R ($Rf \geqq 0$ if $f \geqq 0$) that has often been made and that we shall *not* make. Strangely enough, we found that (2) implies that R is positive, but this fact is gotten only after the representation theorem. Under assumption (2), our final result (Theorem 2 below) gives a complete classification of Reynolds operators in terms of conditional expectation and one-parameter semigroups of measure-preserving transformations.

2. **Motivation and history.** Reynolds operators first arose in connection with a problem in partial differential equations which has never been fully settled. Let $N(f) = g$ be the Navier-Stokes equations, with an external acting force g (we do not write them down explicitly because their specific form is irrelevant for the present discussion). The problem is to find all operators R such that if f is a solution, then Rf is a solution of $N(Rf) = g'$, possibly with a different external acting force g'. The idea is that the function Rf should depend on "fewer degrees of freedom"; it should be in some sense an average of f. A simple computation shows that this transformation is possible by a linear operator R only if R satisfies the Reynolds identity. One thus expects the Reynolds identity to express an averaging, or smoothing, property of the operator.

Interesting though this connection with partial differential equations is, we shall not study it in the present work; our concern is largely classificatory. We hope to show in the process that the Reynolds identity is also interesting for reasons other than those that originated it.

In recent years there has been considerable interest in linear operators satisfying algebraic identities. The most spectacular developments were those obtained by Andersen-Atkinson-Baxter-Spitzer and several others, with abstract Wiener-Hopf methods. The operators considered by these authors satisfy an identity very close to the Reynolds identity; this fact alone provides a strong motivation for the study of Reynolds operators. In fact, we hope to show in a separate work (and it is easy to verify formally) that Reynolds operators are "infinitesimal analogs" of those considered by Atkinson-Baxter, etc.

To clarify the "meaning" of the Reynolds identity, we consider some examples. The simplest is conditional expectation, which in an infinite measure space must be defined with some care. Let Σ' be totally σ-finite σ-subfield of Σ (see Halmos, *Measure theory*), and let $A: f \to f'$ be the operator mapping a real function f into the Radon-Nikodym derivative of f relative to Σ'. Then A is a Reynolds operator and an averaging operator. The Radon-Nikodym derivative is the function f', unique in virtue of the Radon-Nikodym theorem, which is measurable relative to Σ' and which has the property that

$$\int_E f' dm = \int_E f \, dm$$

for every E of finite measure in Σ'. Of course f is assumed integrable over every set of finite measure.

Conditional expectation is the typical example of an averaging operator, and in fact, every Reynolds operator satisfying $R^2 = R$ is a generalization of conditional expectation (see the author's Padova Rendiconti paper).

Our second example is somewhat more sophisticated. Let T^t be a one-parameter semigroup of measure-preserving transformations of (S, Σ, m), and define $V^t f(S) = f(T^t S)$, as usual. Since $\|V^t\| = 1$ in L_∞, the operator

$$R = \int_0^\infty e^{-t} V^t \, dt \tag{3}$$

is well defined. To dispose of integrability questions, we may assume that V^t is L_1-continuous, and let the integral be a Bochner integral. We claim that R is a Reynolds operator. To establish this claim, we shall make use of two well-known results:

(a) V^t is a semigroup of operators "arising from" a semigroup of measure-forming transformations in the manner described above if and only if for each t, the operator V^t is a *homomorphism* of L_∞, that is, if and only if $V^t(fg) = (V^t f)(V^t g)$ for all essentially bounded f and g (see Halmos, *Ergodic theory*, for a proof of this result due to von Neumann). (b) If V^t is *any* one-parameter semigroup of bounded operators and R is defined as in (3), then $dV^t R/dt = V^t(R - I)$ (see Hille-Phillips or Dunford-Schwartz, Chapter VIII). Using these two results, we find that

$$\frac{d}{dt} V^t(RfRg) = (V^t(Rf - f))(V^t Rg) + (V^t Rf)(V^t(Rg - g)).$$

Now, integrating by parts identity (3) and using this, we find

$$\int_0^\infty e^{-t} V^t(RfRg) \, dt = [e^{-t} V^t(RfRg)]_0^\infty$$
$$+ \int_0^\infty e^{-t} V^t(Rg(Rf - f) + Rf(Rg - g)) \, dt.$$

Suitably translated, this reads

$$R(RfRg) = -RfRg + R(Rg(Rf - f) + Rf(Rg - g)),$$

which is trivially equivalent to the Reynolds identity.

Operators of the form (3) are a generalization of conditional expectation. Roughly speaking, one "mixes" before averaging. In fact, we have pointed out elsewhere that many of the properties of conditional expectation can be extended to operators of the form (3). For example, the martingale convergence theorems (for *closed* martingales) extend to operators of the form (3), giving the Abel version of the classical ergodic theorems, and in fact giving a unified approach to martingales and ergodic theorems, with some "mixed" cases to boot.

Our second result (Theorem 2) shows that under assumption (2), all Reynolds operators "split" into a product of two commuting operators, one of which is a conditional expectation and the other is of the form (3). It would seem that this result reduces the study of Reynolds operators to ergodic theory. Actually, the converse is just as true. Several questions of ergodic theory, for example, questions of mixing and existence of invariant measure, can be conveniently formulated in terms of the Reynolds operators, where they become easier to attack. In fact, identity (3) shows that Reynolds operators are the *potentials*, in the language of probabilistic potential theory, of semigroups of measure-preserving transformations.

Finally, the Reynolds identity bears a close connection with the identity $D(fg) = fDg + gDf$ characterizing derivations. If R is a Reynolds operator and R^{-1} exists, perhaps as an unbounded operator, then $R^{-1} - I$ is a derivation. Unfortunately, R^{-1} seldom exists, as the example of conditional expectation shows, and Theorem 1 can be compared to the theorem of Singer and Wermer on the nonexistence of bounded derivations, at least for the algebra L_∞ (a version of the Singer-Wermer Theorem for L_∞ is a corollary of Theorem 1 and their entire theorem could be proved by these methods).

Algebraically, the Reynolds identity combines a feature of homomorphisms ($V(fg) = VfVg$), since the range of R is evidently a subalgebra; and a feature of derivations, namely, the "local operator" property, since if $Rf = 0$ then $Rg = 0$ for any g in the ideal generated by f in the range of R that is, any g of the form fRh, as follows easily from the Reynolds identity. These unusual properties make the Reynolds identity in many respects richer and more inclusive than either the "homomorphism" or the "derivation" identities.

A word about the history of the subject. Since Osborne Reynolds, it was Kampé de Fériet who first recognized the importance of studying the averaging and Reynolds identities, and began their study in a series of papers stretching over a period of thirty years. Curiously enough, the averaging identity was being studied at about the same time as Kolmogorov's *Foundations of probability* became known, but the connection with conditional expectation was brought out only many years later in Mrs. Moy's thesis. The Reynolds identity, on the other hand, first made its appearance because of the difficulty of producing averaging operators that commuted with differentiation in Euclidean spaces. The first algebraic study of the identity is Mme. Dubreil's. The first study of averaging operators by the methods of functional analysis is due to Garrett Birkhoff.

3. **Analytic preliminaries.** The two lemmas we shall use from analysis are: the "discontinuous" version of the Stone-Weierstrass Theorem, and the operator characterization of conditional expectation, suitably extended to infinite measure spaces. In both cases the extensions to infinite measure proceed along much the same lines as is done in the author's note in the Padova Rendiconti, and we shall only sketch the arguments here.

LEMMA 1. *Let (S, Σ, m) be a σ-finite measure space, and let* A *be a subalgebra of $L_\infty(S, \Sigma, m)$. Then the closure of* A *in the L_1-topology of L_∞ is a subalgebra of the form $L_\infty(E, \Sigma', m)$, for some measurable subset $E \subseteq S$.*

If in addition $m(S) < \infty$ and A *contains the identity function, then the closure of* A *in $L_2(S, \Sigma, m)$ is of the form $L_2(S, \Sigma', m)$, for some σ-subfield Σ'.*

SKETCH OF PROOF. Let E be a measurable set of finite measure. Consider the subalgebra $\chi_E A$, where χ_E is the characteristic function (or indicator) of the set E. Then an argument like that of Lemma 1 on page 55 of the mentioned paper shows that the L_1-closure of $\chi_E A$ is of the form $L_\infty(E, \Sigma_E, m)$, where Σ_E is a σ-subfield of the restriction of Σ to E. If F is a measurable set and $F \supseteq E$, then it follows easily that Σ_E is the restriction of Σ_F to E. Thus, we can define Σ' as the inductive limit of the Σ_E as E runs through an increasing sequence of sets of finite measure whose union is S. It is then easy to see that the L_1-closure of A is $L_\infty(E, \Sigma', m)$ for some subset $E \in \Sigma$.

Note that the σ-subfield Σ' need not be totally σ-finite, but will evidently be totally σ-finite if A has a set of generators which are square-integrable.

The following lemma is essentially due to Blackwell:

LEMMA 2. *Let A be a selfadjoint projection in $L_2(S, \Sigma, m)$ whose range is $L_2(S, \Sigma', m)$ with a totally σ-finite σ-subfield Σ'. Then A is the conditional expectation relative to Σ'.*

Again the proof results from routine extensions of the arguments given in the above-quoted paper. The reduction to the finite-measure case is accomplished as follows. Let $E, F \in \Sigma'$ be sets of finite measure, and let $g \in L_2(S, \Sigma, m)$. Then, by the selfadjointness of A,

$$\int_S \chi_E \chi_F A g \, dm = \int_S \chi_E \chi_F g \, dm = \int_S \chi_E A(\chi_F g) \, dm.$$

Since this holds for all E, and since Ag and $A(\chi_F g)$ both belong to $L_2(S, \Sigma', m)$, it follows that $\chi_F A g = A(\chi_F g)$. This reduces the proof to the case where S is of finite measure, and in fact proves that the operator A satisfies the averaging identity.

A word about notation. If E is a subset of S and Σ' a σ-subfield of Σ, we write $L_p(E, \Sigma', m)$ to denote the restriction of Σ' to E.

All Banach spaces are taken over the complex field, unless otherwise specified. If R is a Reynolds operator defined on L_∞ over the *real* field, then define $R_1 f = Ru + iRv$ for $f = u + iv$. It is easily verified that R_1 is again a Reynolds operator over the complex field. Similarly for averaging operators.

All our conventions relative to the use of functional-analytic details follow Dunford-Schwartz or Halmos.

4. **Reduction to averaging operators.** We begin by deriving some algebraic identities which are consequences of the Reynolds identity.

PROPOSITION 1. *Let R be a Reynolds operator in any commutative algebra over a field of characteristic zero, and let n be an integer $\geqq 1$. Then, for any element g the following identity holds*:

$$(*) \qquad nR(g(Rg)^{n-1}) = (n-1)R((Rg)^n) + (Rg)^n.$$

PROOF. For $n = 1$ the identity is trivial; for $n = 2$ it follows from the Reynolds identity by setting $f = g$. For $n > 2$ we proceed by induction: assuming the identity

$$(n-1)R(g(Rg)^{n-2}) = (n-2)R((Rg)^{n-1}) + (Rg)^{n-1},$$

we establish (*). In the Reynolds identity, set $f = -(n-2)(Rg)^{n-1} + (n-1)g(Rg)^{n-2}$. It follows from the induction hypothesis that $Rf = (Rg)^{n-1}$. Therefore, substituting this choice of f in the Reynolds identity, we obtain

$$R(-(n-2)(Rg)^n + (n-1)g(Rg)^{n-1} + g(Rg)^{n-1}) = (Rg)^n + R((Rg)^n).$$

Simplifying, identity (*) follows at once.

PROPOSITION 2. *Let R be as in Proposition* 1, *let $p(x)$ be any polynomial in the variable x without constant term. Then the following identity holds for any Reynolds operator, for g in A:*

$$R(p(Rg)) = p(Rg) + R(Rgp'(Rg)) - R(gp'(Rg)),$$

where p' is the derivative of p.

PROOF. If $p(x) = x^n$ the statement reduces to that of Proposition 1. The general case follows at once by linearity.

PROPOSITION 3. *Let R be a continuous Reynolds operator in $L_\infty(S, \Sigma, m)$, and let $q(x)$ be a continuously differentiable function of a real variable defined for x in a compact interval such that $q(0) = 0$. For f in L_∞, let the range of f be contained in the domain of q. Then the function $q(f)$ is in L_∞, and*

$$R(q(Rf)) = q(Rf) + R(Rfq'(Rf)) - R(fq'(Rf)).$$

PROOF. Let D be the domain of q, a compact interval. By a variant of the Stone-Weierstrass Theorem, we can find a sequence p_n of polynomials without constant term such that $p_n \to q$ and $p'_n \to q'$ uniformly on D. In view of the assumed continuity of R, the result follows at once from the preceding proposition.

REMARK. The preceding result is not the most general of its kind, one can easily extend it to the case of several elements, to functions q which are not continuously differentiable, etc.

COROLLARY 1. *Let f be in the range of R and let q be as above. Then $q(f)$ is in the range of R.*

COROLLARY 2. *Let $f(s) \geqq \varepsilon > 0$ for s in $E \subseteq S$, and let f be in the range of R. Then there is a function g in the range of R such that $g(s) \geqq \delta > 0$ for almost all s in E, and $g(s) \geqq 0$ elsewhere.*

PROOF. Let the range of f be contained in a compact interval J containing 0. Choose a continuously differentiable function q such that $q(0) = 0$ and $q(x) > 0$ for $x \neq 0$ in J. Such a function obviously exists. Then $g = q(f)$ is the desired function by Corollary 1.

COROLLARY 3. *If for every $F \subseteq S$ with $m(F) > 0$ there is a function f in the range of R and an $\varepsilon > 0$ such that if $f(s) \geqq \varepsilon$ on F, then there is a g such that $Rg(s) \geqq \varepsilon > 0$ for almost all s in S.*

PROOF. Here we use for the first time the fact that the algebra on which R acts is L_∞. It is convenient to use the compactification of L_∞, so that we can talk about the value of a function at a point. Thus, we may and will assume that R acts on $C(E)$, the space of all continuous functions on an extremally disconnected compact Hausdorff space E. For every s in E there is an open set G_s containing s and nonnegative g_s such that $Rg_s(t) \geqq \varepsilon$ for t in G_s. The family G_s as s ranges through E forms a covering of E, hence it has a finite subcovering $G_{s_2}, \cdots, G_{s_n}$. Then the function $g = g_{s_1} + \cdots + g_{s_n}$ will do the trick.

COROLLARY 4. *Let R be as in the preceding corollary on the space $L_\infty(E, \Sigma, m)$. Then $R\chi_E = \chi_E$, where χ_E is the indicator of E.*

PROOF. Choose a function $f = Rg$ as in the preceding Corollary 3, and choose q so that $q(0) = q'(0) = 0$ and $q(x) = 1, q'(x) = 0$ for $x \neq 0$ in the range of f. Then $q(f) = \chi_E$, and from Proposition 3 it follows that

$$R\chi_E = \chi_E + R((f-g)q'(f)) = \chi_E, \qquad \text{q.e.d.}$$

THEOREM 1. *Let R be a continuous Reynolds operator in $L_\infty(S, \Sigma, m)$. Then R is an averaging operator if and only if it has closed range.*

PROOF. If R is an averaging operator, as well as a Reynolds operator, then $R^2 = R$, so R is a projection and hence its range is closed.

Conversely, suppose R is a Reynolds operator and its range is closed. Since the range is also closed under products, it follows from Lemma 1 that the range of R is of the form $L_\infty(E, \Sigma', m)$, where Σ' is a σ-subfield of Σ. It follows that R maps $L_\infty(E, \Sigma, m)$ into itself, and by Corollary 4 that $R\chi_E = \chi_E$. Hence $R(\chi_E f) = \chi_E Rf$, and we can and will assume that $S = E$ and $R1 = 1$. The proof results from the following steps:

(1) Suppose that Σ' is the trivial σ-subfield, containing only the null set and the whole space. Then Rf is a constant function, say α, and hence $R^2f = \alpha R1 = \alpha = Rf$. Hence R is a projection.

(2) Suppose now that Σ' is not the trivial σ-subfield, and let A be a set of positive measure belonging to Σ'. Let χ_A be the indicator of A. By assumption, $Rf = \chi_A$ for some f. We shall prove that $R\chi_A = \chi_A$. To this end, let $g(x)$ be a continuously differentiable function of the real variable x, for $-1 \leqq x \leqq 2$, with the following properties: (a) $g(x) = 0$ for $-1 \leqq x \leqq \frac{1}{2}$; (b) $g(x) = 1$ for $\frac{3}{4} \leqq x \leqq 2$. Then $g(\chi_A) = \chi_A$, since χ_A takes only the values 0 and 1. Hence, by Proposition 3 we have

$$R(\chi_A) = \chi_A + R((Rf - f)g'(\chi_A))$$

where f is a function such that $Rf = \chi_A$. But $g'(\chi_A)$ vanishes identically, because $g'(0) = g'(1) = 0$. This concludes the proof of this step.

(3) If $R\chi_A = \chi_A$ for the indicator of every set A, it follows by linearity that $Rf = f$ for every step function f in the range of R, and by continuity that $Rg = g$ for every function g in the range of R. But this amounts to saying that $R^2f = Rf$

for every f. Hence R is idempotent. (Since in addition we are assuming that $R1 = 1$, we obtain by setting $g = 1$ in the Reynolds identity that $R^2 = R$.) Now set $g = Rf$ in the Reynolds identity, and get $R(fRf) = (Rf)^2$. Polarizing, the averaging identity follows.

COROLLARY. *Let the algebra $L_\infty(S, \Sigma, \mu)$ be finite-dimensional. Then every Reynolds operator is an averaging operator.*

Similar results can be obtained for operators acting on the sequence space l_∞.

REMARK. The reasoning that led to Theorem 1 can be generalized without much difficulty (but with lengthy technical details) to $C(S)$, the space of all continuous functions on a compact Hausdorff space S. One then obtains a generalization of the Singer-Wermer Theorem on derivations.

5. **Representation.** In the following the continuity of R in L_∞ need not be assumed; we do, however, assume that R is everywhere defined in L_∞, and maps L_∞ into L_∞.

THEOREM 2. *Let R be a Reynolds operator in $L_\infty(S, \Sigma, m)$, $m(S) < \infty$, satisfying the condition $R1 = 1$ and*

$$(*) \qquad \int_S |Rf|^2 \, dm \leqq \int_S |f|^2 \, dm, \qquad f \in L_\infty(S, \Sigma, m).$$

Then there exist:

(1) *A unique σ-subfield Σ_1 of Σ;*

(2) *A unique positive conditional expectation operator A onto $L_\infty(S, \Sigma_1, m)$;*

(3) *A unique semigroup V^t of measure-preserving transformations defined for $t \geqq 0$ on $L_\infty(S, \Sigma_1, m)$, such that:*

(a) *The algebra $L_\infty(S, \Sigma_1, m)$ is invariant under R;*

(b) *The operators A and R commute; and the range of A is the closure of the range of R;*

(c) *The action of R for f in $L_\infty(S, \Sigma, m)$ is given by the formula*

$$Rf = \int_0^\infty e^{-t} V^t A f \, dt.$$

PROOF. (1) From assumption (*) it follows that the domain of R can be uniquely extended to the space $L_2(S, \Sigma, m)$. We denote again by R the resulting operator, since this can cause no confusion. In view of (*), R is an operator of norm one. We now apply a theorem of Nagy (cf. Riesz and Nagy), and infer that $R^*1 = 1$, where R^* is the adjoint operator of R, again acting on $L_2(S, \Sigma, m)$.

(2) It follows from step (1) that the operator $2R - I$ is isometric: that is, for all f in $L_2(S, \Sigma, m)$,

$$\int_S |2Rf - f|^2 \, dm = \int_S |f|^2 \, dm.$$

This can be established as follows. By the Reynolds identity applied to essentially bounded f and g we have

$$\int_S R(fRg + gRf)\, dm = \int_S [RfRg + R(RfRg)]\, dm.$$

Passing to adjoints, we have

$$\int_S (R^*1)(fRg + gRf)\, dm = \int_S [RfRg + (R^*1)(RfRg)]\, dm.$$

Using the conclusion of (1), this simplifies to

$$\int_S (fRg + gRf)\, dm = \int_S 2RfRg\, dm,$$

and passing to adjoints again (f and g may be assumed real without loss of generality)

$$\int_S g(R^*f + Rf)\, dm = \int_S 2gR^*Rf\, dm.$$

Since this is true for all functions g, we infer that

$$R^*f + Rf = 2R^*Rf,$$

for all f in L_∞, and hence, by continuity, also for all f in L_2. Now let $U = 1 - 2R$; then we obtain from the above identity that $U^*U = 1$. Hence $\int (Uf)^2\, dm = \int fU^*Uf\, dm = \int f^2\, dm$, which shows that U is isometric, at least on real functions. The extension to complex functions is immediate.

(3) Since the operator U is isometric in L_2, the ergodic theorem applies to it (cf. Dunford-Schwartz, Riesz-Nagy) and gives an orthogonal projection operator $I - A$ as a strong limit of the Cesàro averages $(1 + U + U^2 + \cdots + U^n)/(n+1)$. The projection $I - A$ has the following properties. (a) The range of $I - A$ consists of the fixpoints of $U = 1 - 2R$, that is, the set of all f such that $Rf = 0$; (b) the range of the orthogonal complement $A = I - (I - A)$ consists of the closed subspace spanned by functions of the form $f + Uf$, that is, the closure of the range R; in particular, since $R1 = 1$, we have $A1 = 1$, (c) A commutes with R. But the range of R, restricted to L_∞, is a subalgebra of L_∞. Hence we can apply Lemma 1 of §3, and conclude that the range of R is a subspace of the form $L_2(S, \Sigma_1, m)$, where Σ_1 is a σ-subfield of Σ. By Lemma 2 of §3, it now follows that A is the conditional expectation operator relative to Σ_1.

(4) It follows from the preceding step that R, restricted to the invariant subspace $L_2(S, \Sigma_1, m)$ is a one-to-one operator. More is actually true, namely, the range of R, restricted to $L_2(S, \Sigma_1, m)$ is dense in $L_2(S, \Sigma_1, m)$. For if it were not, then there would be a function f in $L_2(S, \Sigma_1, m)$ orthogonal to it: for such a function, $R^*f = 0$, that is, $U^*f = f$. But U^* is of norm one, hence, again by the Nagy theorem quoted above, $U^{**}f = Uf = f$. This in turn implies that $Rf = 0$, which is impossible if f lies in $L_2(S, \Sigma_1, m)$.

(5) Restrict R to the invariant subspace $L_2(S, \Sigma_1, m)$, from now on. We first verify that the unbounded closed operator $D = 1 - R^{-1}$ is antisymmetric, that is, D^* is an extension of $-D$. From the identity, already established in step (2), namely,

$$\int_S (Rf - f)Rg\, dm = -\int_S Rf(Rg - g)\, dm$$

we obtain, writing $p = Rf$ and $q = Rg$,

$$\int_S (1 - R^{-1})pq\, dm = -\int_S p(1 - R^{-1})q\, dm.$$

This holds for all p and q in the domain of the operator $D = I - R^{-1}$, and proves that $1 - R^{-1}$ is antisymmetric and the domain of $1 - R^{-1*}$ includes the domain of $I - R^{-1}$.

(6) The spectrum of D lies in the half plane $y \leqq 0$ in the complex plane $(z = x + iy)$. This follows from a variant of the spectral mapping theorem: the spectrum of U is inside the unit disk, hence the spectrum of R lies inside the circle of radius $\frac{1}{2}$ centered at $x = \frac{1}{2}$, and $D = I - R^{-1}$.

(7) From (5) and (6), together with the Hille-Yosida theorem, we conclude that D is a semigroup generator. Let V^t be the one-parameter semigroup generated by D. Since $R = (1 - D)^{-1}$, it follows from a well-known formula of semigroup theory (cf. Hille-Phillips or Dunford-Schwartz) that

$$Rf = \int_0^\infty e^{-t} V^t f\, dt, \qquad f \in L_2(S, \Sigma_1, m).$$

(8) We now prove that $V^t fg = V^t f V^t g$ for bounded f and g. Since the range of R is dense, it will suffice to show this for $f = Rp$ and $g = Rq$.

First, recall that if V^t is *any* one-parameter semigroup of bounded operators and R is defined as in (6), then $dV^t R/dt = V^t(R - I)$ (cf. Hille-Phillips), as follows easily from the relationship between R and V^t given in (6). We adapt to the present setup an argument due to Feller. Consider the function

$$h(s, t) = V^s((V^t Rf)(V^t Rg)),$$

for fixed f and g and variable s and t. An easy computation, using the Reynolds identity, the above remark, and the fact that R commutes with V^t, shows that $\partial h(s, t)/\partial s = \partial h(s, t)/\partial t$, hence $h(s, t) = q(s + t)$ for some function q. The conclusion amounts to saying that $h(t, 0) = h(0, t)$.

(9) The representation in (6) was obtained for functions of class L_2; however, it is easily seen that it can be extended to all functions of class $L_p(S, \Sigma, m)$, $1 \leqq p \leqq \infty$. This comes from the fact that V^t, being a semigroup of measure-preserving transformations, is norm-preserving in all L_p.

(10) The proof of the theorem is now almost complete, except for the passage from the σ-subfield Σ_1 to the σ-field Σ. The projection A is a conditional expectation; therefore it can be extended to any L_p so that it remains bounded. Clearly

$Rf = RAf = ARf$ for any f for which the expression is defined. Therefore on the right of the displayed formula in (7) we can replace f by Af, q.e.d.

REMARK (*Added in proof*). The restriction $m(S) < \infty$ is not essential, and can be removed with a little extra work.

BIBLIOGRAPHY

1. J. Arbault, *Nouvelles propriétés des transformations de Reynolds*, C.R. Acad. Sci. Paris, **239** (1954), 858–860.

2. ———, *Sur les transformations de Reynolds quasi régulières*, C.R. Acad. Sci. Paris, **239** (1954), 949–951.

3. ———, *Transformations de Reynolds sur les ensembles finis*, Conferenze, Centro Internazionale di Matematica Estivo, Varenna, September, 1957.

4. R. R. Bahadur, *Measurable subspaces and subalgebras*, Proc. Amer. Math. Soc. **6** (1955), 565–570.

5. Martin Billik and Gian-Carlo Rota, *On Reynolds operators in finite-dimensional algebras*, J. Math. Mech. **9** (1960), 927–932.

6. G. Birkhoff, *Moyennes des fonctions bornées*, Colloque d'Algèbre et de Théorie des Nombres, pp. 143–153, Centre National de la Recherche Scientifique, Paris, 1949.

7. Barron Brainerd, *On the structure of averaging operators*, J. Math. Anal. Appl. **5** (1962), 347–377.

8. ———, *Sur la structure des opérateurs moyennes*, C.R. Acad. Sci. Paris **252** (1960), 2058–2060.

9. J. Dieudonné, *Sur le théorème de Lebesgue-Nikodym*. III, Ann. Univ. Grenoble Sect. Sci. Math. Phys. (N.S.) **23** (1948), 25–53.

10. M. L. Dubreil-Jacotin, *Propriétés algébriques des transformations de Reynolds*, C.R. Acad. Sci. Paris **236** (1953), 1950–1951.

11. ———, *Propriétés algébriques des transformations de Reynolds*, C.R. Acad. Sci. Paris **236** (1953), 1136–1138.

12. ———, *Propriétés générales des transformations de Reynolds*, C.R. Acad. Sci. Paris **239** (1954), 856–858.

13. ———, *Étude algébrique des transformations de Reynolds*, Colloque d'Algèbre Supérieure, Brussels, December, 1956.

14. ———, *Sur le passage des équations de Navier-Stokes aux équations de Reynolds*, C.R. Acad. Sci. Paris **244** (1957), 2887–2890.

15. ———, *Sur les axiomes des moyennes*, Corsò sulla teoria della turbolenza Vol. 1, pp. 107–114, Centro Internazionale di Matematica Estivo, Libreria Editrice Universitaria Levrotto e Bella, Turin, 1957.

16. N. Dunford and J. Schwartz, *Linear operators*, Interscience, New York, 1958.

17. P. R. Halmos, *Lectures on ergodic theory*, Publications of the Mathematical Society of Japan, no. 3, The Mathematical Society of Japan, 1956.

18. ———, *Measure theory*, rev. ed., Van Nostrand, New York, 1952.

19. ———, *On a theorem of Dieudonné*, Proc. Nat. Acad. Sci. U.S.A. **35** (1949), 38–42.

20. Rudi Hirschfeld, *Sur les semi-groupes de transformations de Reynolds*, C. R. Acad. Sci. Paris **245** (1957), 1493–1495.

21. G. C. Hufford, *One-parameter semigroups of maps*, Duke Math. J. **24** (1957), 443–453.

22. J. Kampé de Fériet, *L'état actuel du problème de la turbulence*, La science Aeriennce **3** (1934), 9–34; II, ibid. **4** (1935), 12–52.

23. ———, *Les fonctions aléatoires stationnaires et la théorie statistique de la turbulence homogène*, Ann. Soc. Sci. Bruxelles Sér. I **59** (1939), 145–194.

24. ———, *La notion de moyenne dans les équations du mouvement turbulent d'un fluide*, 6ième Congrès International de Mécanique Appliquée, Paris, 1946.

25. ———, *Sur un problème d'algèbre abstraite posé par la définition de la moyenne dans la théorie de la turbulence*, Ann. Soc. Sci. Bruxelles Sér. I **63** (1949), 165–180.

26. ———, *Turbulencia*, Vol. I, Instituto Nacional Esteban Terradas de Tecnica Aeronautica, Madrid (to appear).

27. ———, *Averaging processes and Reynolds equations in atmospheric turbulence*, J. Meteorol. **8** (1951), 358–361.

28. ———, *Construction des transformations de Reynolds régulières*, C.R. Acad. Sci. Paris **239** (1954), 934–936.

29. ———, *Transformations de Reynolds opérant dans un ensemble de fonctions mesurables non negatives*, C.R. Acad. Sci. Paris **239** (1954), 787–789.

30. ———, *La notion de moyenne dans la théorie de la turbulence*, Rend. Sem. Mat. Fis. Milano **27** (1955–1956).

31. J. L. Kelley, *Averaging operators on* $C_\infty(X)$, Illinois J. Math. **2** (1958), 214–223.

32. A. Kolomogoroff, *Grundbegriffe der Wahrscheinlichkeitsrechnung*, Springer, Berlin, 1933.

33. V. J. Mizel and M. M. Rao, *Nonsymmetric projections in Hilbert space*, Dept. of Math. Tech. Rep. No. 47, Carnegie Institute of Technology, Pittsburgh, Pa., 1960.

34. Italico Molinaro, *Détermination d'une R-transformation de Reynolds*, C.R. Acad. Sci. Paris **244** (1957), 2890–2893.

35. ———, *Sur les endomorphismes de Reynolds de fonctions définies sur un ensemble fini*, Publ. Sci. Univ. Alger. Sér. A **4** (1957), 87–101.

36. Shu-Teh Chen Moy, *Characterizations of conditional expectations as a transformation on function spaces*, Pacific J. Math. **4** (1954), 47–63.

37. M. Nakamura, *A remark on the integral decomposition of a measure*, Mem. Osaka Univ. Lib. Arts Ed. Ser. B **3** (1954), 25–28.

38. C. W. Oseen, *Das Turbulenzproblem*, 3ième Congrès International de Mécanique Appliquée, Stockholm, tome 1, pp. 3–18, 1930.

39. O. Reynolds, *On the dynamical theory of incompressible viscous fluids and the determination of the criterion*, Philos. Trans. Roy. Soc. Ser. A **186** (1895), 123–164.

40. Gian-Carlo Rota, *On the representation of averaging operators*, Rend. Sem. Mat. Univ. Padova, **30** (1960), 52–64.

41. ———, *Remarks on stochastic solutions of differential equations*, Proc. Sympos. Partial Differential Equations, U.S. Army Research Center, Madison, Wis., 1960.

42. ———, *Spectral theory of smoothing operators*, Proc. Nat. Acad. Sci. U.S.A. **46** (1960), 863–868.

43. ———, *Une généralisation de l'espérance mathématique conditionnelle qui se présente dans la théorie statistique de la turbulence*, C.R. Acad. Sci. Paris **251** (1960), 624–626.

44. ———, *Une théorie unifiée des martingales et des moyennes ergodiques*, C.R. Acad. Sci. Paris **252** (1961), 2064–2066.

45. I. E. Segal, *Equivalence of measure spaces*, Amer. J. Math. **73** (1951), 275–313.

46. ———, *Abstract probability space and a theorem of Kolmogoroff*, Amer. J. Math. **76** (1954), 721–732.

47. Zbyněk Sidak, *On relations between strict sense and wide sense conditional expectations*, Teor. Verojatnost. i Primenen. **2** (1957), 283–288.

48. I. M. Singer and J. Wermer, *Derivations on commutative normed algebras*, Math. Ann. **129** (1955), 260–264.

49. J. Sopka, *On the characterization of Reynolds'-operators on the algebra of all continuous functions on a compact Hausdorff space*, Thesis, Harvard Univ., Cambridge, Mass., 1950.

50. F. B. Wright, *Generalized means*, Trans. Amer. Math. Soc. **98** (1961), 187–203.

51. E. Sparre Andersen, *On the fluctuations of random variables*, Math. Scand. **1** (1953), 263–285; II, ibid. **2** (1954), 195–223.

52. F. Spitzer, *A combinatorial lemma and its applications to probability theory*, Trans. Amer. Math. Soc. **82** (1956), 323–337.

53. G. Baxter, *An operator identity*, Pacific J. Math. **8** (1958), 649–663.

54. ———, *An analytic problem whose solution follows from a simple algebraic identity*, Pacific J. Math. **10** (1960), 731–762.

55. F. V. Atkinson, *Some aspects of Baxter's functional equation*, J. Math. Anal. Appl. 7 (1963), 1–30.

56. E. Hille and R. Phillips, *Functional analysis and semigroups*, Amer. Math. Soc. Colloq. Publ. Vol. 31, Amer. Math. Soc., Providence, R.I., 1958.

57. F. Riesz and B. Nagy, *Leçons d'analyse fonctionnelle*, 2nd ed., Akademiai Kiado, Budapest, 1953.

MASSACHUSETTS INSTITUTE OF TECHNOLOGY,
CAMBRIDGE, MASSACHUSETTS

INDIANA UNIVERSITY,
BLOOMINGTON, INDIANA

ON PROPAGATION IN RANDOM MEDIA OF DISCRETE SCATTERERS

BY

VICTOR TWERSKY

1. **Introduction.** General introductions and bibliographies for the present topic exist in the literature [**1**; **2**; **3**; **4**; **5**], and the physical significance of the subject is discussed there in detail. This section is therefore restricted to stating the primary problem at hand and to summarizing several results. Some introductory analytical material on scattering problems, and on random distributions of discrete scatterers is included in subsequent sections.

Consider the solution Ψ for the scattering of a wave by a given configuration of N scatterers, say $\Psi(\mathbf{1}, \mathbf{2}, \cdots, \mathbf{N})$, where $\mathbf{1}$ stands for all significant properties of scatterer "one" (including its location $\mathbf{r}_1$), etc. We introduce an ensemble of configurations in terms of an appropriate probability distribution function $W(\mathbf{1}, \mathbf{2}, \cdots, \mathbf{N})$, and define the average of Ψ, as

$$(1) \qquad \langle\Psi\rangle = \int \cdots \int \Psi(\mathbf{1}, \mathbf{2}, \cdots, \mathbf{N}) W(\mathbf{1}, \mathbf{2}, \cdots, \mathbf{N})\, d\mathbf{1}\, d\mathbf{2} \cdots d\mathbf{N};$$

we call $\langle\Psi\rangle$ the "coherent field." Similarly, we average the "intensity" (or "energy density") $|\Psi|^2$ over the ensemble, and write the "average total intensity" as

$$(2) \qquad \langle|\Psi|^2\rangle = |\langle\Psi\rangle|^2 + V,$$

where the "coherent intensity" $|\langle\Psi\rangle|^2$ is obtained from (1), and where the "incoherent intensity" V is the average absolute squared deviation of Ψ from its mean value $\langle\Psi\rangle$. We also consider the average of the corresponding normalized "flux" (e.g., the Poynting vector in electromagnetics) $\mathbf{J} = \operatorname{Re}(\bar{\Psi}\nabla\Psi/ik)$, where the bar indicates complex conjugate; we write

$$(3) \qquad \langle\mathbf{J}\rangle = \operatorname{Re}\langle\bar{\Psi}\nabla\Psi/ik\rangle = \operatorname{Re}[\langle\bar{\Psi}\rangle\nabla\langle\Psi\rangle/ik] + \mathbf{I} = \mathbf{C} + \mathbf{I},$$

where $\mathbf{C}$ and $\mathbf{I}$ are the "coherent" and incoherent" components of the flux. (The present definition of $\mathbf{J}$ suffices for observation in "free k-space"; more generally, other physical parameters than the propagation parameter k are also required.)

In general, we proceed by stating conditions on $\Psi(\mathbf{1}, \mathbf{2}, \cdots, \mathbf{N})$ to make the scattering problem for one configuration determinate, then introduce an ensemble of configurations in terms of $W(\mathbf{1}, \mathbf{2}, \cdots, \mathbf{N})$, and then seek the average values defined in (1), (2), and (3). [The average of Ψ^2, and the moments higher than the second are also of interest [**6**]; we will use a formalism for (2) which will enable us to obtain $\langle \Psi^2 \rangle$ by inspection. However, we do not consider the higher moments in the present paper. We also do not consider here the central statistical problem of obtaining explicit forms of W for the various "random distributions" of physical interest [7]; we assume that W is known, and subsequently use the simplest form of W for illustrative purposes.] We have essentially two kinds of representations [**8**] for Ψ: "compact representations" in terms of the solutions of a set of simultaneous integral equations (say Ψ_c), and "expanded" series representations (say Ψ_e). If we work with Ψ_e, then we obtain $\langle \Psi \rangle = \langle \Psi_e \rangle$, etc., by integration; the integrated forms of the terms of the series Ψ_e may be sufficiently simpler than the original and lead to closed or relatively compact forms for $\langle \Psi_e \rangle$. (See for example [9].) More usually [**2**; **3**; **4**], we average the compact representation Ψ_c, proceed heuristically to construct a set of "average equations" that are simpler than the originals, and then solve these to obtain say $\langle \Psi_c \rangle \approx \langle \Psi \rangle$. Most of the explicit results in the literature are of the form $\langle \Psi_c \rangle$; some of these have been shown adequate in specific ranges of parameters by comparison with experiment. (See for example [**10**; **11**].)

A more general introduction than the above, one that applies both to a random distribution of scatterers and to a randomly perturbed continuum, is given by Keller's [5] parallel discussion of "honest" and "dishonest" methods; Keller [5] uses both methods to derive results for scintillations of star-light arising from inhomogeneities in the atmosphere. The conditions for which $\langle \Psi_c \rangle$ approaches $\langle \Psi_e \rangle$ for a class of one-dimensional scattering problems have been determined by Bazer [**12**]. However, for three-dimensional distributions of discrete scatterers, the relationship of the heuristic c-forms of (1, 2, 3) considered by Foldy [**2**], Lax [**3**], Twersky [**4**], and others [**1**], to their corresponding e-forms is largely an open problem area. The present paper deals primarily with this topic.

In §2, we sketch the essentials of the formalism and notation for the scattering of a wave ϕ by a single object, and list several representations for the scattered wave u (surface integral, complex integral, and infinite series). Then, given a set of such "single-scattered" waves u_s, we construct analogous representations of the "multiple-scattered" set U_s for a configuration of scatterers. For brevity, we use operational forms to relate the U's to the presumably known u's: we have a compact "self-consistent" representation in the form of a set of inhomogeneous algebraic equations, and (by iteration) an expanded "successive scattering series" in terms of products of u's ("orders of scattering"). The corresponding representations of $\Psi = \phi + \sum U_s$, are labeled Ψ_c and Ψ_e respectively.

In §3, we introduce some notation and definitions relating to the probabilistic formalism for an ensemble of configurations. This is quite brief, since detailed discussions are given elsewhere, e.g., in [**1**; **2**; **3**].

In §4.1, we consider the averages of the expanded representations $\langle \Psi_e \rangle$ and $\langle |\Psi_e|^2 \rangle$. In §4.2, we give compact heuristic representations $\langle \Psi_c \rangle$ in the integral equation forms obtained by Foldy [**2**], Lax [**3**], and Twersky [**4**], and compare them with $\langle \Psi_e \rangle$. The essential simplification (as discussed previously in [**9**]) is that $\langle \Psi_c \rangle$ neglects terms corresponding to common path differences in a given order of scattering, i.e., each scatterer is "used only once" in a given order of scattering of $\langle\Psi_c\rangle$, so that, e.g., the back and forth interactions between a pair are neglected. An alternative heuristic compact form for $\langle\Psi\rangle$ is constructed to restore those of the "two-body" processes ignored by $\langle\Psi_c\rangle$. In §4.3, we start with a heuristic approximation for $\langle|\Psi|^2\rangle$ determined by $\langle\Psi_c\rangle$ and the "energy theorem" for $\langle\mathbf{J}\rangle$. Then we give heuristic integral equation forms $\langle\overline{\Psi}_c(\mathbf{r})\Psi_c(\mathbf{r}')\rangle$ derived by Foldy **[2]** and Lax **[3]**, and construct an alternative heuristic form that takes into account additional two-body processes. Comparison with the average of the product of the exact series indicates that these heuristic forms $\langle\overline{\Psi}_c\Psi_c\rangle$ are poorer approximations of $\langle\overline{\Psi}_e\Psi_e\rangle$ than the $\langle\Psi_c\rangle$ are of $\langle\Psi_e\rangle$. In order to obtain a form of $\langle\overline{\Psi}_c\Psi_c\rangle$ consistent with the approximation $\langle\Psi_c\rangle$, we introduce into $\langle\overline{\Psi}_e\Psi_e\rangle$ the same simplification that converts $\langle\Psi_e\rangle$ to $\langle\Psi_c\rangle$, e.g., we neglect any "chain" of u's or $\bar{u}$'s or $\bar{u}u$'s involving back and forth interactions between pairs, etc. This simplification in the series $\langle\overline{\Psi}_e\Psi_e\rangle$ leads directly to a relatively simple integral equation whose inhomogeneous term is $\langle\overline{\Psi}_c\rangle\langle\Psi_c\rangle$, and whose kernel involves a "new single scatterer" $u\varepsilon$; the function $u\varepsilon$ satisfies the integral equation analogous to $\langle\Psi_c\rangle$ whose inhomogeneous term is u, i.e., $u\varepsilon$ is the corresponding "Green's function" (in the sense the term is used in physics) for an angle dependent source u. (For the case of "monopole scatterers," Foldy **[2]** obtained two series representations for the kernel function in his integral equation for $\langle\overline{\Psi}_c\Psi_c\rangle$; the initial term of one of these series corresponds to the new integral equation specialized to monopoles.)

In §5, we consider an illustration that exhibits the relationships between the heuristic and exact forms explicitly. We restrict consideration to a very simple class of scattering problems: (1) the radiation field of the individual scatterers are significant only in the "forward half-space," particularly near the forward scattering direction; (2) the scatterers are located within a slab region of space $0 \leqq z \leqq d$ on which a plane wave is normally incident; (3) the scatterers are identical (or, equivalently, the averages over isolated scatterer parameters are identical), and their position statistics are those of a "rare gas." For the e-forms, we work in general with a finite number of scatterers (N) in a finite available volume ($\mathscr{V}$); for the corresponding c-forms, N and $\mathscr{V}$ are infinite but their ratio is bounded.

The illustrative problem is constructed around scatterers which do not need to be taken into account more than once in each order of scattering. Thus, for this case, the heuristic form $\langle\Psi_c\rangle$ used explicitly by Foldy **[2]**, Lax **[3]**, Twersky **[4]**, and used implicitly by practically all papers in the earlier physics literature **[1]**, is the correct limit of $\langle\Psi_e\rangle$ for $N \to \infty$, $\mathscr{V} \to \infty$. However, the situation is quite different for $\langle|\Psi|^2\rangle$: the heuristic form constructed with the aid of the energy theorem **[4]** gives the correct value $\langle|\Psi_e|^2\rangle$ in the appropriate limit; the analog of Foldy's **[2]** heuristic integral equation $\langle|\Psi_c|^2\rangle$, for which we obtain the kernel function in closed form, does not; the "$\langle\Psi_c\rangle$-consistent" heuristic integral equation for $\langle|\Psi_c|^2\rangle$ is identically the limit of $\langle|\Psi_e|^2\rangle$, and this is also the initial term of the analog of one of Foldy's two series **[2]**.

The result for $\langle\Psi_c\rangle$ is of the form $e^{x}\phi$, and the corresponding result $\langle\Psi_e\rangle$ for finite N is simply $(1 + x/N)^N\phi$. We also obtain a simple form involving polynomials as a practical approximation for $\langle|\Psi_e|^2\rangle$. Corresponding results for $\langle\Psi^2\rangle$ are given in the form of integral equations.

2. Scattering formalism.

2.1. ONE SCATTERER. The time-independent scattering problem for an incident wave

$$\phi(\mathbf{i}) = e^{i\mathbf{k}\cdot\mathbf{r}}, \qquad \mathbf{k} = k\mathbf{i} = |k|\mathbf{i}, \qquad \mathbf{r} = r\mathbf{o}, \tag{4}$$

is specified outside the scatterer's surface S by a solution of

$$(\nabla^2 + k^2)\psi(\mathbf{r}) = 0, \qquad \nabla^2 = \partial_x^2 + \partial_y^2 + \partial_z^2, \qquad k = |k|, \tag{5}$$

subject to prescribed conditions at S and subject to conditions at large distances from S (i.e., $r \to \infty$) which insure

$$\psi \to \phi, \qquad \psi - \phi \equiv u \sim f(\mathbf{o}, \mathbf{i})\frac{e^{ikr}}{r}; \qquad r \to \infty. \tag{6}$$

Here u is the "scattered wave," f (which is independent of r) is the "scattering amplitude," and the origin of coordinates is the center of the smallest sphere enclosing the scatterer (henceforth "scatterer center"). The weakest "radiation condition" on u and its normal derivative $\partial_n u$ leading to (6) appears to be that considered by Wilcox [13], i.e., that $\int|\partial_n u - iku|^2\, dS$ vanishes for a closed surface at infinity.

Various "boundary conditions" and "transition conditions" at S are of interest to physics, particularly those that satisfy the "reciprocity relation"

$$\int_S [\psi(\mathbf{i})\partial_n\psi(\mathbf{j}) - \psi(\mathbf{j})\partial_n\psi(\mathbf{i})]\, dS = 0; \qquad \psi(\mathbf{i}) = \psi(\mathbf{r}; \mathbf{i}) = \phi(\mathbf{r}; \mathbf{i}) + u(\mathbf{r}; \mathbf{i}). \tag{7}$$

Equation (7) holds for example if either ψ, or $\partial_n\psi$, or a linear combination $\psi + C\partial_n\psi$ vanishes on S; it also holds if $\psi = A\psi'$ and $\partial_n\psi = B\partial_n\psi'$ on S, and $(\nabla^2 + k'^2)\psi = 0$ inside, such that the discontinuity coefficients A and B are constants while the internal propagation coefficient k' may be a function of $\mathbf{r}$, etc. Special conditions insure that the scatterer is "lossless" in the sense that

$$\int_S [\bar\psi(\mathbf{i})\partial_n\psi(\mathbf{j}) - \psi(\mathbf{j})\partial_n\bar\psi(\mathbf{i})]\, dS = 0, \tag{8}$$

e.g., any of the conditions mentioned after (7) for real values of the coefficients C, A, B, and k'. If (7) and (8) hold on the scatterer's surface, then from Green's theorem and (5), they hold for any surface outside the scatterer.

Various analytical representations exist for u. We obtain the surface integral form by applying Green's theorem to $u(\mathbf{r})$ and

$$\frac{e^{ik|\mathbf{r}-\mathbf{r}'|}}{|\mathbf{r}-\mathbf{r}'|} \equiv E(k|\mathbf{r}-\mathbf{r}'|)$$

in the region outside the scatterer:

$$(9)\qquad \begin{aligned} u(\mathbf{r}) &= -\frac{1}{4\pi}\int [E(k|\mathbf{r}-\mathbf{r}'|)\partial_n u(\mathbf{r}') - u\partial_n E]\, dS(\mathbf{r}') \\ &\equiv \{E(k|\mathbf{r}-\mathbf{r}'|), u(\mathbf{r}';\mathbf{i})\} = \{E(k|\mathbf{r}-\mathbf{r}'|), \psi(\mathbf{r}';\mathbf{i})\}, \end{aligned}$$

where $S(\mathbf{r}')$ is any surface isolating $\mathbf{r}$ from the scatterer. For the conditions leading to (7), integral equations specifying ψ may be obtained from (9). Comparison of the asymptotic form of (9) for $|\mathbf{r}-\mathbf{r}'| \to \infty$ with (6) leads to the surface integral representation for the scattering amplitude:

$$(10)\qquad f(\mathbf{o}, \mathbf{i}) = \{e^{-ik\mathbf{o}\cdot\mathbf{r}'}, u(\mathbf{r}';\mathbf{i})\} = \{e^{-ik\mathbf{o}\cdot\mathbf{r}'}, \psi(\mathbf{r}';\mathbf{i})\}.$$

Definition (10), (6), Green's theorem, plus the reciprocity relation (7) lead to

$$(11)\qquad f(\mathbf{i}, \mathbf{j}) = f(-\mathbf{j}, -\mathbf{i}).$$

Similarly for lossless scatterers, it follows from (8) that

$$(12)\qquad \begin{aligned} -\frac{2\pi i}{k}[f(\mathbf{j}, \mathbf{i}) - \bar{f}(\mathbf{i}, \mathbf{j})] &= \int_\pi \bar{f}(\mathbf{o}, \mathbf{j}) f(\mathbf{o}, \mathbf{i})\, d\Omega_o; \\ \frac{4\pi}{k}\operatorname{Im} f(\mathbf{i}, \mathbf{i}) &= \int_\pi |f(\mathbf{o}, \mathbf{i})|^2\, d\Omega \equiv \sigma_s(\mathbf{i}), \end{aligned}$$

where σ_s is the "total scattering cross-section," and where $\int_\pi d\Omega_o$ means integrate over all directions $\mathbf{o}$.

The surface integral form for a scatterer of "type" s whose "center" is located at $\mathbf{r}_s$ scattering to a point $\mathbf{r}_a$ under excitation $e^{i\mathbf{k}\cdot(\mathbf{r}-\mathbf{r}_s)}$ may be written

$$(13)\qquad u_s^a(\mathbf{i}) = u_s(\mathbf{r}_a - \mathbf{r}_s; \mathbf{i}) = \{E(k|\mathbf{r}_a - \mathbf{r}_s - \mathbf{r}'|), u(\mathbf{r}';\mathbf{i})\},$$

where $\mathbf{r}'$ is measured from the "scatterer's center" $\mathbf{r}_s$ to a point on an inclosing surface. Using essentially Weyl's representation of $E(kr)$ as a complex integral of plane waves, we rewrite (13) in terms of f of (10) as **[8]**

$$(14)\qquad u_s^a(\mathbf{i}) = \frac{ik}{2\pi}\int e^{ik\mathbf{p}\cdot\mathbf{r}_{as}} f_s(\mathbf{p}, \mathbf{i})\, d\Omega_p, \qquad \mathbf{r}_{as} = \mathbf{r}_a - \mathbf{r}_s = r_{as}\mathbf{o}_{as}.$$

Here, in general, $\int d\Omega_p$ represents a double integral over complex paths, the complex solid angle Ω_p being specified by two angles associated with the unit vector $\mathbf{p}$ (each path of the form used by Sommerfeld for the Hankel function of the first kind). The plane wave form is valid at least outside the circumscribing sphere; see **[8]** for weaker restriction. The asymptotic form of u as in (6) follows from a saddle point approximation of (14). More generally, (14) leads to the Sommerfeld convergent series in inverse powers of r and angular derivatives of f [**8**]:

$$u_s^a(\mathbf{i}) = u_s(r_{as}\mathbf{o}_{as};\, \mathbf{i}) = E_{as}[r_{as};\, D(\mathbf{o}_{as})]f_s(\mathbf{o}_{as}, \mathbf{i}),$$

$$(15)\quad E(r;\, D) = \frac{e^{ikr}}{r}\left\{1 + \frac{i}{2kr}D + \left(\frac{i}{2kr}\right)^2 \frac{D(D-2)}{2!} + \cdots + \left(\frac{i}{2kr}\right)^n \frac{D(D - 1\cdot 2)\cdots(D - [n-1]\cdot n)}{n!} + \cdots\right\},$$

$$D(\mathbf{o}) = (-1/\sin^2\theta)[\partial_\omega^2 + \sin\theta\,\partial_\theta(\sin\theta\,\partial_\theta)],$$

where $D(\mathbf{o})$ is Beltrami's operator on the polar angle (θ) and azimuthal angle (ω) associated with the unit vector $\mathbf{o}$. The series converges outside the circumscribing sphere [**13**]. We may also represent u in terms of a symbolic operation on $\phi(\mathbf{i})$ [**3**], as a Bessel–Legendre series ("multipole expansion") [**8**], etc. In particular if f is independent of directions ("monopole scatterers") then E of (15) reduces to its leading term.

For an isolated scatterer at $\mathbf{r}_s$ scattering to $\mathbf{r}_a$, under excitation by $e^{ik\mathbf{i}\cdot\mathbf{r}}$, the scattered field is

$$(16)\qquad u_s^a(\mathbf{i})\phi_s(\mathbf{i}), \qquad \phi_s(\mathbf{i}) = e^{ik\mathbf{i}\cdot\mathbf{r}_s},$$

where any of the above representations may be used for u_s^a. In general, in order to maintain a relatively simple (if not particularly explicit) notation, we indicate (16) symbolically by

$$(17)\qquad u_s^a\phi_s = E_{as}f_s\phi_s.$$

If necessary, auxiliary notation will be introduced.

2.2. Many scatterers. For a configuration of N, not necessarily identical, scatterers located at $\mathbf{r}_1, \mathbf{r}_2, \cdots, \mathbf{r}_N$, we represent the solution outside the scatterers' surfaces by

$$(18)\qquad \Psi(\mathbf{r}) = \phi + \mathscr{U} = \phi + \sum_{s=1}^{N} U_s(\mathbf{r} - \mathbf{r}_s), \qquad (\nabla^2 + k^2)\Psi = 0, \qquad k = |k|,$$

where Ψ satisfies (7) for all surfaces S_s (although the boundary conditions may be different on different surfaces). Using the forms of the previous section operationally, we have [**8**]

$$(19)\qquad U_s^a = U_s(\mathbf{r}_a - \mathbf{r}_s) = E_{as}F_s,$$

where U_s is the "multiple scattered wave" of scatterer s, and F_s is its "multiple scattered amplitude." Equation (19) serves to indicate that U_s and F_s are related to each other as indicated in (15), (14), (10), (6), etc. If the other scatterers recede to infinite distances from s, then U_s and F_s reduce to their known analogs for scatterer s in isolation, i.e., to their "single scattered" values:

$$(20)\qquad U_s^a \to u_s^a\phi_s, \qquad F_s \to f_s\phi_s; \qquad r_{st} = |\mathbf{r}_s - \mathbf{r}_t| \to \infty \quad \text{for fixed } |\mathbf{r}_s - \mathbf{r}_a|.$$

We need not rework any isolated scatterer problems to determine the solution for the configuration. The problem is linear, and since we know the response of scatterer s to $\phi_s(\mathbf{i})$, we can determine its response U_s^a to the present "exciting field"

$$\Phi_s = \phi_s + \sum_t{}' U_t^s, \qquad \sum_t{}' = \sum_{t \neq s} \tag{21}$$

by applying the superposition principle with $U_t^s = E_{st}F_t$ in the plane wave form (14); symbolically we write $U_s^a = u_s^a \Phi_s$, and represent (18) compactly by the operational forms (at a point $\mathbf{r}_c$):

$$\Psi_c = \phi_c + \sum u_s^c \Phi_s, \qquad \Phi_s = \phi_s + \sum_t{}' u_t^s \Phi_t. \tag{22}$$

Equivalently, we have

$$\begin{aligned} \Psi_c &= \phi_c + \sum E_{cs} F_s = \phi_s + \sum E_{cs} f_s \Phi_s, \\ F_s &= f_s \Phi_s = f_s \phi_s + \sum_t{}' E_{st} f_s F_t. \end{aligned} \tag{23}$$

As an explicit illustration, in terms of the plane wave operator E implicit in (14), we have

$$\begin{aligned} \Psi_c &= e^{ik\mathbf{i}\cdot\mathbf{r}_c} + \frac{ik}{2\pi}\sum_s \int e^{ik\mathbf{p}\cdot(\mathbf{r}_c - \mathbf{r}_s)} F_s(\mathbf{p}, \mathbf{i})\, d\Omega_p, \qquad \mathbf{p} = \mathbf{p}(s); \\ F_s(\mathbf{o}, \mathbf{i}) &= f_s(\mathbf{o}, \mathbf{i})\, e^{ik\mathbf{i}\cdot\mathbf{r}_s} + \frac{ik}{2\pi}\sum_t{}' \int f_s(\mathbf{o}, \mathbf{p})\, e^{ik\mathbf{p}\cdot(\mathbf{r}_s - \mathbf{r}_t)} F_t(\mathbf{p}, \mathbf{i})\, d\Omega_p, \end{aligned} \tag{24}$$

where (24) (which holds at least outside mutually exclusive circumscribing spheres) represents the set F_s as the solutions of a system of N integral equations involving the known functions f_s as inhomogeneous terms and in the kernels. Similarly, we may represent E in (23) by the series in (15). See **[8]** for discussions, applications, and other representations.

When no questions of convergence arise, we iterate the "compact" forms (22) and (23) in terms of the single scattered value and write the "expanded" forms Ψ_e (at a point $\mathbf{r}_e$) as a series of "orders of scattering":

$$\begin{aligned} \Psi_e &= \phi_e + \sum u_s^e \phi_s + \sum u_s^e \sum{}' u_t^s \phi_t + \sum u_s^e \sum{}' u_t^s \sum{}' u_m^t \phi_m + \cdots \\ &= \phi_e + \sum E_{es} f_s \phi_s + \sum E_{es} \sum{}' E_{st} f_s f_t \phi_t + \cdots, \end{aligned} \tag{25}$$

which may be converted to more explicit forms by inspection of (24), etc.

The corresponding "intensity" for two "observation points" $\mathbf{r}_c$ and $\mathbf{r}_a$, in the form we consider subsequently, is

$$\bar{\Psi}_c \Psi_a = \bar{\phi}_c \phi_a + \bar{\phi}_c \mathscr{U}_a + \phi_a \bar{\mathscr{U}}_c + \sum\sum \bar{U}_s^c U_t^a. \tag{26}$$

The "flux"

$$\mathbf{J}_{ca} = (\bar{\Psi}_c \nabla_a \Psi_a - \Psi_a \nabla_c \bar{\Psi}_c)/ik, \qquad \mathbf{J}_{cc} = \mathbf{J}_c = \mathbf{J}, \tag{27}$$

may be obtained from (26). For lossless scatterers, it follows from (8) applied to $\bar{\Psi}_c(\mathbf{i})$ and $\Psi_c(\mathbf{i})$, that

$$\int_S \mathbf{J} \cdot d\mathbf{S} = 0, \tag{28}$$

where S incloses any number of scatterers.

In §3 we introduce the probabilistic formalism, and in §4 we apply it to obtain the averages of (22) and (25), and of the corresponding product forms. The operational representations with their lack of detailed structure are adequate for comparison of the essential features of the c and e forms of present interest. However, in general, more structure is required in order to apply such forms to specific problems. To facilitate restoring the arguments of the functions, we keep redundant factors of ϕ, etc., in subsequent manipulations; the appropriate arguments can be determined by starting with ϕ and working from right to left in the "chains" of products of u's that arise. The redundant factors of ϕ, etc., also enable us to obtain the forms for $\langle\Psi^2\rangle$ by inspection of $\langle\bar{\Psi}\Psi\rangle$.

3. **Probabilistic formalism.** The general distribution function $W(\mathbf{1}, \mathbf{2}, \cdots, \mathbf{N})$ used in (1) satisfies $\int \cdots \int W\, d\mathbf{1} \cdots d\mathbf{N} = 1$, when integrated over the full domains of all variables; $W\, d\mathbf{1} \cdots d\mathbf{N}$ is the probability of finding the scatterers in a configuration in the "volume" between $(\mathbf{1}, \mathbf{2}, \cdots, \mathbf{N})$ and $(\mathbf{1}, \mathbf{2}, \cdots, \mathbf{N}) + d\mathbf{1}\, d\mathbf{2} \cdots d\mathbf{N}$. We may factor W into such forms as

$$W(\mathbf{1}, \mathbf{2}, \cdots, \mathbf{N}) = w_s(\mathbf{s})P_s(\mathbf{s}; \text{avb } \mathbf{s}) = w_{st}(\mathbf{s}, \mathbf{t})P_{st}(\mathbf{s}, \mathbf{t}; \text{avb } \mathbf{s}, \mathbf{t}), \tag{29}$$

etc., where "avb" stands for "all variables besides." The one-particle distribution function $w_s(\mathbf{s}) = \int W\, d(\text{avb } \mathbf{s}) \equiv \langle 1\rangle_s$, may be written $w_s(\mathbf{r}_s, \boldsymbol{\xi}_s)$, where $\mathbf{r}_s$ is the position variable, and $\boldsymbol{\xi}_s$ represents various parameters of scatterer s (size, shape, dielectric properties, etc.). Thus $w_s(\mathbf{r}_s) = \int w_s(\mathbf{r}_s, \boldsymbol{\xi}_s)\, d\boldsymbol{\xi}_s$ (i.e., $w_s(\mathbf{s})$ integrated over all values of $\boldsymbol{\xi}_s$) times $d\mathbf{r}_s$ is the probability of finding scatterer s (the center of its circumscribing sphere) in the volume element $d\mathbf{r}_s$ around the point $\mathbf{r}_s$, etc. Similarly $w_{st}(\mathbf{s}, \mathbf{t}) = \int W\, d(\text{avb } \mathbf{s}, \mathbf{t}) \equiv \langle 1\rangle_{st}$ is the two-particle probability distribution function, etc. The P's are the corresponding conditional probability functions, $\int P_s\, d(\text{avb } \mathbf{s}) = \int P_{st}\, d(\text{avb } \mathbf{s}, \mathbf{t}) = 1$, etc. The two-particle function (the "pair distribution function") may be written

$$w_{st}(\mathbf{s}, \mathbf{t}) = w_s(\mathbf{s})p_{st}(\mathbf{s}; \mathbf{t}) = w_t(\mathbf{t})p_{ts}(\mathbf{t}; \mathbf{s}); \tag{30}$$

the conditional probability p_{st} for identical particles whose distribution depends only on $r_{st} = |\mathbf{r}_s - \mathbf{r}_t|$ is the "radial distribution function" discussed in [7].

If W factors into a product of N one-particle functions $w_s(\mathbf{s})$, then we may say we are dealing with a "gas." If the w's are identical functions of the parameters, then it is essentially a "single-component" gas. If the w's are independent of $\mathbf{r}$, then the gas is "homogeneous."

If we are dealing with an "inhomogeneous gas" in the sense that the location and characteristics of each scatterer is independent of the locations and characteristics of the others, and is the same for all scatterers, then

$$W(\mathbf{1}, \mathbf{2}, \cdots, \mathbf{N}) = w(\mathbf{1})w(\mathbf{2}) \cdots w(\mathbf{N}), \qquad w(\mathbf{s}) = w(\mathbf{r}_s, \boldsymbol{\xi}_s). \tag{31}$$

The corresponding "particle density" function for scatterers of type $\boldsymbol{\xi}$ is

$$\rho(\mathbf{s}) = \rho(\mathbf{r}, \boldsymbol{\xi}) = Nw(\mathbf{r}, \boldsymbol{\xi}), \tag{32}$$

such that $\rho(\mathbf{r}) = \int \rho(\mathbf{r}, \boldsymbol{\xi})\, d\boldsymbol{\xi}$ is the number of scatterers per unit volume at $\mathbf{r}$, and $\int \rho(\mathbf{r})\, d\mathbf{r} = N$ is the total number of scatterers; the volume integration is over the available volume $\mathscr{V}$. If ρ is independent of $\mathbf{r}$, then we use $\rho = N/\mathscr{V}$; we may have $N \to \infty$ and $\mathscr{V} \to \infty$ provided that $N/\mathscr{V}$ remains bounded. Gases of scatterers are considered for example in [**2**; **3**; **4**]. A simple model for some phenomena observed in scattering by liquids may be based on a W which factors into products of identical two-particle functions. This was introduced for single-scattering of x-rays by liquids by Zernike and Prins [**14**], and is also considered in [**3**; **9**], and by Mazur, Mandel, Jansen [**15**], and by others.

4. Scattering by random distributions. In general, the ensemble average of the total scattered field at a point $\mathbf{r}_c$ as in (18) may be written

$$\langle \Psi_c \rangle = \phi_c + \langle \mathscr{U}_c \rangle = \phi_c + \sum \langle U_s^c \rangle, \tag{33}$$

where as in (1), $\langle\ \rangle$ means multiply by W and integrate over all variables. Knowing the coherent field $\langle \Psi_c \rangle$, we write the "incoherent intensity" for $\mathbf{r}_c$ and $\mathbf{r}_a$ in the form

$$V_{ca} \equiv \langle \bar{\Psi}_c \Psi_a \rangle - \langle \bar{\Psi}_c \rangle \langle \Psi_a \rangle = \sum\sum [\langle \bar{U}_s^c U_t^a \rangle - \langle \bar{U}_s^c \rangle \langle U_t^a \rangle], \tag{34}$$

from which we ultimately obtain the total average intensity $\langle |\Psi|^2 \rangle = |\langle \Psi \rangle|^2 + V$ and the corresponding flux $\langle \mathbf{J} \rangle = \mathrm{Re}[\bar{\Psi} \nabla \Psi / ik]$. For lossless scatterers, we average (28) to obtain

$$\int \langle \mathbf{J} \rangle \cdot d\mathbf{S} = 0 \tag{35}$$

over a surface inclosing the distribution.

4.1. Expanded representation. Multiplying the series (25) by W as in (29) and integrating over all variables, we obtain

$$\begin{aligned} \langle \Psi_e \rangle &= \phi_e + \langle \mathscr{U}_e \rangle = \phi_e + \sum_s \langle u_s^e \phi_s \rangle + \sum_s \sum_t{}' \langle u_s^e u_t^s \phi_t \rangle \\ &\quad + \sum_s \sum_t{}' \sum_m{}' \langle u_s^e u_t^s u_m^t \phi_m \rangle + \cdots \\ &= \phi_e + \sum_s \int u_s^e \phi_s w_s \, d\mathbf{s} + \sum_s \sum_t{}' \int\int u_s^e u_t^s [\phi_t + u_s^t \phi_s + \cdots] w_{st}\, d\mathbf{s}\, d\mathbf{t} \\ &\quad + \sum_s \sum_t{}' \sum_m{}'' \int\int\int u_s^e u_t^s u_m^t [\phi_m + \cdots] w_{stm}\, d\mathbf{s}\, d\mathbf{t}\, d\mathbf{m} + \cdots, \end{aligned} \tag{36}$$

where $\sum_m''$ means $m \neq t$, $m \neq s$. The original triple sum $\sum_s \sum_t' \sum_m'$ of the third order of scattering contributes essentially two kinds of terms when averaged, i.e., the fact that $m \neq t$ and $t \neq s$ does not rule out $s = m$. Thus there are $N(N-1)$ terms for $m = s$ of the form $\langle u_s^e u_t^s u_s^t \phi_s \rangle$ which are functions only of two variables, and these wave forms differ essentially from the $N(N-1)$ terms $\langle u_s^e u_t^s \phi_t \rangle$ of the second order, and also from the remaining $N(N-1)(N-2)$ terms $\langle u_s^e u_t^s u_m^t \phi_m \rangle$ of the third order. Similarly for the higher orders. The "chains" in which the subscripts of the u's are all different form a sequence, each term of which contains $N!/(N-\nu)!$ terms; this sequence of terms in which each scatterer appears only once terminates with $\nu = N$, the Nth order of scattering. The first three terms of this sequence are shown in (36), which also gives the starting term of the sequence in which one scatterer appears twice. The fourth order of scattering provides a term for each of these sequences and starts a sequence in which two scatterers are used twice. There are an infinite number of such sequences.

Similarly the quadratic functions follow from

$$
\begin{aligned}
\langle \bar{\Psi}_e \Psi_a \rangle &= \bar{\phi}_e \phi_a + \bar{\phi}_e \langle \mathscr{U}_a \rangle + \phi_a \langle \bar{\mathscr{U}}_e \rangle + \sum \int \overline{u_s^e \phi_s} u_s^a \phi_s w_s \, ds \\
&\quad + \sum \sum{}' \iint \{ \overline{u_s^e \phi_s} [u_t^a \phi_t + u_s^a u_t^s \phi_t + u_t^a u_s^t \phi_s + u_t^a u_s^t u_t^s \phi_t + u_s^a u_t^s u_s^t \phi_s + \cdots] \\
&\quad + \overline{u_s^e u_t^s \phi_t} [u_s^a \phi_s + u_t^a \phi_t + u_s^a u_t^s \phi_t + u_t^a u_s^t \phi_s + u_t^a u_s^t u_t^s \phi_t + \cdots] \\
&\quad + \overline{u_s^e u_t^s u_s^t \phi_s} [u_s^a \phi_s + \cdots] + \cdots \} w_{st} \, d\mathbf{s} \, d\mathbf{t} + \cdots,
\end{aligned} \tag{37}
$$

which may be rewritten in terms of $u = Ef$ and the previous representations for E, and specialized to particular distributions. In principle, the functions in (36) and (37) are known so that the evaluation of $\langle \Psi_e \rangle$ and $\langle \bar{\Psi}_e \Psi_a \rangle$ corresponds to carrying out the integrations explicitly and constructing compact forms for the results. However, since even the case $N = 2$ involves an infinite series of orders of scattering (an infinite series inside the double integral containing w_{st}), this program is practical only for special cases. Because of this, most of the work in this subject has been based on heuristic manipulations of the original compact forms which generated the series of orders of scattering.

4.2. Compact representations for the coherent field. Using (29) in (33), we integrate implicitly avb **s** and write

$$
\langle \Psi_c \rangle = \phi_c + \sum \int \langle U_s^c \rangle_s w_s(\mathbf{s}) \, d\mathbf{s}, \tag{38}
$$

where $\langle \ \rangle_s$, which means an average with **s** fixed, is a function only of **s**. Using (22) in (38), we have

$$
\langle \Psi_c \rangle = \phi_c + \sum \int u_s^c \langle \Phi_s \rangle_s w_s(\mathbf{s}) \, d\mathbf{s} = \phi_c + \int \rho(\mathbf{s}) u_s^c \langle \Phi_s \rangle_s \, d\mathbf{s} \tag{39}
$$

with

$$
\langle \Phi_s \rangle_s = \phi_s + \sum{}' \langle u_t^s \Phi_t \rangle_s = \phi_s + \sum{}' \int u_t^s \langle \Phi_t \rangle_{st} p_{st}(\mathbf{s}; \mathbf{t}) \, d\mathbf{t}, \tag{40}
$$

where $\langle\ \rangle_{st}$ is the average with both **s** and **t** fixed. Similarly the expression for $\langle\Phi_t\rangle_{st}$ introduces $\langle\Phi_m\rangle_{stm}$, etc., to generate a hierarchy of equations which truncates when N sets of variables are held fixed. Formal reduction leads to (36), or to more compact series, e.g., with the terms in the first brackets of (36) compacted operationally to $[1 - u_s^t u_t^s]^{-1}[\phi_t + u_s^t \phi_s]$, etc.

Foldy's form. For a gas as in (31) with $N \to \infty$, Foldy's approximation [2]

$$\langle\Phi_s\rangle_s \approx \langle\Psi_s\rangle \tag{41}$$

reduces (39) to the form of an integral equation

$$\langle\Psi_c\rangle = \phi_c + \int \rho(\mathbf{s}) u_s^c \langle\Psi_s\rangle \, d\mathbf{s}. \tag{42}$$

Equations of this form for various scattering problems are considered in practically all the cited references and in the earlier literature [1]. For monopoles, $u_s^c = fE_{as}$ with f independent of directions and E_{as} equal to the free-space Green's function $E(k|\mathbf{r}_a - \mathbf{r}_s|) = [e^{ik|\mathbf{r}_a - \mathbf{r}_s|}]/|\mathbf{r}_a - \mathbf{r}_s|$, Foldy applied $\nabla^2 + k^2$ to both sides of the resulting (42) to obtain

$$[\nabla^2 + K^2(\mathbf{r})]\langle\Psi_c(\mathbf{r})\rangle = 0, \qquad K^2(\mathbf{r}) = k^2 + 4\pi g(\mathbf{r}), \qquad g(\mathbf{r}) = \int \rho(\mathbf{r}, \boldsymbol{\xi}) f(\boldsymbol{\xi}) \, d\boldsymbol{\xi}. \tag{43}$$

Similarly, for more general scatterers, Lax [3] used (41) (with an unknown constant c) and obtained (43) in terms of the forward scattered values of cf with the amplitude f "evaluated in K-space." Alternative representations for K [4] for slab regions $(0 < z < d)$ of homogeneous distributions of arbitrary scatterers have been obtained in terms of k-space amplitudes, and in terms of amplitudes corresponding to excitation in K-space and radiation into k-space (i.e., as suggested by the meaning of the terms in the kernel of (42)); in general, these forms involve the forward scattered value of f, and also the value corresponding to scattering in the direction of geometrical reflection from the slab's face. [The slab geometry for a homogeneous distribution is particularly simple: for this case $\langle\Psi_c\rangle$ consists essentially of only two plane waves (whose directions of propagation are images in the slab face), and consequently the original complicated operation $u_s^c\langle\Phi_s\rangle_s$ approximated by $u_s^c\langle\Psi_s\rangle$ entails at most manipulating a two by two matrix [4]. For monopoles (and dipoles), all forms reduce essentially to (43). The different forms for arbitrary scatterers correspond essentially to different interpretations of the discontinuity represented by a finite sized scatterer within the "synthetic medium" specified by K plus the boundary conditions on $\langle\Psi_c\rangle$ and $\partial_n\langle\Psi_c\rangle$ at interfaces of K- and k-spaces. No rigorous results for finite sized scatterers exist in the literature, and except for limiting cases the relations between various heuristic procedures have not been discussed. We do not consider this matter in the present paper; it is secondary to the relation of the c and e forms, since essentially the same details of explicit integration arise in both forms.]

Lax's form. Approximation (41), if appropriate for a "gas" is not appropriate for a "liquid" specified by w_{st}. For this case the corresponding approximation is

$$\langle \Phi_t \rangle_{st} \approx \langle \Phi_t \rangle_t. \tag{44}$$

Lax [3] used (44) in an analog of (40) to obtain essentially

$$\langle \Phi_s \rangle_s = \phi_s + \int u_t^s \langle \Phi_t \rangle_t \mu(\mathbf{s}; \mathbf{t})\, d\mathbf{t}, \qquad \mu(\mathbf{s}; \mathbf{t}) = \sum_t{}' p_{st}(\mathbf{s}; \mathbf{t}), \tag{45}$$

which together with (39) makes the problem determinate. (Essentially this approximation was also discussed by Twersky [**9**; **4**], who applied it in detail to planar distributions of cylinders [**9**] specified by the one-dimensional form of $\mu(\mathbf{s}; \mathbf{t})$ introduced by Zernike and Prins [**14**].) Using (39) in (45) gives

$$\langle \Phi_s \rangle_s = \langle \Psi_s \rangle - \int u_t^s \langle \Phi_t \rangle_t [\rho(\mathbf{t}) - \mu(\mathbf{s}; \mathbf{t})]\, d\mathbf{t}, \tag{46}$$

which, if $\mu(\mathbf{r}_s; \mathbf{r}_t) \to \rho$ for $|\mathbf{r}_s - \mathbf{r}_t| \to \infty$ (see [7]) is often more convenient to work with. For the case of a "gas" in the sense $\mu = \rho$, (46) reduces to (41).

Alternative form. The physical significance of the above heuristic approximations (41) and (45) was discussed in the report in [**9**] and their limitations were considered for a specific problem. Their limitations are indicated by comparing the iterated form of (42) with the average of the iterated series given in (36). Thus (42) gives

$$\begin{aligned} \langle \Psi_c \rangle = \phi_c &+ \sum \int u_s^c \phi_s w_s \, d\mathbf{s} + \sum\sum \int\int u_s^c u_t^s \phi_t w_s w_t \, d\mathbf{s}\, d\mathbf{t} \\ &+ \sum\sum\sum \int\int\int u_s^c u_t^s u_m^t \phi_m w_m w_s w_t \, d\mathbf{s}\, d\mathbf{t}\, d\mathbf{m} + \cdots \end{aligned} \tag{47}$$

In view of the discussion after (36), we see that (47) includes only the first of the infinite number of different sequences involved in "successive scattering," i.e., only chains in which all scatterers are different appear in (47); no common path differences can occur in higher orders, since (42) corresponds to successive scatterings of the average of the first order. In the best case, for special scatterers such that only the "main line sequence" is significant, the numerical coefficients in (47) are N^ν as compared to $N!/(N - \nu)!$, so that this difference disappears for $N \to \infty$. Essentially the same limitations are shown by the heuristic system (42) plus (45). In addition, whereas the exact series would involve w_{stm}, etc., the iterated integrals give only chains of one and two particle functions $w_s p_{st} p_{tm}$, etc., and this also introduces errors. Thus if we worked with (36), a more realistic value for w_{stm} obtained by the "superposition approximation" [7] would include p_{sm}, etc.

An alternative approximation for $\langle \Phi_s \rangle_s$ which restores "two body" processes lost in the above may be constructed by returning to the definition of Φ_t. Instead of using (44) we start with $\langle \Phi_t \rangle_{st} = \phi_t + u_s^t \langle \Phi_s \rangle_{st} + \sum_m'' \langle U_m^t \rangle_{st}$, where the double prime means $m \neq t$ and $m \neq s$. Thus the rigorous form of $\langle \Phi_t \rangle_{st}$ shows that the excitation of the fixed scatterer t consists essentially of two types of terms: $\langle U_s^t\rangle_{st}$ corresponds to a spherical wave traveling from a fixed scatterer s to excite t; and ϕ_t plus the sum is more or less the average excitation $\langle\Phi_t\rangle_t$. This suggests that we solve the simultaneous equations for $\langle\Phi_t\rangle_{st}$ and $\langle\Phi_s\rangle_{st}$ in order to eliminate $\langle\Phi_s\rangle_{st}$, and then approximate the resulting two-body solution:

$$(48)\quad \langle\Phi_t\rangle_{st} = \frac{[\phi_t + \sum''\langle U_m^t\rangle_{st}] + u_s^t[\phi_s + \sum''\langle U_n^s\rangle_{st}]}{1 - u_s^t u_t^s} \approx \frac{\langle\Phi_t\rangle_t + u_s^t\langle\Phi_s\rangle_s}{1 - u_s^t u_t^s},$$

where the terms of the expanded denominators operate from the left on the numerators. Using (48) in (40), we obtain

$$(49)\quad \begin{aligned}\langle\Phi_s\rangle_s &= \phi_s + \int u_t^s\left[\frac{\langle\Phi_t\rangle_t\mu(\mathbf{s};\mathbf{t})}{1 - u_s^t u_t^s}\right] dt + \int u_t^s\left[\frac{u_s^t\mu(\mathbf{s};\mathbf{t})}{1 - u_s^t u_t^s}\right] dt\langle\Phi_s\rangle_s \\ &= \frac{\phi_s + \int u_t^s\left[\dfrac{\langle\Phi_t\rangle_t\mu(\mathbf{s};\mathbf{t})}{1 - u_s^t u_t^s}\right] dt}{1 - \int u_m^s\left[\dfrac{u_s^m\mu(\mathbf{s};\mathbf{m})}{1 - u_s^m u_m^s}\right] d\mathbf{m}},\end{aligned}$$

which together with (39) provides a determinate system.

4.3. Compact representations for intensity. For the quadratic function (34), we use (29) and integrate implicitly avb **s**, **t** to obtain

$$(50)\quad \begin{aligned}V_{ca} &= \int \sum\langle\bar{U}_s^c U_s^a\rangle_s w_s(\mathbf{s})\, ds \\ &+ \int\int \sum[\sum'\langle\bar{U}_s^c U_t^a\rangle_{st} w_{st}(\mathbf{s}, \mathbf{t}) - \sum\langle\bar{U}_s^c\rangle_s\langle U_t^a\rangle_t w_s(\mathbf{s})w_t(\mathbf{t})]\, ds\, dt;\end{aligned}$$

here $\langle\bar{U}_s^c U_t^a\rangle_{st} = \bar{u}_s^c u_t^a\langle\bar{\Phi}_s\Phi_t\rangle_{st}$, etc. Using $w_{st}(\mathbf{s}, \mathbf{t}) = w_s(\mathbf{s})p_{st}(\mathbf{s};\mathbf{t})$, $\sum w_s(\mathbf{s}) = \rho(\mathbf{s})$, and $\sum_t' p_{st}(\mathbf{s};\mathbf{t}) = \mu(\mathbf{s};\mathbf{t})$, we rewrite (50) as

$$(51)\quad \begin{aligned}V_{ca} &= \int \rho(\mathbf{s})\bar{u}_s^c u_s^a\langle|\Phi_s|^2\rangle_s\, ds \\ &+ \int\int \rho(\mathbf{s})\bar{u}_s^c u_t^a[\langle\bar{\Phi}_s\Phi_t\rangle_{st}\mu(\mathbf{s};\mathbf{t}) - \langle\bar{\Phi}_s\rangle_s\langle\Phi_t\rangle_t\rho(\mathbf{t})]\, ds\, dt.\end{aligned}$$

Expressions for $\langle|\Phi_s|^2\rangle_s$ and $\langle\bar{\Phi}_s\Phi_t\rangle_{st}$ analogous to (40) may be constructed directly. Thus

$$(52)\quad \begin{aligned}\langle|\Phi_s|^2\rangle_s &= \bar{\phi}_s\langle\Phi_s\rangle_s + \phi_s\langle\bar{\Phi}_s\rangle_s - \bar{\phi}_s\phi_s + \sum'\int\langle|U_t^s|\rangle_{st}p(\mathbf{s};\mathbf{t})\, dt \\ &+ \sum'\sum''\int\int\langle\bar{U}_t^s U_n^s\rangle_{stn}p(\mathbf{s};\mathbf{t},\mathbf{n})\, dt\, d\mathbf{n},\end{aligned}$$

$$\langle \Phi_s \Phi_t \rangle_{st} = \bar{\phi}_s \langle \Phi_t \rangle_{st} + \phi_t \langle \Phi_s \rangle_{st} - \bar{\phi}_s \phi_t + \langle \bar{U}_t^s U_s^t \rangle_{st}$$

$$+ \Sigma'' \int [\langle \bar{U}_t^s U_n^t \rangle_{stn} + \langle \bar{U}_n^s U_s^t \rangle_{stn} + \langle \bar{U}_n^s U_n^t \rangle_{stn}] p(\mathbf{s}, \mathbf{t}; \mathbf{n})\, d\mathbf{n}$$

$$+ \Sigma'' \Sigma''' \int \int \langle \bar{U}_n^s U_m^t \rangle_{stnm} p(\mathbf{s}, \mathbf{t}; \mathbf{n}, \mathbf{m})\, d\mathbf{n}\, d\mathbf{m}.$$

Energy approximation. Perhaps the simplest heuristic approximation for the form of $V = V_{cc}$ for lossless scatterers is based on using the energy theorem. Outside a slab region of space ($0 < z < d$) containing a homogeneous distribution of lossless scatterers, (35) for plane wave excitation gives **[4]**

(53) $$\text{Re}[\bar{\Psi} \nabla \Psi / ik] \cdot \mathbf{z}/z = \langle \mathbf{J} \rangle \cdot \mathbf{n} = (\mathbf{C} + \mathbf{I}) \cdot \mathbf{n} = |\langle \Psi \rangle|^2 \mathbf{i} \cdot \mathbf{n} + \mathbf{I} \cdot \mathbf{n} = \text{constant}.$$

For the slab geometry we have explicit approximations for the form of $\langle \Psi \rangle$ in terms of free space amplitudes f. Using the single scattering theorems for f, we then construct the simplest form of **I** which together with $|\langle \Psi \rangle|^2$ satisfies (53), and obtain the corresponding form of V by inspection. The result **[4; 9]** for a gas

(54) $$V \approx \Sigma \int |\langle U_s \rangle|^2 w_s(\mathbf{s})\, d\mathbf{s} = \int \rho(\mathbf{s}) |\langle U_s \rangle|^2\, d\mathbf{s}$$

is also equivalent to using simply $\langle \Phi_s \Phi_t \rangle_{st} \approx \langle \bar{\Psi}_s \rangle \langle \Psi_t \rangle$ in (50).

Foldy's form. For a gas of monopoles, Foldy **[2]** used (41) plus the heuristic approximations

(55) $$\langle |\Phi_s|^2 \rangle_s \approx \langle |\Psi_s|^2 \rangle, \qquad \langle \Phi_s \Phi_t \rangle_{st} \approx \langle \bar{\Psi}_s \Psi_t \rangle,$$

to reduce (51) to

(56) $$V_{ca} = \int \rho(\mathbf{s}) \bar{u}_s^c u_s^a \langle |\Psi_s|^2 \rangle\, d\mathbf{s} + \int \int \rho(\mathbf{s}) \rho(\mathbf{t}) \bar{u}_s^c u_t^a V_{st}\, d\mathbf{t}.$$

Iterating the integral equation for V_{ca}, starting with the single-integral inhomogeneous term, and then using the definition $V_{ca} = \langle \bar{\Psi}_c \Psi_a \rangle - \langle \bar{\Psi}_c \rangle \langle \Psi_a \rangle$ he obtained an integral equation form for $\langle \bar{\Psi}_c \Psi_a \rangle$:

(57)
$$\begin{aligned} \langle \bar{\Psi}_c \Psi_a \rangle &= \langle \bar{\Psi}_c \rangle \langle \Psi_a \rangle + \int L(c, a; s) \langle |\Psi_s|^2 \rangle\, d\mathbf{s}; \\ L(c, a; s) &= \sum_{n=0}^{\infty} L_n(c, a; s); \\ L_0(c, a; s) &= \bar{u}_s^c u_s^a \rho(\mathbf{s}); \\ L_n(c, a; s) &= \int \int \bar{u}_t^c u_m^a \rho(\mathbf{t}) \rho(\mathbf{m}) L_{n-1}(t, m; s)\, d\mathbf{t}\, d\mathbf{m}. \end{aligned}$$

Foldy suppressed the ξ integrations by using g as in (43), and a corresponding average of $|f(\xi)|^2$. He also recast the kernel function L as a series in the K-space Green's function $E(K|\mathbf{r}_a - \mathbf{r}_s|)$. With ds in (57) replaced by $d\mathbf{r}_s$, he used

$$L = \sum M_n;$$

$$M_0(c, a; s) = G(\mathbf{r}_s)\bar{E}(K|\mathbf{r}_c - \mathbf{r}_s|)E(K|\mathbf{r}_a - \mathbf{r}_s|), \qquad G(\mathbf{r}) = \int \rho(\mathbf{r},\xi)|f(\xi)|^2\, d\xi;$$

(58)

$$M_n(c, a; s) = \frac{1}{4\pi}\int\int \{\bar{g}(\mathbf{r}_t)[\nabla_m^2 + K^2(\mathbf{r}_m)] + g(\mathbf{r}_m)[\nabla_t^2 + \bar{K}^2(\mathbf{r}_t)]\}$$

$$\times M_{n-1}(t, m; s)\bar{E}(K|\mathbf{r}_c - \mathbf{r}_t|)E(K|\mathbf{r}_a - \mathbf{r}_m|)\, d\mathbf{r}_t\, d\mathbf{r}_m,$$

to obtain

$$(59)\quad \langle|\Psi_c|^2\rangle = |\langle\Psi_c\rangle|^2 + \int G(\mathbf{r}_s)\langle|\Psi_s|^2\rangle\left\{|E(K|\mathbf{r}_c - \mathbf{r}_s|)|^2 + \sum_1^\infty M_n(c, c; s)\right\} d\mathbf{r}_s.$$

The resulting integral equation obtained by keeping only the first term of the kernel function in (59) is quite plausible physically and was used by Foldy as a practical approximation for comparison with experiment **[10]**; however, the procedure leading to (59) cannot justify neglecting $\sum_1^\infty M_n$.

Lax's form. Lax **[3]** used (55) and (41) (except for a constant multiplier) to obtain essentially

$$V_{ca} = \int \rho(\mathbf{s})\bar{u}_s^c u_s^a\langle|\Psi_s|^2\rangle\, d\mathbf{s}$$

(60)

$$+ \int\int \rho(\mathbf{s})\bar{u}_s^c u_t^a\{\langle\bar{\Psi}_s\Psi_t\rangle[\mu(\mathbf{s}; \mathbf{t}) - \rho(\mathbf{t})] + V_{st}\rho(\mathbf{t})\}\, d\mathbf{s}\, d\mathbf{t},$$

which is an integral equation form analogous to (56) but having a more complicated "inhomogeneous term."

Alternative form. Alternative equations may be obtained by using a different approximation than (55). Thus more or less as for (48), we may group terms in $\langle\Phi_s\Phi_t\rangle_{st}$ to isolate the different wave forms involved, and then introduce approximations. Equivalently, we start by solving the two-body problem corresponding to $\Phi_t = \phi_t + \sum'' U_m^t + U_s^t = R_t(s) + u_s^t\Phi_s$ and $\Phi_s = R_s(t) + u_t^s\Phi_t$, and then average the product of the resulting forms:

$$\langle\Phi_s\Phi_t\rangle_{st} = \left\langle\left[\frac{R_s(t) + u_t^s R_t(s)}{1 - u_t^s u_s^t}\right]\left[\frac{R_t(s) + u_s^t R_s(t)}{1 - u_s^t u_t^s}\right]\right\rangle_{st},$$

(61)

$$R_s(t) = \Phi_s - U_t^s = \phi_s + \sum'' U_m^s.$$

In order to obtain a form consistent with (42), we drop terms which would lead to a scatterer being "used twice" in either an "a-chain" or a "c-chain" of u's (i.e., which would lead to a chain of u's or $\bar{u}$'s having at least one subscript in common) and work with

$$(62)\qquad \langle\Phi_s\Phi_t\rangle_{st} \approx \langle\bar{R}_s(t)R_t(s)\rangle_{st} + \bar{u}_t^s\langle\bar{R}_t(s)R_t(s)\rangle_{st} + u_s^t\langle\bar{R}_s(t)R_s(t)\rangle_{st}.$$

A simple approximation of (62) more general than (55) is

$$\langle \Phi_s \Phi_t \rangle_{st} \approx \langle \bar{\Psi}_s \Psi_t \rangle + \bar{u}_t^s \langle \bar{\Psi}_t \Psi_t \rangle + u_s^t \langle \bar{\Psi}_s \Psi_s \rangle. \tag{63}$$

Substituting into (54) for $\mu(\mathbf{s}; \mathbf{t}) = \rho(\mathbf{t})$, we obtain

$$\begin{aligned} V_{ca} &= \int \rho(s) \bar{u}_s^c u_s^a \langle |\Psi_s|^2 \rangle \, d\mathbf{s} \\ &\quad + \iint \rho(s)\rho(t) \bar{u}_s^c u_t^a [u_s^t \langle |\Psi_s|^2 \rangle + u_t^s \langle |\Psi_t|^2 \rangle + V_{st}] \, d\mathbf{s} \, dt, \end{aligned} \tag{64}$$

which we regard as an integral equation for V.

$\langle \Psi_c \rangle$*-consistent form.* We could determine the physical significance of the above heuristic forms by means of the same procedure we used in (47) for $\langle \Psi \rangle$. Thus the integral equations for $V_{ca} = \langle \bar{\Psi}_c \Psi_a \rangle - \langle \bar{\Psi}_c \rangle \langle \Psi_a \rangle$ could be iterated to eliminate V, and the resulting integral equations for $\langle \bar{\Psi}_c \Psi_a \rangle$ could then be iterated in terms of $\langle \bar{\Psi}_c \rangle \langle \Psi_a \rangle$, and then $\langle \Psi_c \rangle$ could be replaced by the series (47) to finally obtain a form to compare with the exact series (37). This procedure is too tedious (and unrewarding) to attempt for the general case. (Subsequently, we follow a more or less equivalent procedure for the equations that arise in a simple illustration such that we get L of (57) in closed form.) However, it is clear that the $\langle \bar{\Psi}_c \Psi_a \rangle$ are poorer approximations of $\langle \bar{\Psi}_e \Psi_a \rangle$ than the $\langle \Psi_c \rangle$ are of $\langle \Psi_e \rangle$.

It is also tedious to introduce more and more of the omitted features into such forms as (56) to obtain results consistent with (42) or (46). Instead, we go back to the exact result (37), drop the terms that are omitted by (42) (as we have determined by comparing (47) and (36)) as well as the new analogs, and obtain a compact form for the limit of the result for $N \to \infty$.

Thus in (37) we drop all terms containing a backscattered path $u_s^t u_t^s$, $\bar{u}_s^t u_t^s$, etc., replace all coefficients $N!/(N-\nu)!$ by N^ν, and then compact and set aside the expansions of the coherent term $\langle \bar{\Psi}_c \rangle \langle \Psi_a \rangle$ (known from (47)). For the gas, writing $Nw(\mathbf{s}) = \rho(\mathbf{s})$, etc., we obtain

$$\begin{aligned} \langle \bar{\Psi}_e \Psi_a \rangle - \langle \bar{\Psi}_e \rangle \langle \Psi_a \rangle &= \int \rho(\mathbf{s}) [\overline{u_s^e \phi_s} \cdot u_s^a \phi_s]_1 \, d\mathbf{s} \\ &\quad + \iint \rho(\mathbf{s})\rho(\mathbf{t}) \{ [\overline{u_s^e \phi_s} \cdot (u_s^a u_t^s \phi_t + u_t^a u_s^t \phi_s) + \overline{(e \leftrightarrow a)}]_1 + [\overline{u_s^e u_t^s \phi_t} \cdot u_s^a u_t^s \phi_t]_2 \} \, d\mathbf{s} \, dt \\ &\quad + \iiint \rho(\mathbf{s})\rho(\mathbf{t})\rho(\mathbf{m}) \{ [\overline{u_s^e \phi_s} \cdot (u_s^a u_t^s u_m^t \phi_m + u_t^a u_s^t u_m^s \phi_m + u_t^a u_m^t u_s^m \phi_s) + \overline{(e \leftrightarrow a)}]_1 \\ &\quad + [\overline{u_s^e u_t^s \phi_t} \cdot (u_s^a u_m^s \phi_m + u_m^a u_t^m \phi_t + u_t^a u_m^t \phi_m + u_m^a u_s^m \phi_s)]_1 \\ &\quad + [\overline{u_s^e u_t^s \phi_t} \cdot (u_m^a u_s^m u_t^s \phi_t + u_s^a u_m^s u_t^m \phi_t + u_s^a u_t^s u_m^t \phi_m) + \overline{(e \leftrightarrow a)}]_2 \\ &\quad + [\overline{u_s^e u_t^s u_m^t \phi_m} \cdot u_s^a u_t^s u_m^t \phi_m]_3 \} \, d\mathbf{s} \, dt \, d\mathbf{m} + \cdots, \end{aligned} \tag{65}$$

where $\overline{(e \leftrightarrow a)}$ means include the complex conjugate of the analogous terms with e and a interchanged; the subscripts on the brackets will be explained shortly.

The above expansion with terms grouped by the number of integrations (or, equivalently, powers of ρ) is not particularly revealing. However, the structure of the equation becomes transparent if we regroup terms on the basis of the number of common subscripts in such products as $\overline{u_s^c u_t^s u_s^a u_m^s}$, i.e., essentially on the basis of the number of incoherent scattering processes involved. It is this second grouping that is indicated by the subscripts on the brackets in (65).

If we compare the set of one-brackets with the set of two-brackets, with the term in the three-bracket, and keep in mind the expansion of $\langle\Psi\rangle$ given in (47), we see that these three sets are respectively the leading terms of the first three iterations of an integral equation for $\langle\bar{\Psi}_c\Psi_a\rangle$ in terms of $\langle\bar{\Psi}_c\rangle\langle\Psi_a\rangle$. Explicitly, we have

$$
\begin{aligned}
\langle\bar{\Psi}_c\Psi_a\rangle &= \langle\bar{\Psi}_c\rangle\langle\Psi_a\rangle + \int \rho(\mathbf{s})\overline{u_s^c\varepsilon_{cs}\langle\Psi_s\rangle}u_s^a\varepsilon_{as}\langle\Psi_s\rangle\, d\mathbf{s} \\
&\quad + \iint \rho(\mathbf{s})\rho(\mathbf{t})\overline{u_s^c\varepsilon_{cs}u_t^s\varepsilon_{st}\langle\Psi_t\rangle}u_s^a\varepsilon_{as}u_t^s\varepsilon_{st}\langle\Psi_t\rangle\, d\mathbf{s}\, d\mathbf{t} + \cdots \\
&= \langle\bar{\Psi}_c\rangle\langle\Psi_a\rangle + \int \rho(\mathbf{s})\overline{u_s^c\varepsilon_{cs}}u_s^a\varepsilon_{as}\langle|\Psi_s|^2\rangle\, d\mathbf{s}; \\
u_s^c\varepsilon_{cs} &= u_s^c + \int \rho(\mathbf{t})u_t^c(u_s^t\varepsilon_{ts})\, d\mathbf{t}, \qquad \langle\Psi_c\rangle = \phi_c + \int \rho(\mathbf{s})u_s^a\langle\Psi_s\rangle\, d\mathbf{s},
\end{aligned}
\tag{66}
$$

where $u_s^c\varepsilon_{cs}$ is essentially a new single-scatterer function, say v_s^c, such that

$$
u_s^c\varepsilon_{cs} = v_s^c = u_s^c + \int \rho(\mathbf{t})u_t^c v_s^t\, d\mathbf{t}
\tag{67}
$$

satisfies the integral equation analogous to $\langle\Psi_c\rangle$ whose inhomogeneous term is u, i.e., v_s^c is the "Green's function" for an angle dependent source u_s^c. Two special cases are of particular interest:

$$
\begin{aligned}
\langle|\Psi_c|^2\rangle &= |\langle\Psi_c\rangle|^2 + \int \rho(\mathbf{s})|u_s^c\varepsilon_{cs}|^2\langle|\Psi_s|^2\rangle\, d\mathbf{s}, \\
\langle\Psi_c^2\rangle &= \langle\Psi_c\rangle^2 + \int \rho(\mathbf{s})(u_s^c\varepsilon_{cs})^2\langle\Psi_s^2\rangle\, d\mathbf{s};
\end{aligned}
\tag{68}
$$

the first is the average total intensity, and the second plus the first give all second moments of Re Ψ and Im Ψ [6].

For monopole scatterers, we have $u_s^a\varepsilon_{as} = fE(k|\mathbf{r}_a - \mathbf{r}_s|)\varepsilon_{as} = fE(K|\mathbf{r}_a - \mathbf{r}_s|)$ with $E(K|\mathbf{r}_a - \mathbf{r}_s|)$ as the Green's function for the synthetic medium; for this case the leading term of Foldy's M-series of (58) gives the same result as (66) (but the rest of the terms of the M-series are not necessarily negligible). For more general distributions than the gas, we could use (39) plus (45) for $\langle\Psi_s\rangle$ (which, it should be understood, involve heuristic simplifications of the n-body probability functions of the exact series (36)), and similarly replace $\rho(\mathbf{t})$ in the kernel of $u_s^c\varepsilon_{cs}$ by $\mu(\mathbf{s};\mathbf{t})$ (which introduces additional heuristic simplifications), or else construct a more complete representation. The analog of (39) plus (49) may be constructed by isolating the two-body processes in the original series by essentially the formalism introduced for (61).

The simple form (66) indicates the source of difficulties in seeking such forms through the previous heuristic formalism, i.e., $L(c, a; s)$ of (57) should be a product $\bar{v}_s^c v_s^a$ each factor of which satisfies a relatively simple integral equation. Working backwards from the above we construct the integral equation for $P = \bar{v}v$ and iterate it to compare with (57). Thus

$$V_{ca} = \int P(c, a; s)\langle|\Psi_s|^2\rangle\, ds; \qquad P = \sum P_n, \qquad P_0 = L_0,$$

(69) $$P_n(c, a; s) = \int \rho(\mathbf{v})\bar{u}_\nu^c P_{n-1}(\mathbf{v}, \mathbf{a}; \mathbf{s})\, d\mathbf{v} + \int \rho(\boldsymbol{\mu}) u_\mu^a P_{n-1}(\mathbf{c}, \boldsymbol{\mu}; \mathbf{s})\, d\boldsymbol{\mu} - \int\int \rho(\mathbf{v})\rho(\boldsymbol{\mu})\bar{u}_\nu^c u_\mu^a P_{n-1}(\mathbf{v}, \boldsymbol{\mu}; \mathbf{s})\, d\mathbf{v}\, d\boldsymbol{\mu}.$$

(Note that (64) is generated in the course of the first iteration of (69).) Equivalently (69) follows from the gas form of (50) by using

(70) $$\langle \bar{U}_s^c U_t^a\rangle_{st} - \langle \bar{U}_s^c\rangle_s\langle U_t^a\rangle_t = \bar{u}_s^c V_{sa} + u_t^a V_{ct} - \bar{u}_s^c u_t^a V_{st}.$$

5. **Illustration.** The previous sections introduced the general scattering and statistical formalism, and gave certain "compact" (c) and "expanded" (e) representations for several functions. The c-forms based on heuristic approximations are relatively easier to apply to specific problems but we have no analytical criteria for their validity. The e-forms involve no heuristic assumptions, but they are in general too cumbersome to work with. By comparing expansions of c-forms with corresponding e-forms, we can see what terms are omitted by the approximations, and this provides a general avenue that can be followed for obtaining criteria. This should be relatively easy to do for $\langle\Psi\rangle$ (see (47)), but the $\langle|\Psi|^2\rangle$ forms are considerably more complicated. Since $\langle\Psi_c\rangle$ of (42) has proved so useful for interpreting experiments, we now construct an illustration such that $\langle\Psi_c\rangle$ equals the limit of $\langle\Psi_e\rangle$ for $N\to\infty$; this allows us to concentrate on $\langle|\Psi|^2\rangle$ and determine the corresponding $\langle|\Psi_c|^2\rangle$. We first show that it is only the $\langle\Psi_c\rangle$-consistent form among the previous general forms $\langle|\Psi_c|^2\rangle$ that satisfies the energy theorem, and then show that it is also the limit of $\langle|\Psi_e|^2\rangle$ for $N\to\infty$. We consider the e-results in some detail, because even for special distributions such that the terms omitted from the correct c-forms are negligible for $N\to\infty$, we are interested in the differences between e and c results, and in the corrections required for finite N.

In order to exhibit explicitly the relationships between the heuristic c-forms and the exact e-forms we restrict consideration to a very simple class of scattering problems. We restrict the "statistics," we restrict the geometry, and we restrict the type of scatterers. Subject to these restrictions, we also introduce analytical simplifications in evaluating certain integrals that arise. Since *all* simplifications appear equally in the c and e forms, they do not affect the primary aim of determining the significance of the heuristic approximations.

Ensemble. The ensemble we consider is that of a "rare gas" of N identical scatterers, i.e.,

$$W(\mathbf{1}, \mathbf{2}, \cdots, \mathbf{N}) = w^N,$$

where w is independent of position. The scatterers u_s we deal with are thus either identical (e.g., identical ellipsoids which remain at constant orientation), or represent an identical average value over scatterer characteristics (average over orientation, size, etc.); for the second case we incorporate this independent averaging in the definitions of u and f. Thus for either case, we need consider only integrations over position variables explicitly. Treating the scatterers as points uniformly distributed in an available volume $\mathscr{V}$, we take the part of w which we consider explicitly to equal

$$w = 1/\mathscr{V}$$

The corresponding density function

$$\rho = N/\mathscr{V}$$

is the average number of scatterers in unit available volume. We are interested in finite values of N and $\mathscr{V}$, and also in values $N \to \infty$ and $\mathscr{V} \to \infty$ such that ρ remains bounded.

Geometry. We restrict the scatterers to a slab region of space of thickness d, normal to the direction of incidence $\mathbf{i} = \mathbf{n} = \mathbf{z}/z$ (i.e., $0 \leqq z \leqq d$). The dimensions along x and y will be regarded as infinite in order to preserve symmetry perpendicular to $\mathbf{n}$. Infinite limits on x and y also enable us to do various integrations exactly **[4]**; however, this is not significant in the present treatment since we evaluate all integrals by the method of stationary phase (which requires only that the limits be very large compared to k^{-1}, and this we assume). The available volume of the slab region (which is in general a function of the number of scatterers and their individual volumes) will be treated as finite as long as we are dealing with finite N.

Scatterers. We restrict consideration to "forward-type scatterers" such that

$$|f(\mathbf{i}, \mathbf{i})| \ggg |f(-\mathbf{i}, \mathbf{i})|, \qquad \mathbf{i} = \mathbf{n} = \mathbf{z}/z \tag{71}$$

and neglect all radiation into the half-space back toward the source $\phi = e^{ikz}$. Because of (71), we may replace the "forward scattering theorem" for lossless scatterers in (12) by

$$\frac{4\pi}{k} \operatorname{Im} f(\mathbf{i}, \mathbf{i}) \approx \int_{\pi/2} |f(\mathbf{o}, \mathbf{i})|^2 \, d\Omega_0 \approx \sigma_s \tag{72}$$

where $\int_{\pi/2}$ indicates the forward half-space of angles around $\mathbf{o} = \mathbf{i} = \mathbf{n}$. Where convenient, in order to illustrate certain relations explicitly, we may assume that $|f(\mathbf{o}, \mathbf{i})|^2$ is "tightly peaked" around $\mathbf{o} = \mathbf{i}$ and neglect slow variations of factors such as the scalar product $\mathbf{i} \cdot \mathbf{o}$. More generally, we assume that the significant directions $\mathbf{o}$ make small enough angles from the slab normal $\mathbf{n} = \mathbf{i}$ to insure that

$$|f(\mathbf{o}, \mathbf{o})| \ggg |f(\mathbf{o}', \mathbf{o})|, \qquad \mathbf{o}' = 2\mathbf{o} \cdot \mathbf{nn} - \mathbf{o}, \tag{73}$$

where $\mathbf{o}'$ is the image of $\mathbf{o}$ in the slab's face. (These restrictions correspond for example to scatterers whose dimensions are very large compared to k^{-1}, particularly if their index of refraction, etc., differ little from those of the external region. However, we consistently treat the scatterers as points in carrying out essentially the same integrations in c and e forms. In order to avoid discussion of convergence, we assume the too strong condition $\rho\sigma\, d < 1$. Our procedure may suggest that we require $|f(\mathbf{i}, \mathbf{i})|^N \gg |f(-\mathbf{i}, \mathbf{i})|$, and this would be incompatible with convergence for $N \to \infty$. However, if we introduce more structure into the problem, e.g., a simple $\mu(\mathbf{s}; \mathbf{t})$ "hole," we also introduce additional factors which may be adjusted to insure convergence subject to (71). For present purposes, we ignore $f(-\mathbf{i}, \mathbf{i})$.)

In carrying out integrations, in general, we apply the method of stationary phase and use the asymptotic form of the scattered wave

$$u_s^a(\mathbf{i}) \sim f(\mathbf{o}_{as}, \mathbf{i}) \frac{e^{ikr_{as}}}{r_{as}}, \qquad \mathbf{r}_{as} = \mathbf{r}_a - \mathbf{r}_s = r_{as}\mathbf{o}_{as}, \tag{74}$$

i.e., we take E_{as} in the operational forms to be simply the free k-space Green's function and interpret the symbolic forms as ordinary algebraic ones. (For f independent of angles, the form is then that of a monopole as treated by Foldy; however, restriction (71) makes the present scatterers the simpler ones.) Using (74) in the integrals of the previous section, we evaluate them by means of

$$\iint G(x, y)\, e^{ikg(x,y)}\, dx\, dy \sim \frac{2\pi i}{k} \frac{[G\, e^{ikg}]}{[g_{xx}g_{yy} - g_{xy}^2]^{1/2}}, \tag{75}$$

where the brackets indicate that the functions g, G, and the second derivatives of g (i.e., g_{xx}, etc.) are evaluated at the stationary points for which $g_x = g_y = 0$. The integrals we deal with all have two stationary points, but the restriction (73) allows us to neglect the one corresponding to "geometrical reflection" and keep only the one meaning essentially "forward scattering."

Because of the above, we may drop all terms which involve back and forth scatterings between a pair, i.e., we need consider only the "main line sequence" mentioned after (36), and shown in (47) and (65): any terms containing $u_t^s u_s^t$ or $\bar{u}_t^s u_s^t$, etc., are proportional to a back scattered value $f(\mathbf{o}_{st}, \mathbf{o}_{ts}) = f(-\mathbf{o}_{ts}, \mathbf{o}_{ts}) \approx 0$.

5.1. The coherent field.

Compact representation. For the present problem, (42) reduces to

$$\begin{aligned}
&\langle \Psi_c \rangle = \phi_c(\mathbf{i}) + \rho \iiint u_s^c \langle \Psi_s \rangle\, dx_s\, dy_s\, dz_s, && \rho = N/\mathscr{V}; \\
&\phi_c(\mathbf{i}) = e^{i\mathbf{k}\cdot\mathbf{r}_c}, && \mathbf{k} = k\mathbf{i} = k\mathbf{z}/z, \\
&u_s^c = f(\mathbf{o}_{cs}, \mathbf{i}) \frac{e^{ik|\mathbf{r}_c - \mathbf{r}_s|}}{|\mathbf{r}_c - \mathbf{r}_s|}, \\
&\qquad \mathbf{r}_c - \mathbf{r}_s = [(x_c - x_s)^2 + (y_c - y_s)^2 + (z_c - z_s)^2]^{1/2}\mathbf{o}_{cs},
\end{aligned} \tag{76}$$

where we integrate over a slab region ($0 \leqq z \leqq d$, perpendicular to $\mathbf{i} = \mathbf{n} = \mathbf{z}/z$) whose faces may be treated essentially as infinite planes.

It is clear from symmetry that $\langle \Psi \rangle$ depends only on z:

$$\langle \Psi_s \rangle = \langle \Psi(\mathbf{r}_s) \rangle = \langle \Psi(z_s) \rangle: \tag{77}$$

The integrals over x_s and y_s in (76) for arbitrary scatterers, may be evaluated exactly for infinite limits by using the complete forms of u given in §2 (see [4]). For present purposes, we obtain the same result by using the method of stationary phase (75) and the asymptotic form of u, i.e.,

$$\iint \frac{e^{ik|\mathbf{r}_c - \mathbf{r}_s|}}{|\mathbf{r}_c - \mathbf{r}_s|} f(\mathbf{o}_{cs}, \mathbf{i})\, dx_s\, dy_s \sim \frac{2\pi i}{k} e^{\pm ik(z_c - z_s)} f(\pm \mathbf{i}, \mathbf{i}) \quad \text{for } z_c \gtrless z_s, \tag{78}$$

for $\mathbf{i} = \mathbf{z}/z$. Thus the remaining integration over z_s splits into two ranges; the integral for $z_s < z_c$ has a factor $f(\mathbf{i}, \mathbf{i})$ corresponding to forward scattering, and the remaining range has a factor $f(-\mathbf{i}, \mathbf{i})$ corresponding to geometrical reflection. Because of (71) we drop the reflected term, and reduce (76) to

$$\langle \Psi(z_c) \rangle = e^{ikz_c} \left[1 + \frac{i2\pi f(\mathbf{i}, \mathbf{i})}{k} \rho \int_0^{z_c} \langle \Psi(z_s) \rangle\, e^{-ikz_s}\, dz_s \right]. \tag{79}$$

The solution of the integral equation (obtained by inspection or by iteration) equals

$$\langle \Psi(z_c) \rangle = e^{ikz_c + i\Delta z_c}, \qquad \Delta = \frac{2\pi f(\mathbf{i}, \mathbf{i})}{k} \rho, \quad \rho = \frac{N}{\mathscr{V}}, \tag{80}$$

i.e., the "internal coherent wave" is the plane wave

$$\langle \Psi_c \rangle = \phi_c\, e^{i\Delta z_c} \equiv e^{iKz_c}, \qquad K = k + \Delta. \tag{81}$$

Thus the procedure has synthesized a "medium" in which

$$(\nabla^2 + K^2)\langle \Psi_c \rangle = 0, \qquad K = k + \frac{2\pi\rho f(\mathbf{i}, \mathbf{i})}{k}. \tag{82}$$

The field transmitted through the slab is

$$\langle \Psi_c \rangle_{\text{trans}} = e^{ikz_c + i\Delta d}, \qquad z > d, \tag{83}$$

and the corresponding "coherent intensity" is

$$|\langle \Psi(d) \rangle|^2 = e^{-2\,\text{Im}\,\Delta d}, \quad 2\,\text{Im}\,\Delta d = \left[\frac{4\pi}{k} \text{Im}\, f(\mathbf{i}, \mathbf{i}) \right] \rho d. \tag{84}$$

For lossless scatterers, in view of (72), we have

$$2\,\text{Im}\,\Delta d = \sigma_s \rho d = \rho d \int_{\pi/2} |f(\mathbf{o}, \mathbf{i})|^2\, d\Omega, \tag{85}$$

so that the "coherent attenuation coefficient" 2 Im Δ is simply the total scattering cross section of one scatterer times the number of scatterers per unit volume. Since the scatterers are lossless (i.e., there are no sinks for **J**), the "losses" shown in (84) must be made up by the "incoherent component" which we consider subsequently.

The above is a very sketchy discussion of matters treated elsewhere in detail **[4]**. In basing the discussion on free-space scattering amplitudes $f(\mathbf{i}, \mathbf{i})$, we are avoiding a central problem of the subject: clearly our treatment of the immediate neighborhood of the scatterers, and of the face planes $z = 0$ and d are cursory. However, these are secondary questions pertaining to parameters that play the same roles in both the c and e forms and will not be discussed in the following.

Expanded representation. For the present problem, (36) with $w = 1/\mathscr{V}$ reduces to

$$\text{(86)} \quad \begin{aligned} \langle \Psi_e \rangle = \phi_e &+ Nw \int u_s^e \phi_s \, d\mathbf{r}_s + N(N-1)w^2 \int\int u_s^e u_t^s \phi_t \, d\mathbf{r}_s \, d\mathbf{r}_t \\ &+ N(N-1)(N-2)w^3 \int\int\int u_s^e u_t^s u_m^t \phi_m \, d\mathbf{r}_s \, d\mathbf{r}_t \, d\mathbf{r}_m + \cdots, \end{aligned}$$

where, because of (71), we retained only the "main line sequence"; to be more explicit, we could write $u_s^e(\mathbf{o}_{st}) u_t^s(\mathbf{i}) \phi_t(\mathbf{i})$, etc. Using the forward scattered value of (78), i.e.,

$$\text{(87)} \quad w \int\int u_t^s \phi_t \, dx_t \, dy_t = \frac{2i\pi w}{k} f(\mathbf{i}, \mathbf{i}) \phi_s \equiv i\delta\phi_s = i\frac{\Delta}{N}\phi_s$$

which states simply that a uniform plane of spherical scatterers excited by a plane wave regenerates the plane wave, we reduce (86) to

$$\text{(88)} \quad \begin{aligned} \langle \Psi_e \rangle &= \phi_e \left\{ 1 + iN\delta \int_0^{z_e} dz_s + N(N-1)(i\delta)^2 \int_0^{z_e} dz_s \int_0^{z_s} dz_t + \cdots \right\} \\ &= \phi_e \left\{ 1 + Ni\delta z_e + N(N-1)\frac{(i\delta z_e)^2}{2} + \cdots + \frac{N!}{(N-\nu)!}\frac{(i\delta z_e)^\nu}{\nu!} + \cdots \right\} \\ &= \phi_e(1 + i\delta z_e)^N. \end{aligned}$$

The present result obtained without the heuristic approximation $\langle \Phi_s \rangle_s \approx \langle \Psi_s \rangle$ which lead to (81) is valid down to $N = 1$ (the only case for which the single scattering approximation is exact, and also measurable in microwave experiments on a moving scatterer).

For comparison with (81), we use $N\delta = \Delta$ and write

$$\text{(89)} \quad \langle \Psi \rangle = \phi(1 + i\delta z)^N = \phi\left(1 + i\frac{\Delta}{N}z\right)^N,$$

where $Nw = N/\mathscr{V}$ in Δ is bounded for $N \to \infty$. Since $(1 + i\Delta z/N)^N \to e^{i\Delta z}$ for $N \to \infty$, we see that the heuristic approximation $\langle \Phi_s \rangle \approx \langle \Psi \rangle$ is valid for large N for the present problem, i.e., the corresponding $\langle \Psi_c \rangle$ is the limit of $\langle \Psi_e \rangle$ for $N \to \infty$.

If we replace $N!/(N - \nu)!$ in (86) and (88) by N^ν, we get the series that follow from iterating (76) and (79) respectively. We also note for subsequent manipulations of more complicated series than (86) (in which, essentially, the present ϕ is replaced by an unknown function), that we could just as well have started with the left hand "head" instead of the right hand "tail" of a chain of integrals. Thus, for example, in the double integral of (86) we may integrate first over $\mathbf{r}_s$ and then over $\mathbf{r}_t$. Using (75), we integrate over the $x_s y_s$-plane and (because of (73)) keep only the forward stationary point to obtain

$$w \int\int u_s^a(\mathbf{o}_{st}) u_t^s(\mathbf{i})\, dx_s\, dy_s = w \int\int f(\mathbf{o}_{as}, \mathbf{o}_{st}) f(\mathbf{o}_{st}, \mathbf{i}) E_{as} E_{st}\, dx_s\, dy_s \tag{90}$$
$$\sim E_{at} f(\mathbf{o}_{at}, \mathbf{i}) \left[\frac{i2\pi w f(\mathbf{o}_{at}, \mathbf{o}_{at})}{k \cos \theta_{at}} \right] = u_t^a(\mathbf{i}) i\delta_{at},$$

where δ_{at} is the propagation factor (analogous to $\delta_i = \delta$ of (87)) associated with the direction $\mathbf{o}_{at}$, and $\cos \theta_{at} = \mathbf{n} \cdot \mathbf{o}_{at}$; analogous to (87), the present result states that a uniform plane of spherical scatterers excited by a spherical source regenerates the spherical wave of the source in the forward half-space. Multiplying (90) by ϕ_t we integrate over x_t and y_t by using (87) (which also converts δ_{at} of (90) to $\delta_i = \delta$), and are left with $N(N - 1)[i\delta]^2 \int_0^{z_e} dz_t \int_{z_t}^{z_e} dz_s$ which of course gives the same result as the corresponding term of (88).

We also note that we may obtain the "transmission coefficient" $T_N = (1 + i\delta z)^N$ of (89) algebraically from elementary physical considerations, i.e., we have essentially

$$T_N = T_1^N, \qquad T_1 = 1 + i\delta z = 1 + S_1, \tag{91}$$

where S_1 represents the forward scattering amplitude for a "planar scatterer" whose back scattering is zero. From elementary "transmission line" considerations, we write $T_N = T_1^N$ directly. The binomial coefficients of the individual terms in the expansion of T_N, i.e., the coefficient in $[N!/(N - \nu)!\nu!]S^\nu$ merely indicates the number of possible order-preserving forward-scattering combinations for ν out of N scatterers. From this viewpoint, we would not expect S to depend on z (i.e., we have factored out the plane wave excitation, and we are dealing simply with in-phase forward scattering), and it actually does not. For planar scatterers the available volume for an observation point z within the distribution is $\mathscr{V} = \mathscr{A} z$, where "$\mathscr{A}$" is a redundant area factor. Thus $S = i\delta z$ reduces to $S = i2\pi f/k\mathscr{A}$; this same value follows if our planar scatterers have finite thickness "b," since z in both numerator and denominator would then be replaced by $z - Nb$.

5.2. Total intensity.

Energy approximation. For the present problem, (54) equals

$$V_a = \langle|\Psi_a|^2\rangle - |\langle\Psi_a\rangle|^2 \approx \rho\int |u_s^a|^2|\langle\Psi_s\rangle|^2\, d\mathbf{r}_s$$

(92)

$$= \rho\iiint \frac{|f(\mathbf{o}_{as}, \mathbf{i})|^2}{|\mathbf{r}_a - \mathbf{r}_s|^2} e^{-2\mathrm{Im}\Delta z_s} dx_s\, dy_s\, dz_s.$$

Using

$$\frac{\cos\theta_{as}\, dx_s\, dy_s}{|\mathbf{r}_a - \mathbf{r}_s|^2} = d\Omega_{as},$$

we integrate over z_s for constant θ_{as} and obtain

$$(93)\qquad V_a \approx \rho\int \frac{|f(\mathbf{o}, \mathbf{i})|^2}{\cos\theta} d\Omega \int_0^d e^{-2\,\mathrm{Im}\,\Delta z}\, dz = \frac{(1 - e^{-2\,\mathrm{Im}\,\Delta d})}{2\,\mathrm{Im}\,\Delta}\rho\int \frac{|f(\mathbf{o}, \mathbf{i})|^2}{\cos\theta} d\Omega.$$

For practical measurement purposes, we would restrict the integration over Ω to a cone of, say, half-angle α corresponding to the receiver's main lobe. (More generally we would work with a spherical source and introduce angular factors corresponding to antenna factors for transmitter and receiver horns [11].)

The corresponding incoherent flux is

$$\mathbf{I} \approx \mathrm{Re}\left[\frac{\rho}{ik}\int \bar{u}_s^a \nabla_a u_s^a |\langle\Psi_s\rangle|^2\, d\mathbf{r}_s\right] \mathrel{\dot{\approx}} \rho\int \frac{|f(\mathbf{o}_{as}, \mathbf{i})|^2}{|\mathbf{r}_a - \mathbf{r}_s|^2} e^{-2\,\mathrm{Im}\,\Delta z_s}\mathbf{o}_{as}\, d\mathbf{r}_s$$

(94)

$$= (1 - e^{-2\,\mathrm{Im}\,\Delta d})(\rho/2\,\mathrm{Im}\,\Delta)\int_\alpha |f(\mathbf{o}, \mathbf{i})|^2(\mathbf{o}/\cos\theta)\, d\Omega,$$

where we differentiated only the exponent of E_{as} and then proceeded as for (93); in the final form, α is the "receiver's cone angle" mentioned above. The coherent flux transmitted through the slab (from (83)) is simply

$$(95)\qquad \mathbf{C} = \mathrm{Re}\left[\frac{\langle\bar{\Psi}\rangle\nabla\langle\Psi\rangle}{ik}\right] = |\langle\Psi\rangle|^2\mathbf{i} = e^{-2\,\mathrm{Im}\,\Delta d}\mathbf{i}, \qquad \mathbf{i} = \mathbf{n}.$$

The component of the total flux (in a cone α) normal to the slab for $z > d$ is thus

$$(96)\qquad \langle\mathbf{J}\rangle\cdot\mathbf{n} = (\mathbf{C} + \mathbf{I})\cdot\mathbf{n} = e^{-2\,\mathrm{Im}\,\Delta d} + \frac{(1 - e^{-2\,\mathrm{Im}\,\Delta d})}{2\,\mathrm{Im}\,\Delta}\rho\int_\alpha |f(\mathbf{o}, \mathbf{i})|^2\, d\Omega,$$

where we used $\mathbf{n}\cdot\mathbf{o}_{as} = \cos\theta_{as}$. The incident flux, the only component of flux for $z < 0$, is

$$(97)\qquad \mathbf{J} = \mathrm{Re}(\bar{\phi}\nabla\phi/ik) = \mathbf{i}.$$

For lossless scatterers, theorem (53) states that the component of average total flux normal to the slab is a constant in the external region; from (97), the constant must equal $\mathbf{i}\cdot\mathbf{n} = 1$. For $\alpha = \pi/2$ (a "point receiver"), we use (85) in (96) for lossless scatterers to reduce the incoherent term to $(1 - e^{-2\,\mathrm{Im}\,\Delta d})$. Thus (96) gives $\langle\mathbf{J}\rangle\cdot\mathbf{n} = 1$ in accord with (97).

The basis for the form (92) is thus the energy theorem for lossless scatterers. There are no total energy losses in such problems, and loss effects shown by the coherent component must be compensated by the corresponding incoherent term. We use simply the coherent intensity as excitation in (92) and (94) (instead of the total) and then let the scatterers radiate directly to free space without further multiple scattering; however, this must yield a result in accord with the energy principle. There can be no additional "coherent" losses in the problem; since the "incoherent scattering" cannot become "coherent," it may be treated as radiating directly to free space.

We note that V of (93) differs from $\mathbf{I}\cdot\mathbf{n}$ of (96) only by the factor $\cos\theta$, and this will also hold for more complicated forms we consider subsequently. To facilitate checking whether approximations for V are in accord with the energy theorem for lossless scatterers, we may use $\cos\theta \approx 1$ (which is appropriate if $|f(\mathbf{o},\mathbf{i})|^2$ is peaked sharply around $\mathbf{o} = \mathbf{n} = \mathbf{i}$), and use simply

$$(98)\quad \mathbf{I}\cdot\mathbf{n} \approx V, \qquad \mathbf{C}\cdot\mathbf{n} = |\langle\Psi\rangle|^2, \qquad \langle\mathbf{J}\rangle\cdot\mathbf{n} = 1 \approx |\langle\Psi\rangle|^2 + V = \langle|\Psi|^2\rangle.$$

Thus any proposed approximation for V, in the limit of tightly peaked lossless $|f|^2$ must reduce as follows:

$$(99)\quad V = \langle|\Psi|^2\rangle - |\langle\Psi\rangle|^2 = \int L\langle|\Psi|^2\rangle\, d\mathbf{r}_s \to V = 1 - |\langle\Psi\rangle|^2 = \int L\, d\mathbf{r}_s.$$

In view of (92) ff., the simplest limiting forms of L satisfying (99) are

$$(100)\qquad L(c, c; s) = \rho|u_s^c|^2\, e^{-2\,\mathrm{Im}\,\Delta z_s}, \qquad \rho|u_s^c|^2\, e^{-2\,\mathrm{Im}\,\Delta(z_c - z_s)}.$$

We use (99) and (100) as checks in the following.

Foldy's integral equation form. For the present problem, the kernel function L required for Foldy's form (57) can be evaluated explicitly by using the results of the integration (90), and performing the remaining elementary integrations over z. Thus

$$L_0(c, a; s) = \rho\bar{u}_s^c(\mathbf{i})u_s^a(\mathbf{i}),$$

$$L_1(c, a; s) = \rho^2\int\int \bar{u}_t^c(\mathbf{o}_{ts})u_m^a(\mathbf{o}_{ms})[\rho\bar{u}_s^t(\mathbf{i})u_s^m(\mathbf{i})]\, d\mathbf{r}_m\, d\mathbf{r}_t$$

$$= \rho\overline{u_s^c i\Delta_{cs}}\, u_s^a i\Delta_{as}\int_{z_s}^{z_c} dz_t \int_{z_s}^{z_a} dz_m$$

$$= \rho\overline{u_s^c i\Delta_{cs}(z_c - z_s)}u_s^a i\Delta_{as}(z_a - z_s),$$

$$(101)\quad L_2(c, a; s) = \rho^2\int\int \bar{u}_t^c(\mathbf{o}_{ts})u_m^a(\mathbf{o}_{ms})[\rho\overline{u_s^t(\mathbf{i})i\Delta_{ts}(z_t - z_s)}u_s^m(\mathbf{i})i\Delta_{ms}(z_m - z_s)]\, d\mathbf{r}_m\, d\mathbf{r}_t$$

$$= \rho\overline{u_s^c(\mathbf{i})(i\Delta_{cs})^2}u_s^a(\mathbf{i})(i\Delta_{as})^2\int_{z_s}^{z_c}(z_t - z_s)\, dz_t\int_{z_s}^{z_a}(z_m - z_s)\, dz_m$$

$$= \rho\bar{u}_s^c(\mathbf{i})\,\frac{\overline{[i\Delta_{cs}(z_c - z_s)]^2}}{2}\cdot u_s^a(\mathbf{i})\,\frac{[i\Delta_{as}(z_a - z_s)]^2}{2},$$

$$L_n(c, a; s) = \rho\bar{u}_s^c(\mathbf{i})\,\frac{\overline{[i\Delta_{cs}(z_c - z_s)]^n}}{n!}\, u_s^a(\mathbf{i})\,\frac{[i\Delta_{as}(z_a - z_s)]^n}{n!},$$

where

$$\Delta_{as} = N\delta_{as} = \frac{\rho 2\pi f(\mathbf{o}_{as}, \mathbf{o}_{as})}{k \cos \theta_{as}}.$$

Since the zeroth order Bessel function $J_0(x)$ may be written

$$\sum_{n=0}^{\infty} \left[\frac{ix}{2}\right]^{2n} \frac{1}{(n!)^2},$$

and since

$$I_0(x) = J_0(ix) = \sum \left(\frac{x}{2}\right)^{2n} \frac{1}{(n!)^2},$$

we may rewrite (101) in the closed form

$$L(c, a; s) = \sum_{n=0}^{\infty} L_n = \rho \bar{u}_s^c(\mathbf{i}) u_s^a(\mathbf{i}) I_0(2\sqrt{\bar{\Delta}_{cs}(z_c - z_s)\Delta_{as}(z_a - z_s)}). \tag{102}$$

In particular, for $c = a$, we use $L(c, c; s)$ of (102) in the corresponding form of (57) to obtain

$$\begin{aligned} \langle|\Psi_c|^2\rangle - |\langle\Psi_c\rangle|^2 &= \rho \int |u_s^c(\mathbf{i})|^2 \langle|\Psi_s|^2\rangle I_0(2|\Delta_{cs}|(z_c - z_s))\, d\mathbf{r}_s \\ &= \rho \int [|f(\mathbf{o}, \mathbf{i})|^2/\cos\theta]\, d\Omega \int \langle|\Psi_s|^2\rangle I_0(2|\Delta_{cs}|(z_c - z_s))\, dz_s. \end{aligned} \tag{103}$$

Thus we have "solved" the original integral equation form, to obtain an actual integral equation for $\langle|\Psi|^2\rangle$ in terms of $|\langle\Psi\rangle|^2$. However, we do not regard (103) as correct: the limiting form of the kernel function for lossless tightly peaked $|f|^2$ is not in accord with (100). More explicitly, in this limit we have $\langle|\Psi|^2\rangle \to 1$, $\cos\theta \to 1$, and the right and left hand sides give different values for

$$V = \langle|\Psi|^2\rangle - |\langle\Psi\rangle|^2 = 1 - |\langle\Psi\rangle|^2;$$

the right hand side of (103) gives $2\,\mathrm{Im}\,\Delta\int_0^{z_c} I_0(2|\Delta|(z_c - z_s))\, dz_s$ which does not equal $1 - e^{-2\,\mathrm{Im}\,\Delta z_s}$ obtained from the left side.

The $\langle\Psi_c\rangle$-consistent integral equation. In order to apply $\langle\bar{\Psi}_c\Psi_a\rangle$ of (66), we must first determine the new scattering function $u_s^c\varepsilon_{cs}$. We have

$$\begin{aligned} u_s^c(\mathbf{j})\varepsilon_{cs} &= u_s^c(\mathbf{j}) + \rho \int u_t^c(\mathbf{o}_{ts}) u_s^t(\mathbf{j})\varepsilon_{ts}\, d\mathbf{r}_t = u_s^c(\mathbf{j})\left[1 + i\Delta_{cs}\int_{z_s}^{z_c} \varepsilon_{ts}\, dz_t\right], \\ \varepsilon_{cs} &= 1 + \Delta_{cs}\int_{z_s}^{z_c} \varepsilon_{ts}\, dz_t = e^{i\Delta_{cs}(z_c - z_s)}, \end{aligned} \tag{104}$$

where we used (90) and then followed essentially the same procedure as for $\langle\Psi\rangle$ of (79) in solving the integral equation for ε. Using (104) in (66), we obtain

$$\begin{aligned} \langle|\Psi_c|^2\rangle &= |\langle\Psi_c\rangle|^2 + \rho \int |u_s^c e^{i\Delta(z_c - z_s)}|^2 \langle|\Psi_s|^2\rangle\, d\mathbf{r}_s \\ &= e^{-2\,\mathrm{Im}\,\Delta z_s} + \rho \int \frac{|f(\mathbf{o}_{cs}, \mathbf{i})|^2}{\cos\theta_{cs}}\, d\Omega_{cs} \int \langle|\Psi_s|^2\rangle\, e^{-2\,\mathrm{Im}\,\Delta(z_c - z_s)}\, dz_s, \end{aligned} \tag{105}$$

which clearly satisfies the energy theorem in the appropriate limit (see (99) and (100)). We also show subsequently that (105) is the required limit of the corresponding explicit approximation of $\langle|\Psi_e|^2\rangle$ for $N \to \infty$.

From (104), we see that we have also constructed the K-space Green's function for the present problem. In terms of $z_{as} = z_a - z_s = \cos\theta_{as} r_{as}$, we have

$$E(K_{as}r_{as}) = E(kr_{as})\varepsilon_{as} = \frac{e^{ikr_{as}+i\Delta_{as}r_{as}\cos\theta_{as}}}{r_{as}} \equiv \frac{e^{iK_{as}r_{as}}}{r_{as}},$$
(106)
$$K_{as} = k + \Delta_{as}\cos\theta_{as} = k + 2\pi\rho f(\mathbf{o}_{as}, \mathbf{o}_{as})/k,$$

where $K_{as} = K(\mathbf{o}_{as})$ differs from $K = K(\mathbf{i})$ of (82) only in the argument of f. Thus if $f(\mathbf{i}, \mathbf{i})$ is independent of direction (i.e., if the scatterer is spherically symmetric, or if u represents a symmetrical average over all orientations of ellipsoids, etc.) then $E(Kr)$ is also independent of direction.

Foldy's recast kernel function. Foldy obtained $\sum M_n$ of (58) by operating on $\sum L_n$ of (57) with the wave equation (43). The propagation parameter of (43) equals $K^2 = k^2 + 4\pi\rho f$ for identical (or averaged) monopoles, while the present K^2 (as in (82)) has an additional term in f^2; to facilitate comparison, we assume suitable restrictions for neglecting the difference and apply $E(Kr_{as})$ of (106) to (58).

Since $\sum L_n$ gives an inadequate result, so does the recast form $\sum M_n$. However, because the initial term M_0 gives the correct $\langle\Psi_c\rangle$-consistent form of $\langle|\Psi_c|^2\rangle$, it is of interest to consider (58) further. Using essentially the same procedure as for (101), we obtain

$$M_0(c, a; s) = \rho\bar{u}_s^c(\mathbf{i})u_s^a(\mathbf{i})\, e^{\overline{i\Delta_{cs}z_{cs}}+i\Delta_{as}z_{as}}, \qquad z_{cs} = z_c - z_s;$$

$$M_1(c, a; s) = -\rho^2 f(\mathbf{o}_{as}, \mathbf{i})E(Kr_{as})\overline{\int f(\mathbf{o}_{ct}, \mathbf{o}_{ts})f(\mathbf{o}_{ts}, \mathbf{i})E(Kr_{ct})E(Kr_{ts})\, d\mathbf{r}_t}$$
(107)
$$-\rho^2\overline{f(\mathbf{o}_{cs}, \mathbf{i})E(Kr_{cs})}\int f(\mathbf{o}_{am}, \mathbf{o}_{ms})f(\mathbf{o}_{ms}, \mathbf{i})E(Kr_{am})E(Kr_{ms})\, d\mathbf{r}_t$$
$$= -M_0(c, a; s)[\overline{i\Delta_{cs}z_{cs}} + i\Delta_{as}z_{as}];$$
$$M_2(c, a; s) = M_0(c, a; s)[\tfrac{1}{2}\overline{(i\Delta_{cs}z_{cs})}^2 + 2\overline{(i\Delta_{cs}z_{cs})}(i\Delta_{as}z_{as}) + \tfrac{1}{2}(i\Delta_{as}z_{as})^2].$$

From (107), we have symbolically

$$\sum M_n = L_0\, e^{A+B}[1 - A - B + \tfrac{1}{2}A^2 + 2AB + \tfrac{1}{2}B^2 + O(A^3)]$$
(107′)
$$= L_0[1 + AB + O(A)^3],$$

so that M_1 provides a first order "correction" to M_0, and successive terms serve to cancel additional essential terms of the exponent. Comparison with the result of (101) for the same number of iterations, i.e.,

(101′) $$\sum L_n = L_0[1 + AB \mp \tfrac{1}{4}A^2B^2 + O(A^6)],$$

shows that $\sum L_n$ is the more rapidly converging series in A, B. Both series converge to $\sum L_n = \sum M_n = L$ of (102), which is an incorrect form for the energy theorem.

Other representations. Similarly the heuristic form (64) may be rewritten in the form (57) with the kernel function L replaced by

$$N = L_0[1 + A + B + AB + \tfrac{1}{2}AB(A + B) + \tfrac{1}{4}A^2B^2 + O(A^5)], \tag{108}$$

where we followed essentially the same procedure as for (101).

Comparing the above expansions with the analogous two stages of the expansion of the kernel function of (105), i.e., with

$$\rho \bar{u}_s^c u_s^a \bar{\varepsilon}_{cs} \varepsilon_{as} = L_0 e^{A+B} = L_0[1 + A + B + AB + \tfrac{1}{2}A^2 + \tfrac{1}{2}B^2 + O(A^3)], \tag{109}$$

we see that (108) is the only expansion that has the proper leading terms to provide the first corrections to the single scattering approximation.

In the above we showed that the $\langle \Psi_c \rangle$-consistent form of $\langle |\Psi_c|^2 \rangle$ gave results in accord with the energy theorem. In the following we show explicitly that this form is also the limit of $\langle |\Psi_e|^2 \rangle$ for $N \to \infty$ (as is, of course, required by the development leading to (66) subject to the present restrictions).

Expanded representation. We use (37) with $w = 1/\mathscr{V}$ but because of the present restrictions, we drop all terms involving back-scattered values of f; thus we obtain a finite sequence. We group the terms on the basis of their numerical coefficient in N: analogous to (65), we have

$$\begin{aligned} \langle \bar{\Psi}_e \Psi_a \rangle &= \bar{\phi}_e \phi_a + Nw \int (\bar{\phi}_e u_s^a \phi_s + \overline{u_s^e \phi_s} \phi_a + \overline{u_s^e \phi_s} u_s^a \phi_s) \, d\mathbf{r}_s \\ &\quad + N(N-1)w^2 \iint [\overline{u_s^e \phi_s} u_t^a \phi_t + \bar{\phi}_e u_s^a u_t^s \phi_t + \overline{u_s^e u_t^s \phi_t} \phi_a \\ &\qquad + \overline{u_s^e \phi_s}(u_s^a u_t^s \phi_t + u_t^a u_s^t \phi_s) + \overline{(u_s^e u_t^s \phi_t + u_t^e u_s^t \phi_s)} u_s^a \phi_s \\ &\qquad + \overline{u_s^e u_t^s \phi_t} u_s^a u_t^s \phi_t] \, d\mathbf{r}_s \, d\mathbf{r}_t + \cdots \end{aligned} \tag{110}$$

where (as usual, for brevity) the suppressed directions of incidence in the u's are determined by the terms on their right. Using (87) and (90) and performing the integrations over x, y, we evaluate all integrals of the form considered in previous sections. Thus in terms of

$$\begin{aligned} &\delta = \frac{2\pi f(\mathbf{i}, \mathbf{i})}{k} w, \quad \delta_{as} = \frac{2\pi f(\mathbf{o}_{as}, \mathbf{o}_{as})}{k \cos \theta_{as}} w, \quad z_{es} = z_e - z_s; \\ &W_{ea}(s) = \frac{w}{\bar{\phi}_e \phi_a} \int \overline{u_s^e \phi_s} u_s^a \phi_s \, d\mathbf{r}_s, \quad W_{ee}(s) = w \int \frac{|f(\mathbf{o}_{es}, \mathbf{i})|^2}{\cos \theta_{es}} \int_0^{z_e} dz_s = Q(\mathbf{o}_{es}, \mathbf{i}) \int_0^{z_e} dz_s, \end{aligned} \tag{111}$$

we obtain initially

$$
\begin{aligned}
\frac{\langle\overline{\Psi}_e\Psi_a\rangle}{\bar{\phi}_e\phi_a} = 1 &+ N\{(\overline{i\delta z_e} + i\delta z_a) + W_{ea}(s)\} \\
&+ N(N-1)\{\tfrac{1}{2}(\overline{i\delta z_e} + i\delta z_a)^2 \\
&\qquad + W_{ea}(s)[\overline{i\delta_{es}z_{es}} + i\delta_{as}z_{as} + 2\,\mathrm{Re}\, i\delta z_s] + W_{ea}(s)W_{ss}(t)\} \\
&+ N(N-1)(N-2)\Big\{\frac{1}{3!}(\overline{i\delta z_e} + i\delta z_a)^3 \\
&\qquad + W_{ea}(s)\tfrac{1}{2}[\overline{i\delta_{es}z_{es}} + i\delta_{as}z_{as} + 2\,\mathrm{Re}\, i\delta z_s]^2 \\
&\qquad + W_{ea}(s)W_{ss}(t)[\overline{i\delta_{es}z_{es}} + i\delta_{as}z_{as} + 2\,\mathrm{Re}\, i\delta_{st}z_{st} + 2\,\mathrm{Re}\, i\delta z_t] \\
&\qquad + W_{ea}(s)W_{ss}(t)W_{tt}(m)\Big\} + \cdots.
\end{aligned}
\tag{112}
$$

Succeeding may b• obtained by inspection, e.g., the next term is

$$
\begin{aligned}
\frac{N!}{(N-4)!}\Big\{&\frac{1}{4!}(\overline{i\delta z_e} + i\delta z_a)^4 + W_{ea}(s)\frac{1}{3!}[\overline{i\delta_{es}z_{es}} + i\delta_{as}z_{as} + 2\,\mathrm{Re}\, i\delta z_s]^3 \\
&+ W_{ea}(s)W_{ss}(t)\tfrac{1}{2}[\overline{i\delta_{es}z_{es}} + i\delta_{as}z_{as} + 2\,\mathrm{Re}\, i\delta_{st}z_{st} + 2\,\mathrm{Re}\, i\delta z_t]^2 \\
&+ W_{ea}(s)W_{ss}(t)W_{tt}(m)[\overline{i\delta_{es}z_{es}} + i\delta_{as}z_{as} + 2\,\mathrm{Re}\, i\delta_{st}z_{st} + 2\,\mathrm{Re}\, i\delta_{tm}z_{tm} \\
&\qquad + 2\,\mathrm{Re}\, i\delta z_m] \\
&+ W_{ea}(s)W_{ss}(t)W_{tt}(m)W_{mm}(n)\Big\}.
\end{aligned}
\tag{112'}
$$

As a check on the above, and for its own interest, we temporarily specialize (112) to tightly peaked $|f|^2$. For this case, all the δ's are identical and the chains of δz's in the square brackets in (112) collapse to $\overline{i\delta z_e} + i\delta z_a$; similarly, all Q's in $W_{ss}(t)$, etc., are identical, and we may integrate over all the remaining z's, except z_s which is involved in $W_{ea}(s)$. The relationship of the resultant form to the binomial expansion of the Nth power of 1 plus the first term in braces in (112) is that expected from elementary physical considerations. To make the relationship explicit, we then let $\mathbf{r}_a = \mathbf{r}_e$, integrate over the remaining z_s, and obtain simply

$$
\begin{aligned}
\langle|\Psi|^2\rangle &= 1 + N(-2\,\mathrm{Im}\,\delta + Q)z + \frac{N(N-1)}{2}(-2\,\mathrm{Im}\,\delta + Q)^2z^2 + \cdots \\
&= (1 - 2\,\mathrm{Im}\,\delta z + Qz)^N.
\end{aligned}
\tag{113}
$$

We thus have an intensity transmission coefficient $\mathcal{T}_N = \mathcal{T}_1^N$ analogous to the wave coefficient T_N, and the result may be rederived by the elementary "transmission line" algebraic procedure mentioned after (91). For the present case of peaked $|f|^2$, we may use $\cos\theta \approx 1$ in Q of (111). Thus for lossless scatterers, we have $Q \approx \sigma w = 2\,\mathrm{Im}\,\delta$, and (113) reduces to $\langle|\Psi|^2\rangle = 1$ as required by the energy theorem.

More generally, we regroup the terms of (112) into the coherent component plus other components corresponding to products of the operator W:

$$\begin{aligned}\frac{\langle\bar{\Psi}_e\Psi_a\rangle}{\bar{\phi}_e\phi_a} &= (1+\overline{i\delta}z_e+i\delta z_a)^N + NW_{ea}(s)(1+\overrightarrow{i\delta}_{es}z_{es}+i\delta_{as}z_{as}+2\,\mathrm{Re}\,i\delta z_s)^{N-1}\\ &\quad + N(N-1)W_{ca}(s)W_{ss}(t)(1+\overline{i\delta}_{es}z_{es}+i\delta_{as}z_{as}\\ &\qquad + 2\,\mathrm{Re}\,i\delta_{st}z_{st}+2\,\mathrm{Re}\,i\delta z_t)^{N-2}+\cdots.\end{aligned}\tag{114}$$

We first specialize this to a more practical form for finite N, and then proceed to the limit $N\to\infty$.

For a finite relatively small number of elements, we would compute the intensity for $\mathbf{r}_e=\mathbf{r}_a$ from

$$\begin{aligned}\langle|\Psi_e|^2\rangle &= \frac{\langle\bar{\Psi}_e\Psi_e\rangle}{\bar{\phi}_e\phi_e}\\ &= (1+2\,\mathrm{Re}\,i\delta z_e)^N + NW_{ee}(s)(1+2\,\mathrm{Re}\,i\delta_{es}z_{es}+2\,\mathrm{Re}\,i\delta z_s)^{N-1}\\ &\quad + N(N-1)W_{ee}(s)W_{ss}(t)(1+2\,\mathrm{Re}\,i\delta_{es}z_{es}\\ &\qquad + 2\,\mathrm{Re}\,i\delta_{st}z_{st}+2\,\mathrm{Re}\,i\delta z_t)^{N-2}+\cdots\\ &\quad + \frac{N!}{(N-\nu)!}\left[\prod_{n=1}^{\nu}W_{e^{(n-1)}e^{(n-1)}}(e^{(n)})\right]\left[1+2\,\mathrm{Re}\sum_{m=1}^{\nu}i\delta_{e^{(m-1)}e^{(m)}}z_{e^{(m-1)}e^{(m)}}\right.\\ &\qquad \left. + 2\,\mathrm{Re}\,i\delta z_{e^{(\nu)}}\right]^{N-\nu}\end{aligned}\tag{115}$$

(from which we also obtain $\langle\Psi^2\rangle/\phi_e^2$ by dropping Re, and using the first form of W of (111) without bars). For practical purposes, for peaked $|f|^2$ (but not going quite to the limiting form of (113)) we regard the δ's as identical and integrate over all z's except z_s to obtain the transmitted intensity ($z_e>d$)

$$\begin{aligned}\langle\mathbf{J}\cdot\mathbf{i}\rangle \approx \langle|\Psi|^2\rangle &= (1-2\,\mathrm{Im}\,\delta d)^N + NW_{dd}(s)\{(1-2\,\mathrm{Im}\,\delta d)^{N-1}\\ &\qquad + (N-1)(1-2\,\mathrm{Im}\,\delta d)^{N-2}Qz_s+\cdots\}\\ &= (1-2\,\mathrm{Im}\,\delta d)^N + NQ_\alpha\int_0^d(1-2\,\mathrm{Im}\,\delta d+Qz_s)^{N-1}\,dz_s\end{aligned}\tag{116}$$

where the subscript α on Q corresponds to the half-angle of the cone of observation. Integrating over z_s, we obtain

$$\begin{aligned}\langle\mathbf{J}\cdot\mathbf{i}\rangle &\approx \langle|\Psi|^2\rangle\\ &= (1-2\,\mathrm{Im}\,\delta d)^N + \frac{Q_\alpha}{Q}[(1-2\,\mathrm{Im}\,\delta d+Qd)^N-(1-2\,\mathrm{Im}\,\delta d)^N],\end{aligned}\tag{117}$$

which we leave in the present grouping to facilitate comparison with measurements, i.e., we can measure the coherent term and the incoherent term (proportional to

Q_α/Q) separately. For practical measurements involving a spherical source of finite cone angle α_t, both Q_α and Q would also depend on α_t; for lossless scatterers, the corresponding $Q(\alpha_t)$ would equal $2\,\mathrm{Im}\,\delta$ only in an appropriate limit of α_t. The form (117) may also prove useful as a first approximation for all scatterers very large compared to wavelength, i.e., even for "nontenuous" scatterers provided that $|f(\mathbf{i},\mathbf{i})| \gg |f(-\mathbf{i},\mathbf{i})|$. For this case and plane wave excitation, $Q \neq w\sigma_s$ should still represent a large fraction of the total scattering cross section of one object.

Returning to (114) we introduce the symbols,

$$\Delta = N\delta, \qquad \rho = Nw = N/\mathscr{V}, \qquad P_{ea}(s) = NW_{ea}(s),$$

(118)

$$P_{ee}(s) = NW_{ee}(s) = q(\mathbf{o}_{es}, \mathbf{i})\int_0^{z_e} dz_s, \qquad q_\alpha = NQ_\alpha,$$

and proceed to the limit $N \to \infty$ by using $N!/(N-\nu)! \to N^\nu$, $(1 + x/N)^N \to e^x$, etc. Thus (114) reduces to

(119)

$$\frac{\langle \overline{\Psi}_e \Psi_a \rangle}{\bar{\phi}_e \phi_a} = e^{\overline{i\Delta z_e} + i\Delta z_a} + P_{ea}(s)\, e^{\overline{i\Delta}_{es} z_{es} + i\Delta_{as} z_{as} + 2\,\mathrm{Re}\, i\Delta z_s}$$

$$+ P_{ea}(s)P_{ss}(t)\, e^{\overline{i\Delta}_{es} z_{es} + i\Delta_{as} z_{as} + 2\,\mathrm{Re}\, i\Delta_{st} z_{st} + 2\,\mathrm{Re}\, i\Delta z_t} + \cdots,$$

where succeeding terms correspond to successive iterations of the coherent term $e^{\overline{i\Delta z_e} + i\Delta z_a}$ in the operator $P_{ea}(s)\, e^{\overline{i\Delta}_{es} z_{es} + i\Delta_{as} z_{as}}$. Compacting the representation, we obtain the integral equation

(120)

$$\langle \overline{\Psi}_c \Psi_a \rangle = \langle \overline{\Psi}_c \rangle \langle \Psi_a \rangle + \rho \int \bar{u}_s^e(\mathbf{i}) u_s^a(\mathbf{i})\, e^{\overline{i\Delta}_{es} z_{es} + i\Delta_{as} z_{as}} \langle |\Psi_s|^2 \rangle\, d\mathbf{r}_s,$$

$$\langle \Psi_a \rangle = e^{i\mathbf{k}\cdot\mathbf{r}_a + i\Delta z_a}, \quad u_s^a(\mathbf{i})\, e^{i\Delta_{as} z_{as}} = f(\mathbf{o}_{as}, \mathbf{i})\, \frac{e^{ikr_{as} + i\Delta_{as} z_{as}}}{r_{as}},$$

which is of course the special case of (66) obtained by using the present u and (104). For $\mathbf{r}_c = \mathbf{r}_a$, (120) reduces to the $\langle \Psi_c \rangle$-consistent form $\langle |\Psi_c|^2 \rangle$ of (105).

In terms of the total cross section for one scatterer $(4\pi/k)\,\mathrm{Im}\, f(\mathbf{i},\mathbf{i}) = \sigma = \sigma_a + \sigma_s$ (absorption plus scattering), we rewrite (105) as

(121)
$$\langle |\Psi_a|^2 \rangle = e^{-\rho\sigma(\mathbf{i}) z_a} + \rho \int \frac{|f(\mathbf{o}_{as}, \mathbf{i})|^2}{r_{as}^2} \langle |\Psi_s|^2 \rangle\, e^{-\rho\sigma(\mathbf{o}_{as}) r_{as}}\, d\mathbf{r}_s$$

where $\sigma(\mathbf{o}) = (4\pi/k)\,\mathrm{Im}\, f(\mathbf{o},\mathbf{o})$. For lossless scatterers, $\sigma(\mathbf{i})$ reduces to the total scattering cross section $\sigma_s(\mathbf{i}) = \int |f(\mathbf{o},\mathbf{i})|^2\, d\Omega$.

The limit of the practical form (116) is also of interest. For this case, we have

(122)

$$\langle \mathbf{J}\cdot\mathbf{i} \rangle \approx \langle |\Psi|^2 \rangle = e^{-2\,\mathrm{Im}\,\Delta d} + q_\alpha \int_0^d e^{-2\,\mathrm{Im}\,\Delta d + q\zeta}\, d\zeta$$

$$= e^{-2\,\mathrm{Im}\,\Delta d} + q_\alpha \int_0^d e^{-2\,\mathrm{Im}\,\Delta (d-\zeta)} [e^{(-2\,\mathrm{Im}\,\Delta + q)\zeta}]\, d\zeta,$$

where

$$q = NQ = \rho \int \frac{|f(\mathbf{o}, \mathbf{i})|^2}{\cos\theta} \, d\Omega \approx \sigma_s \rho.$$

The function in brackets is the present approximation for the total average internal intensity $\langle |\Psi(\zeta)|^2 \rangle$, and the remainder of the integrand is the remains of the Green's function. Integrating over ζ, we obtain the analog of (117)

$$\langle \mathbf{J}\cdot\mathbf{i} \rangle \approx e^{-\rho\sigma d} + \frac{q_\alpha}{q}(e^{-\rho\sigma d + qd} - e^{-\rho\sigma d}). \tag{123}$$

For the present lossless scatterers, $\rho\sigma = q = 2 \operatorname{Im} \Delta$, and (122) reduces to the result given previously in (96). However, as mentioned after (117), the present forms may also provide general first approximations for very large, nontenuous scatterers.

The average of $\langle \Psi^2 \rangle$. As mentioned in the introduction, averages of functions other than Ψ, $|\Psi|^2$, and $\mathbf{J}$ are also of interest, e.g., Ψ^2, $(\operatorname{Re}\Psi)^2$, etc. [6]. For completeness as far as quadratic functions are concerned, we note that $\langle \Psi_e \Psi_a \rangle$ may be obtained by inspection of (114), (120), etc., i.e., by simply removing the bar throughout all definitions and replacing $2 \operatorname{Re} i\delta$, etc., by $2i\delta$, etc.; it was because of this extension (used in (68) and mentioned after (115)) that we kept the redundant factors of ϕ in the definitions of W and P in (111) and (118). The corresponding analog of (121) is the integral equation

$$\langle \Psi_a^2 \rangle = \langle \Psi_a \rangle^2 + \rho \int [u_s^a(\mathbf{i}) \, e^{i\Delta_{as}(z_a - z_s)}]^2 \langle \Psi_s^2 \rangle \, d\mathbf{r}_s, \tag{124}$$

where $\langle \Psi_a \rangle = \phi_a \, e^{i\Delta z_a}$. We may work with

$$\langle \Psi_a^2 \rangle = \langle \Psi_a \rangle^2 + \rho \int^* [f(\mathbf{o}_{as}, \mathbf{i})\phi_s E(K|\mathbf{r}_a - \mathbf{r}_s|)]^2 \langle \Psi_s^2 \rangle \, d\mathbf{r}_s \tag{125}$$

where * indicates an artifice to avoid the singularity at $r_{as} = 0$, e.g., a minimum separation for the points. For forward peaked $|f|^2$ and small angles, we use (75) to obtain

$$\begin{aligned} \langle \Psi_a^2 \rangle &= e^{i2\mathbf{k}\cdot\mathbf{r}_a + i2\Delta z_a} \left\{ 1 + \frac{i2\pi\rho f^2(\mathbf{i}, \mathbf{i})}{2k} \int^* \frac{\langle \Psi^2(z_s) \rangle}{z_a - z_s} e^{-i2\mathbf{k}\cdot\mathbf{r}_s - i2\Delta z_s} \, dz_s \right\} \\ &= \langle \Psi_a \rangle^2 \left\{ 1 + \frac{if(\mathbf{i}, \mathbf{i})\Delta}{2} \int^* \frac{\langle \Psi^2(z_s) \rangle}{\langle \Psi_s \rangle^2 (z_a - z_s)} \, dz_s \right\}. \end{aligned} \tag{126}$$

The transmitted form of (125) for $z_a \gg d = (z_s)_{\max}$ equals

$$\langle \Psi^2 \rangle = \phi^2 \, e^{i2\Delta d} \left\{ 1 + \frac{if\Delta}{2z} \int_0^d F(\zeta) \, d(\zeta) \right\}, \tag{127}$$

where $F(\zeta) = \langle\Psi^2(\zeta)\rangle/\langle\Psi(\zeta)\rangle^2$ satisfies the integral equation

$$F(\zeta) = 1 + \frac{if(\mathrm{i}, \mathrm{i})\Delta}{2} \int^* \frac{F(\zeta)}{z - \zeta}\, d\zeta. \tag{128}$$

The leading term of (127) is simply

$$\langle\Psi^2\rangle \sim \phi^2\, e^{i2\Delta d} \left(1 + \frac{if\Delta d}{2z}\right). \tag{129}$$

References

1. V. Twersky, *Multiple scattering of waves*, J. Res. Nat. Bur. Standards Sect. D **64** (1960), 715–730; J. E. Burke and V. Twersky, *On scattering of waves by many bodies*, Report EDL–L23, Sylvania Electronic Defense Labs., Mt. View, Calif., 1963; J. Res. Nat. Bur. Standards Sect. D (1964) (to appear).

2. L. L. Foldy, *The multiple scattering of waves,* Phys. Rev. (2) **67** (1945), 107–119.

3. M. Lax, *Multiple scattering of waves.* I, Rev. Modern Phys. **23** (1951), 287–310; II. *The effective field in dense systems*, Phys. Rev. (2) **88** (1952), 621–629.

4. V. Twersky, *On scattering of waves by random distributions.* I. *Free-space scattering formalism*, J. Mathematical Phys. **3** (1962), 700–715; II. *Two-space scatterer formalism*, ibid. **3** (1962), 724–734.

5. J. B. Keller, *Wave propagation in random media*, Proc. Sympos. Appl. Math. Vol. 13, pp. 227–246, Amer. Math. Soc., Providence, R. I., 1962; *Stochastic equations and wave propagation in random media*, Proc. Sympos. Appl. Math. Vol. 16, pp. 145–170, Amer. Math. Soc., Providence, R. I., 1964.

6. V. Twersky, *Signals, scatterers, and statistics*, Report EDL–E72, Sylvania Electronic Defense Labs., Mt. View, Calif., 1962; IEEE Trans. **AP–11** (1963), 668–680.

7. G. H. A. Cole, *Classical theory of the equilibrium liquid pair distribution*, Advances in Phys. **7** (1962), 224–251.

8. V. Twersky, *Multiple scattering by arbitrary configurations in three dimensions*, J. Mathematical Phys. **3** (1962), 83–91.

9. ———, *Multiple scattering of waves by planar random distributions of parallel cylinders and bosses*, Research Report EM–58, Courant Inst. Math. Sci., New York Univ., New York, 1953; *Scattering by quasi-periodic and quasi-random distributions*, IRE Trans. **AP–7** (1959), S307–319.

10. E. I. Carstensten and L. L. Foldy, *Propagation of sound through a liquid containing bubbles*, J. Acoust. Soc. Amer. **19** (1947), 481.

11. C. I. Beard and V. Twersky, *Forward coherent and incoherent scattering from volume distributions of spheres*, Report EDL–E46, Sylvania Electronic Defense Labs., Mt. View, Calif., 1960; *Off-forward scattering from volume distributions of spheres*, Report EDL–E47, ibid.

12. J. Bazer, *Multiple scattering in one dimension*, Research Report EM–122, Courant Inst. Math. Sci., New York Univ., New York, 1959.

13. C. H. Wilcox, *A generalization of theorems of Rellich and Atkinson*, Proc. Amer. Math. Soc. **7** (1956), 271.

14. F. Zernike and J. A. Prins, *Die Beugung von Röntegen Strahlen in Flussigkeiten als Effekt der Mölekulanordnung*, Z. Physik **41** (1927), 184.

15. P. Mazur and M. Mandel, *On the theory of molecular polarization in gases*, Physica **22** (1956), 289; L. Jansen and P. Mazur, Physica **21** (1955), 193.

Technion, Israel Institute of Technology,
Haifa, Israel
Sylvania Electronic Defense Laboratories,
Mountain View, California

WAVE PROPAGATION IN A GENERAL RANDOM CONTINUOUS MEDIUM

BY

W. C. HOFFMAN

1. **Introduction.** The problem of wave motion in a randomly inhomogeneous medium is of considerable importance in mathematical physics, where it arises naturally in the following contexts: propagation of electromagnetic or acoustic waves through a turbulent medium, the statistical mechanics of a continuous medium, and the molecular scattering of light. The present paper is devoted primarily to the mathematics associated with the first of these three topics, i.e., the theoretical problem of wave motion in a medium which, while isotropic, is characterized by having a random point function for refractive index. This problem will henceforth be referred to as the "random continuum" problem, and for a continuous medium is equivalent to "turbulent scatter."

An admirably complete and lucid treatment of the statistical mechanics of a continuous medium has been given by Kampé de Fériet in another of these symposium volumes [**1**]. The third type of phenomenon, that involving scattering from random configurations of elementary scatterers, is discussed elsewhere in this symposium volume [**2**].

Theoretical approaches to the random continuum problem have generally been devised in connection with the problem of turbulent scatter, and may be broadly subsumed under the following heads: perturbation theory (including in particular the Born approximation), the integral equation formulation, transformation to a spatial analogue of the Riccati equation,[1] and the diffusion equation approach (which is meant to include ray theory, transport equations, and the Fokker–Planck equation). It is clear from a casual consideration of these headings that most investigators have approached the problem more from the point of view of differential equations and electromagnetic waves than from the stochastic aspects, and in point of fact probabilistic considerations have often languished in comparison to those of classical analysis. As examples one may cite the fact that the correlation function $\exp\{-\alpha|x|\}$ was used for some time in engineering formulations of a turbulent scatter theory in spite of the fact that it was known from a theorem of Doob [**3**] that such a correlation function could only correspond to a Brownian motion process, i.e., one whose first derivative is everywhere discontinuous, an unfortunate feature for a hydrodynamic flow. Again, as Kampé de Fériet has pointed out [**4**], the application of time or spatial averaging to integral

[1] This is referred to in the Russian literature as Rytov's method.

representations of field quantities, as has been commonly done in most engineering analyses, requires justification in the form of an as yet nonexistent ergodic theorem, and what should actually be calculated therefore are mathematical expectations rather than time or volume averages, the statistical inference problem being left for later on.

We shall therefore pay special attention in the present discussion to the probabilistic aspects of the problem, in particular to the meaning of derivative or integral of a random function and to the concept of random integral of a partial differential equation, to the various forms of spectral representation for the random functions involved, and the appropriate aspects of functional analysis.

Kampé de Fériet [1] has recognized three aspects of random integrals of partial differential equations: (i) random integrals of particular initial value or boundary value problems (e.g., the heat equation, Laplace equation, wave equation, etc.); (ii) the matter of defining a probability measure on the function space of regular integrals; and (iii) partial differential equations with random functions for coefficients. It is this third aspect that occupies us here, since our concern lies mainly with the reduced wave equation

$$\Delta U + k^2(\mathbf{x})U(\mathbf{x}) = 0 \tag{1.1}$$

which follows from the wave equation $\Delta u - v^{-2}(\mathbf{x})u_{tt} = 0$ under the assumption of harmonic time dependence: $e^{i\omega t}$. The essential feature of (1.1) is that $k(\mathbf{x})$ is a random function of position, and so also therefore is $U(\mathbf{x})$. Thus the field quantity is defined as a functional of the random refractive index process.

Nearly all studies to date of wave propagation in a random continuum have assumed harmonic time dependence, i.e., the reduced wave equation (1.1). Silver [5] has pointed out that the applicability of this assumption (or that of quasi-monochromaticity) requires verification. A medium that is swirling just as rapidly as the wave propagates through it will clearly give rise to frequency shifts that invalidate the assumption of monochromaticity. Thus hot or very energetic media are excluded. In general, use of the reduced wave equation appears proper whenever the time variation in the refractive properties of the medium is of a much lower order than the propagation time of the wave.

2. **Mathematical analysis for random functions.** The analysis of random functions can be approached in several different ways [6], but for our purposes that based on mean square convergence suffices. Thus *regular random functions* are those for which

$$E\{|X(\omega, \xi)|^2\} < \infty, \tag{2.1}$$

and by mean square convergence of a sequence $\{X_n\}$ we mean

$$\lim_{n\to\infty} E\{|X_n(\omega) - X(\omega)|^2\} = 0 \iff \operatorname{l.i.m.} X_n = X$$

and mean square convergence of random functions means

$$\lim_{\xi\to\xi_0} E\{|X(\omega, \xi) - X(\omega, \xi_0)|^2\} = 0 \iff \operatorname*{l.i.m.}_{\xi\to\xi_0} X(\omega, \xi) = X(\omega, \xi_0). \tag{2.2}$$

The connection between mean square convergence and the covariance function $\Gamma(\xi_1, \xi_2) = E\{X(\omega, \xi_1)X^*(\omega, \xi_2)\}$ (where it has been assumed that $EX(\omega, \xi) = 0$) is immediately clear from (2.2):

$$\begin{aligned} E\{|X(\omega, \xi + h) - X(\omega, \xi)|^2\} &= E\{[X(\omega, \xi + h) - X(\omega, \xi)][X^*(\omega, \xi + h) - X^*(\omega, \xi)]\} \\ &= 2\Gamma(0) - \Gamma(h) - \Gamma(-h) = 2 \operatorname{Re} [\Gamma(0) - \Gamma(h)]. \end{aligned}$$

It follows that continuity of the covariance function at $\xi_1 = \xi_2$ in the ordinary sense is enough to guarantee the continuity of $X(\omega, \xi)$ in the mean square sense, and it is a general rule that mean square properties of a random function are implied by the corresponding ordinary calculus properties of its covariance function Γ. Thus for mean square properties to hold, $X(\omega, \xi)$ must have finite variance.

If stronger properties than mean square ones are desired, e.g., ordinary continuity or differentiability almost everywhere (or, in probability measure, "almost certainly") then we are faced with a somewhat more difficult problem, but one which can be resolved on the basis of the following criterion for almost certain convergence [**6**]: If

$$E\{|X(\omega, \xi) - X(\omega, \xi_0)|^{p+1}\} < C|\xi - \xi_0|^{q+1} \qquad (p, q > 0), \tag{2.3}$$

then

$$X(\omega, \xi) \to X(\omega, \xi_0) \text{ almost certainly as } \xi \to \xi_0.$$

It follows from this criterion that $X(\omega, \xi)$ is almost certainly continuous if it is once mean square differentiable, and that a sufficient condition for $X(\omega, \xi)$ to be n times almost certainly differentiable is that it be $(n + 1)$-times m. s. differentiable.

The mean square partial derivative $\partial X(\omega, \xi_1, \cdots, \xi_n)/\partial\xi_j$ of $X(\omega, \boldsymbol{\xi}_n)$ will exist at $\boldsymbol{\xi}_n^0$ if

$$\lim_{h\to 0} E\left\{\left|\frac{X(\omega, \xi_1, \cdots, \xi_j + h, \cdots, \xi_n) - X(\omega, \xi_n)}{h} - \frac{\partial X}{\partial \xi_j}\right|^2\right\} = 0,$$

and similarly for higher derivatives. A n. a. s. c. for the mean square existence of the partial derivative of order p is that the corresponding ordinary derivative of order $2p$ of the covariance function of $X(\omega, \boldsymbol{\xi}_n)$ exist at the origin [**6**].

Alternatively, if $X(\omega, \boldsymbol{\xi}_n)$ has a spectral representation

$$X(\omega, \boldsymbol{\xi}_n) = \int_{R_n} e^{i\sigma\cdot\boldsymbol{\xi}_n} dZ(\omega, \boldsymbol{\sigma}_n)$$

(which will be defined more fully below) then a n. a. s. c. for the existence of a mean square derivative of order p is the existence of the multiple integral

$$\int_{R_n} [D^{2p}_{\boldsymbol{\xi}_n} e^{i\boldsymbol{\sigma}_n\cdot\boldsymbol{\xi}_n}]_{\boldsymbol{\xi}_n=0}\, dZ(\omega, \boldsymbol{\sigma}_n),$$

where

$$D^{2p}_{\boldsymbol{\xi}_n} = \prod_1^n \frac{\partial^{2p_i}}{\partial \xi_i^{\,2p_i}}, \qquad \sum_1^n p_i = p.$$

Thus for our purposes the reduced wave equation can be taken as equivalent to the condition

$$E\left\{\left|\sum_1^3 \frac{\partial^2 U}{\partial x_i^2} + k^2(\mathbf{x})U(\mathbf{x})\right|^2\right\} = 0,$$

or, if we wish to deal with realizations $U(\mathbf{x}_3)$ that are almost certainly twice continuously differentiable, then $U(\mathbf{x}_3)$ must be three times mean square differentiable, and

$$E\{[\Delta U(\mathbf{x}) - (-k^2(\mathbf{x}+\mathbf{h}))U(\mathbf{x}+\mathbf{h})][\Delta U^*(\mathbf{x}) + k^{*2}(\mathbf{x}+\mathbf{h})U^*(\mathbf{x}+\mathbf{h})]\} \leqq C|\mathbf{h}|^2$$

uniformly in $\mathbf{x}$.

We note that the rules for differentiation in ordinary calculus carry over to mean square differentiation, including the rule for partial and total differentiation of functions of functions, provided certain general conditions on mean square majorants are satisfied [**6**].

Stochastic Riemann, Stieltjes, and Lebesgue integrals of a random function are defined as the limits in mean square of the corresponding approximating sums, when they exist. If $X(\omega, \xi)$ is a regular random function with continuous covariance function, then apart from possible equivalences, the mean square indefinite integral

$$Y(\omega, \xi) = \int_a^\xi X(\omega, \eta)\, d\eta$$

exists and is mean square differentiable with mean square derivative $X(\omega, \xi)$. Further, if $\mathcal{Y}(\omega, \xi)$ is a primitive of $X(\omega, \xi)$ in mean square, then $Y(\omega, \xi) = \mathcal{Y}(\omega, \xi) - \mathcal{Y}(\omega, a)$ [**7**]. We thus have a basis for the formulation of mean square Volterra and Fredholm integral equations.

3. **Spectral representations.** The extension of the usual probability concepts associated with random variables to stochastic processes is accomplished via the probability field $(\Omega, \mathfrak{F}, P)$, where Ω is the space of all real functions, $\mathfrak{F}$ is a Borel field of sets generated in the usual way from the elementary events S in the space, and P is a probability measure defined on $\mathfrak{F}$. Any function $X(\omega, \xi) \in \Omega$ is called, for fixed ω, a *realization*, or sample function of the process, and is often written simply $X(\xi)$. However, the argument ω will often be omitted from the process itself in the sequel if the meaning is clear from the context. For any finite set $\xi_1, \cdots, \xi_n$ of parameter values of the process $\{X(\omega, \xi), \xi \in R\}$, the corresponding multivariate distribution F_n of the random variables $X(\omega, \xi_1), \cdots, X(\omega, \xi_n)$ is called a *finite-dimensional* distribution of the process and plays a fundamental role in the definition of a stochastic process after Kolmogoroff. According to Kolmogoroff's fundamental theorem [**8**; **9**], if the F_n satisfy the *consistency relations*

$$F_m(X(\omega, \xi_1), \cdots, X(\omega, \xi_m)) = F_n(X(\omega, \xi_1), \cdots, X(\omega, \xi_m), \infty, \cdots, \infty)$$
$$(m < n, \quad -\infty < \xi_i < \infty),$$

then the family $\{F_n\}$ of distribution functions uniquely determines the probabilities $P(S)$ of all events $S \in \mathfrak{F}$, and conversely any system $\{F_n\}$ of distribution functions defines a probability field $(\Omega, \mathfrak{F}, P)$, provided the distribution functions satisfy the consistency relations.

Kolmogoroff's theorem makes possible a mathematically rigorous treatment of stochastic processes, but, due to the complexity of the calculations involved in the general multivariate distribution, is not of much use in practice. If the structure of the process is of first interest, e.g., its continuity or measurability or that it satisfies a certain functional equation, then the process is best analyzed either as an abstract function by imbedding it in a suitable Banach space or else in terms of a spectral representation. The class of second order, or *regular*, functions that we have encountered above is such as to admit spectral representations, and in view of the suitability of regular functions for random analysis, this class of functions seems particularly well suited to our purposes. We shall therefore adopt this approach in the sequel except where explicitly stated to the contrary.

A general form of the spectral theorem for regular processes has been given by Blanc-Lapierre and Fortet **[10]**. This asserts the existence of the following spectral representation for the (not necessarily stationary) stochastic process $X(\boldsymbol{\xi})$:

$$X(\boldsymbol{\xi}) = \int_{R_3} e^{i\boldsymbol{\xi}\cdot\boldsymbol{\eta}}\, dZ(\boldsymbol{\eta}),$$

where $Z(\boldsymbol{\eta})$ is a stochastic process in $\boldsymbol{\eta}$-space such that the covariance has the representation

$$\operatorname{cov}\,[X(\boldsymbol{\xi}), X(\boldsymbol{\xi}')] = \int_{R_3\times R_3} e^{i(\boldsymbol{\xi}\cdot\boldsymbol{\eta}-\boldsymbol{\xi}'\cdot\boldsymbol{\eta}')}\, d^2\Sigma(\boldsymbol{\eta}, \boldsymbol{\eta}'),$$

and

$$d^2\Sigma(\boldsymbol{\eta}, \boldsymbol{\eta}') = E\{dZ(\boldsymbol{\eta})\, dZ^*(\boldsymbol{\eta}')\}$$

is such as to be absolutely integrable over all of $(\boldsymbol{\eta}, \boldsymbol{\eta}')$-space. These conditions require that the covariance function be uniformly bounded and continuous over the product space $R_3 \times R_3$, which in turn implies that $X(\boldsymbol{\xi})$ is continuous in mean square in the whole space.

For stationary second order processes, the spectral representation is somewhat more straightforward, and we have that

$$Y(\boldsymbol{\xi}) = \int_{R_3} e^{i\boldsymbol{\xi}\cdot\boldsymbol{\eta}}\, d\Pi(\boldsymbol{\eta})$$

where $\Pi(\boldsymbol{\eta})$ is a stochastic process with orthogonal increments.

Further, apart possibly from a set of realizations of probability zero, the $\Pi(\boldsymbol{\eta})$ process is determined *uniquely* **[9]** in terms of the $Y(\boldsymbol{\xi})$ process by the equation

$$\tfrac{1}{2}[\Pi(\boldsymbol{\eta}_2+) + \Pi(\boldsymbol{\eta}_2-)] - \tfrac{1}{2}[\Pi(\boldsymbol{\eta}_1+) + \Pi(\boldsymbol{\eta}_1-)]$$

$$= (2\pi)^{-3} \underset{A\to\infty}{\text{l.i.m.}} \iiint_{-A}^{A} \prod_{j=1}^{3} \frac{e^{-i\eta_{2j}\xi_j} - e^{-i\eta_{1j}\xi_j}}{-i\xi_j}\, Y(\boldsymbol{\xi})\, d\boldsymbol{\xi}$$

where η_1 and η_2 range over all of $(\eta_1 \times \eta_2)$-space. This gives us a uniqueness theorem (up to a set of measure zero) for what are essentially Fourier transforms of second order stationary random functions.

Silverman [11] has drawn a distinction between what he calls a globally stationary process, meaning one which is stationary in the wide sense over the whole space, and locally stationary processes, which he defines as follows: A centered random process $X(\omega, \xi)$, defined for all real ξ, is said to be locally stationary (wide sense) if its covariance $\Gamma(\xi_1, \xi_2) = E\{X(\omega, \xi_1)X^*(\omega, \xi_2)\}$ can be put in the form

$$\Gamma(\xi_1, \xi_2) = \Gamma_1(\tfrac{1}{2}(\xi_1 + \xi_2))\Gamma_2(\xi_1 - \xi_2),$$

where Γ_1 is a non-negative function and Γ_2 is a stationary covariance function. Γ_1 describes the global structure of $X(\xi)$, i.e., its behavior over the whole real line, while Γ_2, which is invariant under translation, can be thought of as describing its local behavior. The Fourier transform of $\Gamma(\xi_1, \xi_2)$, i.e., the corresponding two-dimensional spectral density, is factorable into a non-negative function and the Fourier transform of a non-negative function. The harmonic analysis of locally stationary random processes appears more suited to physical problems than that for globally stationary processes, since the Fourier transform of the latter will not exist in general except as a stochastic integral. The Fourier transform of a locally stationary process can also be interpreted as an ensemble of integrals over distinct realizations. For globally stationary processes the variance $\Gamma(\xi, \xi)$ is a positive constant and the Fourier transform over the whole line of the sample function $X(\omega_0, \xi)$ will therefore fail to exist, with probability one. Locally stationary processes will probably prove to be of considerable significance in physical applications since their use removes the unphysical assumption that, with probability one, the sample functions (realizations) possess infinite energy. Locally stationary processes (though not under this name) have recently been studied in connection with spectral estimation for turbulence theory by Kampé de Fériet and Frenkiel [12], and this type of process certainly deserves further investigation.

The following table of covariance functions and associated spectra is taken from Wheelon [13]:

TABLE I

Covariance Function	Spectral Density
$\exp\{-\rho/\rho_0\}$	$8\pi \dfrac{E\{X^2\}\rho_0^3}{[1 + k^2\rho_0^2]^2}$
$\exp\{-\rho^2/\rho_0^2\}$	$\pi^{3/2}E\{X^2\}\rho_0^3 \exp\{-1/4\, k^2\rho_0^2\}$
$(\rho/\rho_0)K_1(\rho/\rho_0)$	$6\pi^2 \dfrac{E\{X^2\}\rho_0^3}{[1 + k^2\rho_0^2]^{5/2}}$
$[1 + (\rho/\rho_0)^2]^{-2}$	$\pi^2 E\{X^2\}\rho_0^3 \exp\{-k\rho_0\}.$

These are the covariance functions that have been assumed in theoretical analyses of turbulent scattering of electromagnetic waves. They have no basis in any physical theory of turbulence,[2] but do aid materially in evaluating the integrals that arise (each one is a well-known kernel). The question of the proper covariance function for an atmospheric refractive index subject to turbulent fluctuations is an important problem that still remains open.

Bugnolo [**14**] has given a heuristic discussion of the question of stationarity when the refractive index of the medium constitutes a stochastic process in space and time. He concludes that, in the application to turbulent scattering in the troposphere at least, the refractive index process must be nonstationary, and therefore proposes a redefinition of the expected value of the process that would be consistent with the result for a deterministic inhomogeneous medium.

4. **Ergodicity.** Ergodic properties refer to those features of a stochastic process which are equivalent under either of the operations: mathematical expectation or sample average. Thus ergodic theorems consitute the basis for statistical estimation and inference, for in any given practical situation we observe only realizations, and the ergodic property constitutes the bridge connecting theory and experiment. The principal area in which the development of ergodic theory has taken place is that of statistical mechanics. There the statement of ergodic theorems generally involves the shift operator and the trajectories in phase space. The situation is somewhat different with respect to the reduced wave equation, which represents a different type of flow.

An *invariant set* is a measurable set E such that $TE = E$; an *invariant function*, a measurable function such that $f(x) = f(T_\xi x)$ almost everywhere in Ω. The transformation T_ξ is said to be metrically transitive if the only invariant sets are the null set and the whole space Ω (in the case of functions, if the only functions invariant with probability one are constants). In statistical mechanics metric transitivity means that with probability one a trajectory covers almost all of Ω. For stationary stochastic processes metric transitivity is entirely equivalent to the ergodic property, and may be expressed by the Birkhoff–Khintchine theorem: For a measurable, stationary, metrically transitive, continuous parameter process $\{X(\omega, t)\}$, $-\infty < t < \infty$, with finite expectation,

$$EX = \lim_{T\to\infty} \frac{1}{2T} \int_{-T}^{T} X(t)\, dt$$

with probability 1. That a stationary process is not necessarily ergodic is shown by the discrete-parameter process

$$X_t = a\varepsilon + Y_t, \qquad -\infty < t < \infty$$

[2] And some could only correspond to a Brownian motion, not to a turbulent motion in a continuous medium.

where a is a nonrandom constant, the Y_t are independent and equidistributed and are further independent of the random variable ε. (In this example $n^{-1}\sum_1^n \rho_\nu = a^2/(1 + a^2) \neq 0$ as $n \to \infty$, which violates a n. a. s. c. for ergodicity.) This limiting condition on the correlation function is equivalent to the requirement that there be no line of frequency zero in the spectrum of the process, or alternatively that the spectrum of the process be continuous at $\omega = 0$.

Though ergodicity has received considerable investigation over the past few years [**7**; **15**], usable criteria for ergodic properties are still somewhat limited in scope. A particularly useful result, but one which applies only to Gaussian processes, is due to G. Maruyama [**16**]. It states that a Gaussian process is ergodic if and only if its spectral function is continuous. This theorem has been applied by Kampé de Fériet [**1**] to the important case of random solutions of $u_{tt} = c^2 u_{xx}$ in a homogeneous medium.

The ergodic properties of wave propagation through a random time-varying medium has been investigated by T. J. Skinner [**17**], who showed that for the solution of (1.1) the time-varying medium can be replaced by a time independent probability space provided that on the boundary of the time-varying medium the scalar field $u(\mathbf{x}, t) = A(\mathbf{x}, t) \exp \{i\phi(\mathbf{x}, t) + i\omega t\}$ has the properties:

(i) $A(\mathbf{x}, t)$ and $\phi(\mathbf{x}, t)$ are ergodic;

(ii) the absolute value of any frequency component of either $A(\mathbf{x}, t) \sin \phi(\mathbf{x}, t)$ or $A(\mathbf{x}, t) \cos \phi(\mathbf{x}, t)$ is less than $\omega/(2\pi)$, the mean frequency of the source; and

(iii) $u(\mathbf{x}, t)$ is quasi-monochromatic.

5. **The radiation problem for an unbounded random medium.** After this prefatory material on the probabilistic aspects of the problem we come now to the particular functional equations involved. Keller [**18**] has formulated the radiation problem corresponding to equation (1.1) as follows:

$$(5.1)\qquad \begin{cases} \Delta U + k_0^2 n^2(\mathbf{x}) U(\mathbf{x}) = -4\pi\delta(\mathbf{x}) \\ \lim\limits_{|\mathbf{x}|\to\infty} |\mathbf{x}| \left(\dfrac{\partial U}{\partial |\mathbf{x}|} + ik_0 n(\mathbf{x}) U \right) = 0 \end{cases}$$

where k_0 is the free-space wave number and $k^2(\mathbf{x}) = k_0^2 n^2(\mathbf{x})$, $n(\mathbf{x})$ being an as yet unspecified random function of position $\mathbf{x}$. The second of equations (5.1) is the Sommerfeld radiation condition which guarantees that the waves from the unit source $\delta(\mathbf{x})$ at the origin will be outgoing at infinity.

One can proceed in several different directions from the general problem (5.1). As mentioned in the introduction, the following approaches have been considered: (i) perturbation theory [**18**; **19**]; (ii) transformation to an equivalent spatial Riccati equation via the so-called Rytov transformation [**20**; **21**]; (iii) the integral equation formulation [**19**; **21**; **22**]; and (iv) what is in fact a special case of (i) or (iii), the Born approximation [**13**; **23**]. The simplification resulting from taking the reduced wave equation to be one-dimensional

$$(5.2)\qquad Y'' + k^2(x) Y(x) = 0,$$

i.e., the transmission line equation, has also received considerable attention [**24**; **25**]. One can also more or less bypass equations (5.1) in the form given and instead adopt what is essentially a transport equation approach, e.g., ray-tracing [**18**; **20**; **26**; **27**; **28**]; invariant imbedding [**29**]; and diffusion of the electromagnetic field by multiple scattering [**30**]. In the transport context attention is directed not so much at the field quantity itself but at some function associated with it, e.g., spectral-density, ray paths, transition probabilities, or the like [**31**; **32**; **33**]. In other connections, notably quantum field theory, still other approaches have been adopted, in particular integration in functional spaces (the so-called Wiener integrals) [**34**; **35**; **36**], and these techniques, properly generalized appear to have promise for problem (5.1). A start in a similar direction has been made by Kraichnan [**37**].

6. **Perturbation theory.** If the refractive index of the medium exhibits only small departures from its equilibrium value, then a perturbation expansion in terms of a small parameter ε may be adopted:

$$n(\mathbf{x}) = 1 + \sum_{1}^{\infty} \nu_m(\mathbf{x})\varepsilon^m, \qquad \varepsilon \ll 1. \tag{6.1}$$

If the field variable also has a perturbation expansion

$$U = \sum_{0}^{\infty} U_m(\mathbf{x})\varepsilon^m, \qquad \varepsilon \ll 1 \tag{6.2}$$

then (5.1) gives rise to the following ascending hierarchy of radiation problems (in powers of ε):

$$\begin{cases} \Delta U_0 + k_0^2 U_0 = -4\pi\delta(\mathbf{x}), \\ \lim\limits_{|\mathbf{x}|\to\infty} |\mathbf{x}| \left(\dfrac{\partial U_0}{\partial|\mathbf{x}|} + ik_0 U_0\right) = 0, \end{cases} \tag{6.3}$$

$$\begin{cases} \Delta U_1 + k_0^2 U_1 = -2k_0^2 \nu_1 U_0(\mathbf{x}), \\ \lim\limits_{|\mathbf{x}|\to\infty} |\mathbf{x}| \left(\dfrac{\partial U_1}{\partial|\mathbf{x}|} + ik_0 U_1 + 2ik_0\nu_1 U_0\right) = 0, \end{cases} \tag{6.4}$$

$$\vdots \qquad\qquad \vdots$$

$$\begin{cases} \Delta U_p + k_0^2 U_p = -k_0^2 \sum\limits_{q=1}^{p} U_{p-q} \sum\limits_{m=0}^{q} \nu_{q-m}\nu_m, \\ \lim\limits_{|\mathbf{x}|\to\infty} |\mathbf{x}| \left(\dfrac{\partial U_p}{\partial|\mathbf{x}|} + ik_0 U_p + ik_0 \sum\limits_{m=0}^{p-1} \nu_{p-m} U_m\right) = 0. \end{cases} \tag{6.5}$$

The solution of (6.3) is given by the well-known expression for an outgoing spherical wave

$$U_0(\mathbf{x}) = \frac{e^{-ik_0|\mathbf{x}|}}{|\mathbf{x}|}. \tag{6.6}$$

Then Green's theorem yields the solution of (6.4) immediately in the form

$$U_1(\mathbf{x}) = 2k_0^2 \int_{R_3} \frac{e^{-ik_0|\mathbf{x}-\mathbf{x}'|}}{|\mathbf{x}-\mathbf{x}'|} \nu_1(\mathbf{x}')U_0(\mathbf{x}')\, d\mathbf{x}' \tag{6.7}$$

and in general

$$U_p(\mathbf{x}) = k_0^2 \int_{R_3} \frac{e^{-ik_0|\mathbf{x}-\mathbf{x}'|}}{|\mathbf{x}-\mathbf{x}'|} \sum_{q=1}^{p} \left(\sum_{m=0}^{q} \nu_{q-m}(\mathbf{x}')\nu_m(\mathbf{x}') \right) U_{p-q}(\mathbf{x}')\, d\mathbf{x}'. \tag{6.8}$$

(In particular, for $p = 2$,

$$U_2(\mathbf{x}) = k_0^2 \int_{R_3} \frac{e^{-ik_0|\mathbf{x}-\mathbf{x}'|}}{|\mathbf{x}-\mathbf{x}'|} ([\nu_1^2 + 2\nu_2]U_0(\mathbf{x}') + 2\nu_1(\mathbf{x}')U_1(\mathbf{x}'))\, d\mathbf{x}'.) \tag{6.9}$$

Each of the above integral formulas is to be understood in the mean square sense, as is also the convergence of the perturbation series (6.2). We recognize in formula (6.7) the so-called Born approximation to the solution of (5.1). This formula has served as the basis for nearly all the past work on turbulent scattering [**13**]. A good summary of the mathematical rationale of this approach may be found in [**18**]. The formulas (6.7)–(6.9) have proved particularly useful in determining the moments of $U(\mathbf{x})$. Keller's principal result is that to terms $O(\varepsilon^2)$ the mean value of the field quantity U propagates as if it traveled through an "effective" medium with complex refractive index

$$n_{\text{eff.}} = \left\{ 1 + \varepsilon^2 \left(1 - 2ik_0 \int_0^\infty [e^{2ik_0 r} - 1]\Gamma(r)\, dr \right) \right\}^{1/2}.$$

A similar conclusion has also been obtained by Ament [**19**].

7. **Born approximation.** The first approximation in the iteration-perturbation solution of the scattering integral equation is called the Born approximation. In the electromagnetic case the Born approximation expresses the total field $\mathbf{E}(\mathbf{x})$ (incident plus scattered) in terms of the unperturbed incident field $\mathbf{E}_0(\mathbf{x})$ as follows [**13**]:

$$\mathbf{E}(\mathbf{x}) = \mathbf{E}_0(\mathbf{x}) - k_0^2 \int d^3\mathbf{x}' G_0(\mathbf{x}, \mathbf{x}')\Delta\varepsilon(\mathbf{x}'; t)\mathbf{E}_0(\mathbf{x}') \sin \mathsf{X} \tag{7.1}$$

where V is the randomly inhomogeneous volume comprised in the intersection of transmitter and receiver beams, X is the angle between $\mathbf{E}_0$ and the Poynting vector of the scattered wave, and $\Delta\varepsilon$ is the random residual for the "dielectric constant," or permittivity. Equation (7.1) or the equivalent mean square power equation

$$\mathbf{P}_{\text{rec.}} = A_r E\{|\mathbf{E}_{sc}|^2\} = P_t(\pi/\lambda_0)^2 \int\int_{V\times V} \frac{e^{-i(k_0-k_1)(|\mathbf{x}-\mathbf{x}'|-|\mathbf{x}-\mathbf{x}''|)}}{|\mathbf{x}-\mathbf{x}'|^2|\mathbf{x}-\mathbf{x}''|^2}\sqrt{G_r G_t G_r' G_t'} \cdot \Gamma_{\Delta\varepsilon}(\mathbf{x}'-\mathbf{x}'')\, d\mathbf{x}'\, d\mathbf{x}'' \tag{7.2}$$

where A_r is the capture cross-section of the receiving antenna, $\mathbf{E}_{sc} \equiv \mathbf{E} - \mathbf{E}_0$, $\mathbf{P}_t$ is the transmitted power, with associated gain function $G_t(\theta, \varphi)$, V the common volume of the two beams, $\mathbf{k}_1$ is the propagation vector of the transmitted wave, and $G_r(\theta, \varphi)$ is the gain function of the receiving antenna. The polarization factors involving sin X have been dropped. In the far-zone approximation (7.2) becomes

$$\mathbf{P}_{\text{rec.}} = \mathbf{P}_t(\pi/\lambda_0)^2 \int_V \frac{G_r G_t}{|\mathbf{x}-\mathbf{x}'|^2|\mathbf{x}-\mathbf{x}''|^2} \int_V e^{i(\mathbf{k}_1-\mathbf{k}_2)\cdot\boldsymbol{\rho}}\,\Gamma_{\Delta\varepsilon}(\boldsymbol{\rho})\, d\boldsymbol{\rho}\, d\mathbf{r} \tag{7.3}$$

where

$$\boldsymbol{\rho} = \mathbf{x}' - \mathbf{x}'', \qquad \mathbf{r} = \mathbf{x}' + \mathbf{x}''.$$

Equation (7.3) has provided the basis for nearly all theoretical analyses of "forward scatter" of radio waves in a turbulent atmosphere. We note that it is subject to the following hypotheses: (i) multiple scattering can be neglected, (ii) the scattering is isotropic, and (iii) the random variations of the permittivity are small and slowly varying in time. The first and second hypotheses appear somewhat unrealistic when applied to the terrestrial atmosphere and the third can apply only in a "cool" medium wherein particle energies are low (for example, stellar atmospheres are excluded, as are also "hot" plasmas in general). Attempts to remove the restriction to single-scattering phenomena have been made by Wheelon **[13]**, who introduced the second approximation to the iteration-perturbation solution, and by Ament, who employed ray-tracing between successive scatterers **[26]**, Bremmer, who based his analysis on diffusion of the joint probability density for position and direction of a unit of radiation energy **[30]**, and Bugnolo, who considered diffusion of the spectral density function of an electromagnetic field under multiple scattering **[31]**. The latter approaches will receive further discussion below under the head of transport equations.

Generalization of (7.2) to the case where the refractive index is anisotropic (as, e.g., when the scale of turbulence is different in the horizontal and vertical directions) has been carried out by Staras **[38]** and Booker **[39]**. The covariance function is simply assumed to be of the form

$$\Gamma(\mathbf{x} - \mathbf{x}') = \Gamma\left(\frac{x - x'}{l_0}, \frac{y - y'}{l_0}, \frac{z - z'}{l_v}\right), \tag{7.4}$$

and its introduction into (7.2) makes the problem anisotropic. It presently appears that partial reflections from flattened atmospheric cells ("platelets" or "feuillets") constitute the most tenable explanation of tropospheric "forward scatter" phenomena, and the distinction between the "feuillet" approach and that embodied in (7.4) is worthy of note. In the former it is not scattering from turbulence but rather partial reflections from stable horizontal laminae having gradients of refractive index that are large relative to the turbulent medium in which they are imbedded that give rise to "forward scatter." In principle the anisotropic scattering theory could be extended to take account of "feuillet" phenomena, but such a generalization is lacking at present. The "feuillet" approach has received considerable attention, starting with the pioneering work of Friis, Crawford and Hogg [**40**]. The interested reader is referred to the report by Bremmer [**30**] for an excellent description of the investigations in this field.

Other work on scattering by an anisotropic randomly inhomogeneous medium has been carried out by Bowhill [**41**; **42**] and Yeh [**43**]. Bowhill considered the case of a medium with stationary Gaussian inhomogeneities having different scales along three space axes and the effect this would work upon the usual model of a succession of equivalent diffracting screens. He attempted to employ for this purpose the theory of emergent angular power spectrum but found that the diffractive phase shifts as the wave passed from one inhomogeneity to a neighboring, correlated one rendered such an approach invalid. However, spatial spectra and correlation functions for the emergent wave were determined for anisotropic "random shallow phase screens" for both vertical and oblique incidence.

Yeh's analysis [**43**], based upon Karavainikov's perturbation theory for a spherical wave in an inhomogeneous medium,[3] prescribes the phase and amplitude fluctuations of a spherical wave propagating through a medium containing anisotropic (elongated) inhomogeneities. The medium is assumed to have a refractive index whose correlation function is ellipsoidally symmetric and of Gaussian form in the arguments. Yeh thus obtains first order approximations to the covariance functions for phase fluctuations and logarithmic amplitude.

8. **Formulation as a random integral equation.** Let us consider instead of (5.1) the corresponding radiation problem for the inhomogeneous reduced wave equation

$$\begin{cases} \Delta V(\mathbf{x}) + k_0^2 n^2(\mathbf{x}) V(\mathbf{x}) = -f(\mathbf{x}), \\ \lim_{|\mathbf{x}|\to\infty} |\mathbf{x}| \left(\dfrac{\partial V}{\partial |\mathbf{x}|} + i k_0 V(\mathbf{x}) \right) = 0. \end{cases} \tag{8.1}$$

The forcing function $f(\mathbf{x})$, arising perhaps from a current distribution or acoustic pressure, is assumed to vanish everywhere outside some finite region of space, and the form of the radiation condition in (8.1) requires that $n(\mathbf{x}) \to 1$ as $|\mathbf{x}| \to \infty$. Green's theorem applied to the pair of functions $V(\mathbf{x})$ and the free-space Green's function $G_0(\mathbf{x}, \mathbf{x}') = \exp\{-ik_0|\mathbf{x} - \mathbf{x}'|\}/|\mathbf{x} - \mathbf{x}'|$ yields the integral equation

$$V(\mathbf{x}) - \Lambda_0 \int_{R_3} G_0(\mathbf{x}, \mathbf{x}') \nu(\mathbf{x}') V(\mathbf{x}')\, d\mathbf{x}' = F(\mathbf{x}) \tag{8.2}$$

[3] Very similar in approach to Rytov's method leading to equations (9.19).

where

$$F(\mathbf{x}) = \frac{1}{4\pi}\int G_0(\mathbf{x}, \mathbf{x}')f(\mathbf{x}')\, d\mathbf{x}', \tag{8.3}$$

$$\nu(\mathbf{x}) = n^2(\mathbf{x}) - 1, \tag{8.4}$$

$$\Lambda_0 = k_0^2/(4\pi).$$

It is clear from (8.2)–(8.4) that $V(\mathbf{x})$ is given by the usual integral formula over the region where $n(\mathbf{x}) = 1$. Let D denote the region where $\nu(\mathbf{x})$ is different from zero (the compact support of ν). In view of the radiation condition, D must be finite.[4] Consider then the integral equation for $\mathbf{x}, \mathbf{x}' \in D$:

$$V(\mathbf{x}) - \Lambda_0\int_D G_0(\mathbf{x}, \mathbf{x}')\nu(\mathbf{x}')V(\mathbf{x}')\, d\mathbf{x}' = F(\mathbf{x}). \tag{8.5}$$

Equation (8.5) differs from a standard Fredholm integral in two respects: (i) in general the kernel $G_0(\mathbf{x}, \mathbf{x}')\nu(\mathbf{x}')$ is not in L_2, and (ii) $\nu(\mathbf{x})$ and $V(\mathbf{x})$ are random functions. Provided $\nu(\mathbf{x})$ is uniformly bounded with probability 1 in D (a not unrealistic hypothesis), the first difficulty can be removed in the usual way via introduction of the iterated kernel:[5]

$$K_2(\mathbf{x}, \mathbf{x}'') = \int_D G_0(\mathbf{x}, \mathbf{x}')\nu(\mathbf{x}')G_0(\mathbf{x}', \mathbf{x}'')\nu(\mathbf{x}'')\, d\mathbf{x}'. \tag{8.6}$$

Thus the following integral equation is nonsingular with probability 1 and is equivalent to (8.5):

$$V(x) - \Lambda_0^2\int_D K_2(\mathbf{x}, \mathbf{x}')V(\mathbf{x}')\, d\mathbf{x}' = H(\mathbf{x}), \tag{8.7}$$

where

$$H(\mathbf{x}) = F(\mathbf{x}) + \Lambda_0\int_D G_0(\mathbf{x}, \mathbf{x}')\nu(\mathbf{x}')F(\mathbf{x}')\, d\mathbf{x}'. \tag{8.8}$$

---

[4] However, so large that the radiation condition permits one to neglect the surface integral that would otherwise appear in (8.5). This assumes that $\nu(\mathbf{x})$ decreases smoothly near the boundary of D.

[5] Since $\Pr\{|\nu(\mathbf{x})| < m;\ \mathbf{x} \in D\} = 1$, we have with probability 1 that

$$\int_{D\times D} |G_0(\mathbf{x}, \mathbf{x}')\nu(\mathbf{x}')G_0(\mathbf{x}', \mathbf{x}'')\nu(\mathbf{x}'')V(\mathbf{x}'')|\, d\mathbf{x}'\, d\mathbf{x}'' \leqq m^2\int_{D\times D} |G_0(\mathbf{x}, \mathbf{x}')G_0(\mathbf{x}', \mathbf{x}'')V(\mathbf{x}'')|\, d\mathbf{x}'\, d\mathbf{x}''.$$

Now $\Pr\{|V| > \eta\} \leqq \eta^{-2}E|V|^2$, and since V is regular in D by hypothesis, $\Pr\{|V| > \eta\}$ can be made arbitrarily small by taking η large enough. Therefore almost everywhere in D, with probability 1,

$$\int_{D\times D} |G_0(\mathbf{x}, \mathbf{x}')\nu(\mathbf{x}')G_0(\mathbf{x}', \mathbf{x}'')\nu(\mathbf{x}'')V(\mathbf{x}'')|\, d\mathbf{x}'\, d\mathbf{x}'' \leqq m^2V_0\int_{D\times D} |G_0(\mathbf{x}, \mathbf{x}')G_0(\mathbf{x}', \mathbf{x}'')|\, d\mathbf{x}'\, d\mathbf{x}''.$$

The integral on the right with respect to $d\mathbf{x}'$ is known to be in L_2. Therefore the original integrand is absolutely integrable with probability 1, and Fubini's theorem permits the inversion of integration leading to (8.6) almost everywhere in the probability space.

The probabilistic features of regularity (second order random functions) and boundedness with probability 1 enter strongly in the above argument. These hypotheses in essence enable us to refer the problem to the corresponding deterministic one. The kernel in (8.7) is not symmetric as it stands, but can easily be made so by multiplying (8.7) through by $\sqrt{\nu(\mathbf{x})}$ and introducing the new functions

$$W(\mathbf{x}) = \sqrt{\nu(\mathbf{x})}V(\mathbf{x}), \qquad L(\mathbf{x}) = \sqrt{\nu(\mathbf{x})}H(\mathbf{x}) \tag{8.9}$$

and new kernel

$$K(\mathbf{x}, \mathbf{x}') = \sqrt{\nu(\mathbf{x})}K_2(\mathbf{x}, \mathbf{x}')\sqrt{\nu(\mathbf{x}')}. \tag{8.10}$$

The Fredholm theory applies in any case,[6] and a regular solution can be determined by the usual techniques for Fredholm equations.

For the case that the refractive index constitutes a Gaussian random process, and so will be unbounded, Hoffman **[21]** has shown that (8.1) is solved by the mean square convergent Neumann series

$$V(\mathbf{x}) = F(\mathbf{x}) + \sum_{m=1}^{\infty} \Lambda_0^m \int_D d\mathbf{x}_1 G_0(\mathbf{x}, \mathbf{x}_1)\nu(\mathbf{x}_1) \int_D d\mathbf{x}_2 \cdots \int_D G_0(\mathbf{x}_{m-1}, \mathbf{x}_m)\nu(\mathbf{x}_m)F(\mathbf{x}_m)\, d\mathbf{x}_m$$

provided (i) the Neumann series solution for the corresponding deterministic equation

$$V(\mathbf{x}) = F(\mathbf{x}) + \Lambda_0 \int_D G_0(\mathbf{x}, \mathbf{x}')V(\mathbf{x}')\, d\mathbf{x}'$$

converges in the ordinary way; and (ii)

$$|\Lambda_0 \sqrt{\operatorname{var} \nu}\, B| < 1.$$

where

$$\left| \int_D G_0(\mathbf{x}, \mathbf{x}')F(\mathbf{x}')\, d\mathbf{x}' \right|^2 < B.$$

9. **Equivalent spatial Riccati equation.** The so-called Rytov transformation **[20]**

$$U(\mathbf{x}) = A_0 \exp\{-ik_0\psi(\mathbf{x})\} \tag{9.1}$$

takes (1.1) into the nonlinear differential equation

$$(\nabla\psi)^2 + \frac{i}{k_0}\nabla^2\psi = n^2(\mathbf{x}), \tag{9.2}$$

where

$$\psi(\mathbf{x}) = S(\mathbf{x}) + \frac{i}{k_0}\ln[A(\mathbf{x})/A_0], \tag{9.3}$$

$A(\mathbf{x})$ and $S(\mathbf{x})$ being the "amplitude" and "phase" associated with representation of $U(\mathbf{x})$ as

$$U(\mathbf{x}) = A(\mathbf{x}) \exp\{-ik_0 S(\mathbf{x})\}. \tag{9.4}$$

[6] Although the Hilbert–Schmidt theory may not, since the kernel is not necessarily definite.

The following approach is suggested by an analysis of Burgers [**44**] for the one-dimensional case. Let

$$\boldsymbol{\Theta} = \nabla \psi. \tag{9.5}$$

Equation (9.2) then becomes the three-dimensional analogue of the Riccati equation:

$$\nabla \cdot \boldsymbol{\Theta} - ik_0\Theta^2 = -ik_0 n^2(\mathbf{x}). \tag{9.6}$$

If we now introduce the asymptotic expansions

$$n^2(\mathbf{x}) = En^2(\mathbf{x}) + \sum_1^\infty \nu_m(\mathbf{x})\varepsilon^m,$$

and

$$\boldsymbol{\Theta}(\mathbf{x}) \sim \sum_{m=0}^\infty \boldsymbol{\Theta}_m(\mathbf{x})\varepsilon^m,$$

the following system of equations results

$$\begin{cases} \dfrac{i}{k_0}\nabla \cdot \boldsymbol{\Theta}_0 + \Theta_0^2 = En^2(\mathbf{x}), \\ \dfrac{i}{k_0}\nabla \cdot \boldsymbol{\Theta}_m + \sum_{p=0}^m \boldsymbol{\Theta}_p \cdot \boldsymbol{\Theta}_{m-p} = \nu_m(\mathbf{x}) \qquad (m = 1, 2, \cdots). \end{cases} \tag{9.7}$$

Provided $\nabla\psi_0 = \boldsymbol{\Theta}_0$, which corresponds to the case of a refractive index whose deterministic component is everywhere constant, we may introduce the spectral representations

$$\nu_1(\mathbf{x}) = \int_{R_3} e^{i\boldsymbol{\alpha}\cdot\mathbf{x}}\, d\eta_1(\boldsymbol{\alpha}) \quad \text{and} \quad \boldsymbol{\Theta}_1(\mathbf{x}) = \int_{R_3} e^{i\boldsymbol{\alpha}\cdot\mathbf{x}}\boldsymbol{\gamma}_1(\boldsymbol{\alpha})\, d\xi_1(\boldsymbol{\alpha}),$$

where $\eta_1(\boldsymbol{\alpha})$ and $\xi_1(\boldsymbol{\alpha})$ are processes with orthogonal increments and $\boldsymbol{\gamma}_1(\boldsymbol{\alpha})$ is a sure vector function of $\boldsymbol{\alpha}$. The Fourier transform of (9.7) with $m = 1$ then yields the following relation [**21**] connecting the spectral density functions of the refractive index and gradient of generalized phase function $\boldsymbol{\Theta}$:

$$d\xi_1(\boldsymbol{\alpha}) = k_0 \frac{d\eta_1(\boldsymbol{\alpha})}{2k_0\boldsymbol{\Theta}_0 \cdot \boldsymbol{\gamma}_1(\boldsymbol{\alpha}) - \boldsymbol{\alpha}\cdot\boldsymbol{\gamma}_1(\boldsymbol{\alpha})}. \tag{9.8}$$

The covariance function of $\boldsymbol{\Theta}_1$ is then given by the following formula, provided the Fourier transform exists:

$$\Gamma_1(\mathbf{x} - \mathbf{x}') = k_0^2 \int_{R_3(\boldsymbol{\alpha})} e^{i(\mathbf{x}-\mathbf{x}')\cdot\boldsymbol{\alpha}} \frac{d\sigma_1(\boldsymbol{\alpha})}{[2k_0\boldsymbol{\Theta}_0 \cdot \boldsymbol{\gamma}_1(\boldsymbol{\alpha}) - \boldsymbol{\alpha}\cdot\boldsymbol{\gamma}_1(\boldsymbol{\alpha})]^2} \tag{9.9}$$

where

$$d\sigma_1(\boldsymbol{\alpha}) = E\{d\eta_1(\boldsymbol{\alpha})\, d\eta_1^*(\boldsymbol{\alpha}')\}.$$

For nonconstant $\nabla\psi_0$, a similar approach [21] leads to the following integral equation connecting the respective spectral density functions

$$(\boldsymbol{\alpha}\cdot\boldsymbol{\alpha})d\xi(\boldsymbol{\alpha}) = k_0^2\int_{R_3(\beta)}\{m(\boldsymbol{\alpha}-\boldsymbol{\beta}) + d\eta(\boldsymbol{\alpha}-\boldsymbol{\beta})\}\,d\xi(\boldsymbol{\beta}), \tag{9.10}$$

where $m(\boldsymbol{\alpha})$ is the Fourier transform of $En^2(\mathbf{x})$.

The above approach has the virtue of making full use of the probabilistic structure of the process but perhaps falls short in terms of analytical results. Following Rytov [20], we introduce the deviation $\Psi = \psi - \psi_0$ of the solution of (9.2) from that of the deterministic equation (first of (9.7)), and obtain the differential equation

$$\nabla(\Psi + 2\psi_0)\cdot\nabla\Psi + \frac{i}{k_0}\Delta\Psi = \nu(\mathbf{x}) \equiv n^2(\mathbf{x}) - En^2(\mathbf{x}). \tag{9.11}$$

Provided

$$E|\nabla\Psi|^2 \ll 4, \qquad En^2 = 1, \qquad \psi_0 = x, \tag{9.12}$$

(9.11) reduces to

$$2\frac{\partial\Psi}{\partial x} + \frac{i}{k_0}\Delta\Psi = \nu(\mathbf{x}). \tag{9.13}$$

These conditions correspond physically to a weakly inhomogeneous medium. If now (9.13) has a solution of the form

$$\Psi(\mathbf{x}) = e^{+ik_0x}w(\mathbf{x}), \tag{9.14}$$

then w will satisfy the differential equation

$$\Delta_3 w + k_0^2 w = -ik_0\,e^{-ik_0x}\nu(\mathbf{x}) = -4\pi f(\mathbf{x}). \tag{9.15}$$

Equation (9.14) has the well-known solution

$$w(\mathbf{x}) = \int_{R_3}\frac{e^{-ik_0|\mathbf{x}-\mathbf{x}'|}}{|\mathbf{x}-\mathbf{x}'|}f(\mathbf{x}')\,d\mathbf{x}', \tag{9.16}$$

which, expressed in terms of Ψ, reads as follows

$$\Psi(\mathbf{x}) = \frac{i}{2\lambda_0}\int_{R_3}\frac{e^{-ik_0(R-[x-x'])}}{R}\nu(\mathbf{x}')\,d\mathbf{x}'. \tag{9.17}$$

The first of conditions (9.12) requires that

$$\int_{R_3\times R_3}E\{|\nu(\mathbf{x}')\nu(\mathbf{x}'')|\}\left(\frac{2k_0}{R}+\frac{1}{R^2}\right)\left(\frac{2k_0}{R'}+\frac{1}{R'^2}\right)d\mathbf{x}'\,d\mathbf{x}'' \ll 16\lambda_0^2 \tag{9.18}$$

in order that formula (9.17) be applicable. If (9.18) holds, then, to first order, the phase and amplitude fluctuations are described respectively by

$$S(\mathbf{x}) = x + \frac{1}{2\lambda_0}\int_{R_3} \frac{\sin\{k_0(R - [x - x'])\}}{R}\,\nu(\mathbf{x}')\,d\mathbf{x}',$$

(9.19)

$$A(\mathbf{x}) = A_0 \exp\left(\frac{\pi}{\lambda_0^2}\int_{R_3} \frac{\cos\{k_0(R - [x - x'])\}}{R}\,\nu(\mathbf{x}')\,d\mathbf{x}'\right).$$

Expressions (9.19) are taken to hold in the mean square sense.

A one-dimensional form of the spatial Riccati equation (9.6) results from the "ansatz"

$$\mathbf{\Theta} = \Theta_1(x)\mathbf{i} + \Theta_2(y)\mathbf{j} + \Theta_3(z)\mathbf{k},$$

and

$$-ik_0 n^2(x, y, z) = f_1(x) + f_2(y) + f_3(z).$$

In that event (9.6) reduces to a system of three independent equations of the form

$$\Theta_j' - ik_0\Theta_j^2 = f_j(x_j), \qquad (j = 1, 2, 3).$$

This equation is essentially the classical Riccati equation

$$y'(x) + y^2(x) = -p(x) \tag{9.20}$$

where

$$x = -ik_0 x_j, \qquad y = \Theta_j, \qquad p = \frac{1}{ik_0} f_j(x_j).$$

Equation (9.20) has been the object of much study. The following iterative solution

$$y(x) = -\underset{n\to\infty}{\text{l.i.m.}}\left(\int_0^x d\xi_{n-1}\left(\int^{\xi_{n-1}} d\xi_{n-2}\cdots\int^{\xi_3} d\xi_2\left(\int_0^{\xi_2} d\xi_1 P^2(\xi_1) + P(\xi_2)\right)^2 + \cdots + P(\xi_{n-1})\right)^2 + P(x)\right) \tag{9.21}$$

to the nonlinear integral equation for $z(x) = y^2(x)$, $y(0) = 0$:

$$z(x) = \left[\int_0^x z(\xi)\,d\xi + P(x)\right]^2, \qquad P(x) = \int_0^x p(\xi)\,d\xi \tag{9.22}$$

appears to offer some potential value in the probabilistic case.

If $p(x)$ is an analytic random function, so that

$$p(x) = \sum_0^\infty p_m x^m,$$

the p_m being random variables, then (9.20) can be solved by the following recurrence relation for the random coefficients η_m occurring in the power series for $y(x)$:

$$m\eta_m = -\sum_{l=0}^{m-1} \eta_l \eta_{m-1-l} - p_{m-1} \qquad (m = 1, 2, \cdots).$$

Knowledge of the sure coefficient η_0 is therefore enough to specify the wave function for the analytic case.

10. **The one-dimensional problem.** The second order linear ordinary differential equation (5.2) with random wave number $k(x)$ has also received considerable attention, both because it occurs naturally as the transmission line equation and also because it is the simplest case of (1.1).

Kay and Silverman [**24**] have studied the multiple scattering of a plane wave by a stack of N dielectric slabs, all of the same thickness d, but each of which has permittivity $1 \pm \Delta\varepsilon$, with probability 1/2 for each value. If a scalar plane wave $e^{-ik_0 z}$ is incident from $-\infty$ on such a stack of Bernoulli slabs, the resultant field satisfies the reduced one-dimensional wave equation

$$\left\{\frac{d^2}{dz^2} + k_0^2[1 + \Delta\varepsilon(z)]\right\} Y(z) = 0. \tag{10.1}$$

A Neumann series solution is then obtained for the corresponding Fredholm integral equation:

$$\begin{aligned} Y(z) = e^{-ik_0 z} + \sum_{n=1}^{\infty} (\tfrac{1}{2}ik_0)^n \int_0^{Nd} & \\ \cdots \int_0^{Nd} \exp\,[-ik_0\{|z - z_1| + \cdots + |z_{n-1} - z_n|\} - ik_0 z_n] & \\ \cdot \prod_{m=1}^{n} \Delta\varepsilon(z_m)\, dz_m. & \end{aligned} \tag{10.2}$$

Kay and Silverman next define transmission and reflection coefficients T and R in terms of integral expressions like (10.2) according to the relations

$$Y(z) = \begin{cases} T\, e^{-ik_0 z}, & z \geqq Nd, \\ e^{-ik_0 z} + R\, e^{+ik_0 z}, & z < 0. \end{cases}$$

The integrals in T and R are then estimated and used to show the existence of stochastic majorants for the Neumann series for $E|R|^2$ and $E|T|^2$. For those terms in the Neumann series whose order is $<N$ the convergence is considerably more rapid than in the corresponding deterministic case. This feature is attributed to an enhanced attenuation by multiple scattering arising out of the random character of the medium, and is adduced by the authors in support of the common use of the Born approximation, or single-scattering model, in "forward scatter" theories.

11. **Wave propagation as a transport process.**

11.1. GEOMETRIC OPTICS OF A RANDOM MEDIUM. Geometric optics constitutes a "ballistic" (or zero wavelength) approximation to wave propagation phenomena. The trajectories along which field disturbances propagate are thus the ray paths. The geometrical optics approximation involves an assumption that wave-fronts behave locally like plane waves. This implies that the only admissible solutions of a reduced wave equation are those of the form (9.4), whence we obtain the eikonal equation for the optical path length $S(\mathbf{x})$:

$$(\nabla S)^2 + o(\lambda_0) = n^2 \tag{11.1}$$

while for the amplitude function $A(\mathbf{x})$:

$$\nabla \ln A \cdot \nabla S + \tfrac{1}{2}\nabla^2 S = 0. \tag{11.2}$$

Now introduce the unit vector in the ray direction at $\mathbf{x}$:

$$\hat{\mathbf{s}} = \nabla S/n. \tag{11.3}$$

Equation (11.3) is equivalent to (11.1) to within terms $o(\lambda_0)$. Letting $\hat{\boldsymbol{\rho}}$ denote a unit vector at $\mathbf{x}$ directed along the radius of curvature ρ, we have, since

$$\frac{d\mathbf{s}}{ds} = (\mathbf{s} \cdot \nabla)\mathbf{s} = -\mathbf{s} \times (\nabla \times \mathbf{s}),$$

that

$$\frac{\hat{\boldsymbol{\rho}}}{\rho} = -\hat{\mathbf{s}} \times (\nabla \times \hat{\mathbf{s}}),$$

and the ray curvature at $\mathbf{x}$ is therefore given by

$$\frac{1}{\rho} = \hat{\boldsymbol{\rho}} \cdot \nabla \ln n. \tag{11.4}$$

Keller [18] has formulated the initial value problem for (11.1) in the well-posed form

$$\begin{aligned} (\hat{\mathbf{s}} \cdot \nabla)(n\hat{\mathbf{s}}) &= \nabla n, \\ S(\mathbf{0}) &= 0, \\ \hat{\mathbf{s}}(\mathbf{0}) &= \mathbf{1}. \end{aligned} \tag{11.5}$$

The first of these equations can also be derived variationally from Fermat's principle [20].

We now consider $n^2(x)$ to be a regular random function $n^2(\omega; x)$, whence it follows that $S(\omega; x)$ is a differentiable regular random function. Then mean square differentiation and integration can be invoked and the preceding equations (and their consequences to follow) have a meaning in the case of regular random functions.

The pioneering work in the application of geometric optics to random continuous media appears to be that of P. G. Bergmann **[28]**. Bergmann began with the eikonal equation (11.1) together with the equation

$$\nabla \cdot \left(\frac{\phi}{n} \nabla S\right) = 0, \tag{11.6}$$

where $\phi(\mathbf{x})$ is the field intensity (flux density) at $\mathbf{x}$, and assumed a refractive index of the form $n = 1 + \varepsilon v$, $\varepsilon \ll 1$. He thus obtained integral formulas for the first order solutions of (11.1) and (11.6) from which the mean square deviation of optical path length from the geometrical path length and the variance of signal level fluctuations can be determined.

Since 1946 the geometrical optics of a random medium has received considerable further investigation (see the extensive bibliographies in **[30]**, **[20]**, **[45]**, and **[13]**). Keller **[18]** has given a thorough and penetrating treatment of the problem, and he as well as Chernov **[20]** and Kharanen **[27]** have analyzed ray propagation in a random medium under the hypothesis that the refractive index constitutes a Markov process. Keller's form of the analysis will be followed here.

Keller denotes our $\mathbf{s}$ by $\mathbf{x}'$ and is then able to write equations (11.5) as

$$\begin{aligned} (n\mathbf{x}')' &= \nabla n, \\ \mathbf{x}(0) &= 0, \\ \mathbf{x}'(0) &= \mathbf{u}, \end{aligned} \tag{11.6$'$}$$

where $\mathbf{x}(s, \varepsilon)$ is the position vector of the terminus of a ray that departed from the origin in the direction of the unit vector $\mathbf{u}$. Assuming that the perturbation expansion of n extends only to the first order in ε:

$$n(\mathbf{x}, \varepsilon) = 1 + \varepsilon\mu(\mathbf{x}), \tag{11.7}$$

with the usual form of the perturbation series for $\mathbf{x}(s, \varepsilon)$, one is led to the second order expansion

$$\mathbf{x}(s, \varepsilon) = \mathbf{x}_0(s) + \varepsilon\mathbf{x}_\varepsilon(s) + \tfrac{1}{2}\varepsilon^2\mathbf{x}_{\varepsilon\varepsilon}(s) + o(\varepsilon^2), \tag{11.8}$$

where

$$\mathbf{x}_0(s) = s\mathbf{u}, \tag{11.9}$$

$$\mathbf{x}_\varepsilon(s) = \int_0^s (s - t)\nabla_T\mu(t\mathbf{u})\, dt, \tag{11.10}$$

$$\begin{aligned} \mathbf{x}_{\varepsilon\varepsilon}(s) = 2\int_0^s (s - t)\Big[(\mathbf{x}_\varepsilon \cdot \nabla_T)\nabla_T\mu - \tfrac{1}{2}\nabla_T\mu^2 - \mathbf{u}\nabla_T\mu \cdot \int_0^t \nabla_T\mu(\tau\mathbf{u})\, d\tau \\ - \mathbf{u} \cdot \nabla\mu \int_0^t \nabla_T\mu(\tau\mathbf{u})\, d\tau\Big]\, dt \end{aligned} \tag{11.11}$$

and ∇_T denotes the gradient transverse to the unit vector $\mathbf{x}' = \mathbf{u}$; i.e.,

$$\nabla_T = \nabla - \mathbf{x}_0'(\mathbf{x}_0' \cdot \nabla).$$

It is then a straightforward matter to obtain moments of various orders under the hypothesis that the μ-process is stationary in the wide sense:

(11.12) $$E\{\mu(\mathbf{x}_1)\mu(\mathbf{x}_2)\} = \gamma(|\mathbf{x}_1 - \mathbf{x}_2|) = E|\mu^2|\rho(|\mathbf{x}_1 - \mathbf{x}_2|).$$

Thus

(11.13) $$E\mathbf{x}(s, \varepsilon) = s\mathbf{u} + \varepsilon^2 E\mu^2 \int_0^s (s - t)^2 t^{-1} \rho(t)\, dt + o(\varepsilon^2),$$

while for the variance of the transverse displacement δ of the endpoint of a ray of length s from the corresponding extension of the initial unit vector $\mathbf{u}$:

(11.14) $$E\delta^2 \approx -\tfrac{4}{3}\varepsilon^2 E\mu^2 s^3 \int_0^\infty r^{-1}\rho(r)\, dr + o(\varepsilon^2),$$

and for the mean square value of $\mathbf{x}' - \mathbf{u}$:

(11.15) $$E\{(\mathbf{x}' - \mathbf{u})^2\} = 2[1 - E \cos \alpha(s, \varepsilon)] \approx -4\varepsilon^2 E\mu^2 s \int_0^\infty r^{-1}\rho(r)\, dr + o(\varepsilon^2).$$

We now pass to a consideration of the Markovian ray tracing, i.e., $\mathbf{x}'(s, \varepsilon)$ is assumed to constitute a continuous parameter Markov process. This appears physically plausible, since Huyghen's principle is the optical analogue of the Chapman–Kolmogorov equation. However, it is clear that $\mathbf{x}(s, \varepsilon)$ in the form (11.8) could not in general constitute a wide-sense Markov process, for instance, since the necessary and sufficient condition for the process to be Markovian (wide sense) is that **[9]**

(11.16) $$\Gamma(s, \sigma) = \Gamma(s, s')\Gamma(s', \sigma),$$

($\Gamma(s, \sigma)$ being the covariance function of $\mathbf{x}'(s, \varepsilon)$ and $\mathbf{x}'(\sigma, \varepsilon)$) is violated. The left-hand side of (11.16) is $O(\varepsilon^2)$ whereas the right-hand side is $O(\varepsilon^4)$, and in addition the integrand of the right-hand side involves the product $\kappa(t, t')\kappa(t'', \tau)$, $t' \neq t''$, where $\kappa(t, t')$ is the covariance function of $\nabla_T\mu(t)$ and $\nabla_T\mu(t')$. Even if the ε's do not enter and the $\nabla\mu$ process is wide sense Markovian, the equation

(11.17) $$\int_0^s \int_0^{s'} \kappa(\sigma, \sigma')\, d\sigma\, d\sigma' = \int_0^s \int_0^t \int_0^t \int_0^{s'} \kappa(\sigma, \tau)\kappa(\tau', \sigma')\, d\sigma\, d\tau\, d\tau'\, d\sigma'$$

would have to hold if the $x(s, \varepsilon)$ process were to be Markovian.

Even so, it is plausible that, insofar as its next position is concerned, only the present location of the end of the ray path is required and not the entire previous trajectory, and as mentioned above, several authors have adopted the Markov process approach to the geometric optics of a randomly inhomogeneous medium. The state space as well as the parameter space are continuous, the state at s being the direction of the ray path there:

$$\alpha(s) = (\theta, \varphi).$$

If the Markovian hypothesis is tenable, then the transition probability $p(s, \alpha; s + \Delta s, \alpha + \Delta\alpha)$ would satisfy the Fokker–Planck equation [20]

$$\frac{\partial p}{\partial s} = \frac{1}{2}\frac{\partial^2}{\partial\theta^2}\left(\lim_{\Delta s\to 0}\frac{E(\Delta\theta)^2}{\Delta s}\sin\theta\, p\right) + \frac{\partial^2}{\partial\theta\partial\varphi}\left(\lim_{\Delta s\to 0}\frac{E\{(\Delta\theta)(\Delta\varphi)\}}{\Delta s}\sin\theta\, p\right)$$
$$(11.18)\qquad + \frac{1}{2}\frac{\partial^2}{\partial\varphi^2}\left(\lim_{\Delta s\to 0}\frac{E(\Delta\varphi)^2}{\Delta s}\sin\theta\, p\right) - \frac{\partial}{\partial\theta}\left(\lim_{\Delta s\to 0}\frac{E(\Delta\theta)}{\Delta s}\sin\theta\, p\right)$$
$$- \frac{\partial}{\partial\varphi}\left(\lim_{\Delta s\to 0}\frac{E(\Delta\varphi)}{\Delta s}\sin\theta\, p\right).$$

After some trigonometric reductions (11.18) can be reduced to the following form (which is formally the same as the Fokker–Planck equation for the rotational motion of a Brownian particle):

$$(11.19)\qquad \frac{\partial p}{\partial s} = D\left\{\frac{1}{\sin\theta}\frac{\partial}{\partial\theta}\left(\sin\theta\frac{\partial p}{\partial\theta}\right) + \frac{1}{\sin^2\theta}\frac{\partial^2 p}{\partial\varphi^2}\right\},$$

where

$$D = \lim_{\Delta s\to 0}\frac{E\alpha^2}{4\Delta s} + o(\varepsilon^2).$$

For the case that p is independent of φ, the solution of the initial value problem consisting of (11.19) and the initial absolute probability $p(0, \alpha) = \delta(\theta)$ is given by

$$(11.20)\qquad p(0, \alpha; s, \alpha) = \frac{1}{4\pi}\sum_{n=0}^{\infty}(2n + 1)P_n(\cos\theta)\, e^{-n(n+1)Ds}.$$

The expectation of $\cos\alpha$ obtained from (11.20) apparently differs from that which follows from (11.15). However, this results from different ranges of validity of the two results, that based on (11.15) holding well for small s while that following from (11.20) applies best for large values of s. The two results do, however, agree to terms of second order in the intermediate, overlapping range of s.

11.2. DIFFUSION AND TRANSPORT EQUATIONS FOR MULTIPLE SCATTERING. Another approach to wave propagation that involves a transport equation rather than the wave equation [31] is based on the connection between the electromagnetic energy flux and the energy density associated with the photon distribution function. According to the differential form of Poynting's theorem, we have that

$$(11.21)\qquad \operatorname{div}\mathbf{P} + \frac{\partial U}{\partial t} = 0,$$

where U is the total electromagnetic energy, related to the photon flux as follows:

$$(11.22)\qquad U = \hbar\int_0^\infty \omega N_\omega\, d\omega = \int d\omega \int_{\text{vel. space}} \omega f_\omega\, dV_v$$

and

N_ω = number of photons per unit volume in the frequency band $(\omega, \omega + d\omega)$,
f_ω = the probability density function for the distribution of photons in positional velocity space.

Now introduce the spectral density function

$$\Sigma(\mathbf{x}, \mathbf{v}, \omega) = \omega f_\omega(\mathbf{x}, \mathbf{v}), \tag{11.23}$$

and supplement (11.21) by a term taking into account the scattering of photons out of $(\omega, \mathbf{v})$. After some reductions one is led to the integro-differential equation

$$\mathbf{v} \cdot \nabla\Sigma = \int\int p(\omega, \omega'|\mathbf{v}, \mathbf{v}')\Sigma(\mathbf{x}, \omega', \mathbf{v}')\, d\omega'\, dV_{v'} - \int Q_T \Sigma(\mathbf{x}, \omega')\, d\omega' \tag{11.24}$$

where

$$p(\omega, \omega'|\mathbf{v}, \mathbf{v}')\, d\omega\, dV_v = \Pr\{\text{a photon at } (\boldsymbol{\omega}', \mathbf{v}') \text{ is scattered into the range } (\omega + d\omega, \mathbf{v} + d\mathbf{v})\}, \tag{11.25}$$

$$Q_T = \text{scattering cross section}$$

$$= \frac{1}{2\pi} \int_{-\infty}^{\infty} e^{-i(\omega-\omega')\tau}\, d\tau \int_{\mathcal{O}} \sigma(\mathbf{K}, 0)\, d\mathcal{O}, \mathbf{K} = \mathbf{k} - \mathbf{k}', \tag{11.26}$$

$$\sigma(\mathbf{K}, \tau) = \frac{\pi^2}{\lambda^4} \sin^2 \gamma \int e^{-i\mathbf{K}\cdot\mathbf{r}}\Gamma(\mathbf{r}, \tau)\, d\mathbf{r}, \tag{11.27}$$

$\Gamma(\mathbf{r}, \tau)$ being the covariance function for dielectric noise (turbulent scattering). It follows from (11.25)–(11.27) that

$$p(\omega, \omega'|\mathbf{v}, \mathbf{v}') = \frac{1}{2\pi} \int_{-\infty}^{\infty} e^{-i(\omega-\omega')\tau}\, \sigma(\mathbf{K}, \tau)\, d\tau.$$

For a source radiating into a semi-infinite half-space, Bugnolo was able to reduce (11.24) to the partial differential equation

$$\frac{\partial\Sigma}{\partial\xi} \simeq \sum_{n=1}^{N} (-1)^n \gamma_{2n}^2 \frac{\partial^{2n}\Sigma}{\partial\omega^{2n}} + \sum_{m=0}^{M} (-1)^m \frac{\alpha_{2m}^2}{4} \left(\frac{\partial^{2m+2}}{\partial\delta^2\partial\omega^{2m}} + \frac{1}{\delta}\frac{\partial^{2m+1}}{\partial\delta\partial\omega^{2m}}\right)\Sigma, \tag{11.28}$$

which was then solved by transform methods to obtain the solution

$$\Sigma(\xi, \theta, \omega) = \frac{1}{2\pi}\int_{-\infty}^{\infty} e^{i\omega s} \int_0^{\infty} J_0(g\theta) \times \exp\left\{\sum_{n=1}^{N} (-i)^{2n}\gamma_{2n}^2 s^2 + \frac{1}{4}\sum_{m=0}^{M} (-i)^{2m}\alpha_{2m}^2 s^{2m} g^2\right\}\xi\Psi(g, s) g\, dg\, ds \tag{11.29}$$

where

$$\Psi(g, s) = \int_{-\infty}^{\infty} e^{-i\omega s} \int_{-\infty}^{\infty} s(\beta, \omega) J_0(g\beta)\beta\, d\beta\, d\omega. \tag{11.30}$$

(For definition of the parameters in (11.28), (11.29), and (11.30), see the original reference [**31**].)

Bugnolo has also studied the application of these results to tropospheric and ionospheric forward scatter of radio waves [**32**; **33**]. He finds that the spectral density is Gaussian, to the first order at least, with a variance proportional to penetration distance x

$$\text{var}_\omega(x, \omega_0) = x\left(\int (\mathbf{K}\cdot\mathbf{V})^2\sigma(\theta)\,d\Omega\right)^2, \tag{11.31}$$

where $\sigma(\theta)$ is the scattering cross section per unit solid angle per unit volume and $\mathbf{V}$ is the mean wind velocity. This realistic feature, viz., the increase in width of the spectral density function with increasing distance, is lacking in the single scatter theories. A mean free path for scattering is also defined:

$$d_0 = \left(\int \sigma(\theta, \varphi)\,d\Omega\right)^{-1} \sim \lambda^2\varepsilon_0^2/[lE(\Delta\varepsilon)^2], \tag{11.32}$$

l being the average scale of turbulence, and, assuming that the scattering constitutes a stationary Markov process, the following expression is determined for the probability that a ray is scattered n times in a distance R:

$$\frac{Q_s^n}{\Gamma(n)}\int_0^R r^{n-1}\,e^{-Q_s r}\,dr,$$

Q_s being the total scattering cross-section per unit volume at wave number k. It turns out that for the odds to be even that a ray will be scattered twice in a distance R, R must be of the order of 1.7 mean free paths.

Another transport equation approach, based on multiply scattered rays, has been given by Ament [**26**], who finds that multiple scattering can take place for path lengths even smaller than the mean free path d_0 under certain circumstances (large cross-sections or large angular deviations). The distribution in angle of the scattered power at distance x is assumed to follow a compound Poisson process

$$P(x; y', z') = \sum_{m=0}^{\infty} (Qx)^m\, e^{-Qm} P_m(y', z')/m!.$$

Ament also gives several diffusion equations which apply to the phase coherence of multiply scattered rays, together with a brief discussion of the appropriate Wiener integrals. We shall discuss the functional integral approach further below.

Bremmer [**30**] has also considered from the standpoint of the diffusion model the probabilistic properties of radiation traversing a turbulent medium. He uses for this purpose the joint probability density $h_z(x, y; \xi, \eta)$ that an energy unit departing from the origin parallel to the z-axis will intersect a transverse plane at distance z in an element of area $dxdy$ in a direction with direction cosines ξ and η. This probability density (actually a transition probability with initial value at the origin) is termed the multiple-scattering diffusion function and is taken to satisfy a Chapman–Kolmogorov equation. The latter leads, once a differential cross-section profile $\sigma(\xi, \eta)$ has been assigned, to a diffusion equation in operator form

$$\left(\xi\frac{\partial}{\partial x} + \eta\frac{\partial}{\partial y} + \frac{\partial}{\partial z}\right) h_z(x, y; \xi, \eta) = \frac{1}{d_0} \ln\left\{d_0 \iint_{-\infty}^{\infty} d\xi'\, dy' \sigma(\xi', \eta') \exp\left[-\xi'\frac{\partial}{\partial \xi} - \eta'\frac{\partial}{\partial \eta}\right]\right\} h_z(x, y; \xi, \eta). \tag{11.33}$$

The corresponding probability density $h_{z,m}(x, y; \xi, \eta)$ for consecutive scattering at m equidistant planes, each with separation distance z/m, has the bivariate Laplace transform [30]:

$$p_1q_1p_2q_2 \exp\left\{\frac{m}{z}\int_0^z d\zeta \ln\left(\frac{z}{m}\iint_{-\infty}^{\infty} d\xi\, d\eta \sigma(\xi, \eta) \cdot \exp\left[-\xi(p_1\zeta + p_2) - \eta(q_1\zeta + q_2)\right]\right)\right\}. \tag{11.34}$$

Bremmer has determined $h_{z,m}$ for the cases of a Gaussian cross-section profile and a so-called Norton profile (the third in Table I). The interested reader is referred to Bremmer's paper [30] for further details.

11.3. INVARIANT IMBEDDING. Invariant imbedding, developed by Bellman and others as an application of dynamic programming, has enjoyed conspicuous success in such transport phenomena as neutron scattering and radiative transfer in stellar atmospheres [46; 47]. Appeal is made to the duality between wave mechanics and particle mechanics to carry over the transport process to wave propagation phenomena. In the deterministic single slab case the method leads to the well-known Riccati equations governing the reflection and transmission coefficients of an inhomogeneous transmission line. In the stochastic case expressions are obtained for reflection and transmission coefficients, R_N and T_N respectively, for a plane wave incident from the right upon a stack of N slabs, each of which has a random wave number which is constant (for any particular realization) in that slab. The approach is as follows: the problem for fixed N is first of all imbedded in the class of problems for $N = 1, 2, \cdots$. Next appeal is made to the so-called localization principle (i.e., partial reflection and transmission occur at each plane section of the stratified medium as the wave passes through) in order to obtain iterative relations between R_N and R_{N-1}, and T_N and R_{N-1} and T_{N-1}. A brief discussion is given in [25] of how to approach the actual probabilistic problem of determining the probability distribution functions associated with these formal expressions, but no real attack on this aspect of the problem appears to have been yet carried out.

12. **Relation to more general theories.** Much of what we have discussed is a good deal more closely allied to classical analysis and what is now classical probability theory than to the modern functional analysis approach. This reflects,

however, the fact that those portions of functional analysis that would be most useful in connection with (5.1) remain in large part still to be developed. Equations (5.1) constitute a non-self-adjoint problem [**48**], even for deterministic constant k^2, and the mathematical apparatus appropriate to spectral representations for non-self-adjoint equations and integration in the appropriate functional spaces is still largely lacking. Though the method of integration in functional spaces [**34**], has enjoyed marked success in problems of quantum mechanics, that is to say for Hilbert space, Wiener integrals would have to be generalized in two directions, (i) to the class of twice continuously differentiable functions and (ii) to more general stochastic processes than the Brownian motion process, to be of use in the present context.

Many of the recently developed techniques of modern partial differential equation theory would also seem to carry over to the random case, e.g., parametrix methods using either a deterministic or simple random function as fundamental solution. The possibilities in this direction are largely unexplored, although the basic constant-coefficient differential equation has been studied by Kampé de Fériet [**1**]. The general question of random equations is discussed elsewhere in this symposium [**49**]. Prior to this work such approaches have in general applied only to first order differential equations or to equations with constant coefficients, the element of randomness arising from the presence of a random forcing function or random boundary conditions. Much the same applies to past studies of random operators on Banach spaces [**50**; **51**; **52**], although the use of Orlicz spaces introduced in this connection may offer considerable promise.

References

1. J. Kampé de Fériet, *Statistical mechanics of continuous media*, Proc. Sympos. Appl. Math. Vol. 13, pp. 165–198, Amer. Math. Soc., Providence, R. I., 1962.

2. V. Twersky, *Propagation in media of discrete scatterers*, Proc. Sympos. Appl. Math. Vol. 16, pp. 84–116, Amer. Math. Soc., Providence, R. I., 1964.

3. J. L. Doob, *The Brownian movement and stochastic equations*, Ann. of Math. (2) **43** (1942), 351–369.

4. J. Kampé de Fériet, *Spectral tensor of homogeneous turbulence*, Symposium on turbulence, U.S. Naval Ord. Lab. Rep. No. 1136, Silver Springs, Md., July 1, 1949.

5. S. Silver, *Delineations and methodology in the subject of scattering by a statistically inhomogeneous medium*, Electromagnetic theory and antennas, E. C. Jordan, ed., Pergamon, London, 1963.

6. J. E. Moyal, *Stochastic processes and statistical physics*, J. Roy. Statist. Soc. **11** (1949), 150–210.

7. M. Loève, *Probability theory*, 2nd ed., Van Nostrand, Princeton, N. J., 1960.

8. A. Kolmogoroff, *Grundebgriffe der Wahrscheinlichkeitsrechnung*, Chelsea, New York, 1946.

9. J. L. Doob, *Stochastic processes*, Wiley, New York, 1953.

10. A. Blanc-Lapierre and R. Fortet, *Théorie des fonctions aléatoires*, Masson, Paris, 1953.

11. R. A. Silverman, *Locally stationary random processes*, Res. Rep. MME-2, New York University Institute of Mathematical Sciences Div. Electromag. Res., New York, 1957.

12. J. Kampé de Fériet and F. N. Frenkiel, *Correlation and spectra for non-stationary random functions*, Math. Comp. **16** (1962), 1–21.

13. A. D. Wheelon, *Radio-wave scattering by tropospheric irregularities*, J. Res. Nat. Bureau Standards Sect. D **63D** (1959), 205–233.

14. D. S. Bugnolo, *Stochastic processes and beyond-the-horizon propagation*, IRE Trans. **AP–9** (1961), 226–228.

15. K. Jacobs, *Neuere Methoden und Ergebnisse der Ergodentheorie*, Springer, Berlin, 1960.

16. G. Maruyama, *The harmonic analysis of stationary stochastic processes*, Mem. Fac. Sci. Kyūsyū Univ. Ser. A **4** (1949), 45–106.

17. T. J. Skinner, *Ergodic theorem in the solution of the scalar wave equation with statistical boundary conditions*, J. Opt. Soc. Amer. **51** (1961), 1246–1251.

18. J. B. Keller, *Wave propagation in random media*, Proc. Sympos. Appl. Math. Vol. 13, pp. 227–246, Amer. Math. Soc., Providence, R. I., 1962.

19. W. S. Ament, *The effect of atmospheric inhomogeneities on radio propagation velocity*, Naval Research Laboratory, Branch Memo. WPR TA–5/50, Washington, D.C., 1950.

20. L. A. Chernov, *Wave propagation in a random medium*, McGraw-Hill, New York, 1960.

21. W. C. Hoffman, *The electromagnetic field in a randomly inhomogeneous medium*, IRE Trans. **AP–7** (1959), Special Suppl., S301–S306.

22. C. Müller, *Zur mathematischen Theorie elektromagnetischer Schwingungen*, Abh. Deutsch. Akad. Wiss. Berlin Kl. Math.-Nat. Klasse 1945/46, No. 3 (1950), 5–56.

23. R. A. Silverman, *Scattering of plane waves by locally homogeneous dielectric noise*, Proc. Cambridge Philos. Soc. **54** (1958), 530–537.

24. I. Kay and R. A. Silverman, *Multiple scattering by a random stack of dielectric slabs*, Nuovo Cimento (10) **9** (1958), Suppl., 626–645.

25. R. Bellman and R. Kalaba, *Invariant imbedding and wave propagation in stochastic media*, Electromagnetic wave propagation, Desirant and Michaels, eds., pp. 243–252, Academic Press, New York, 1960.

26. W. S. Ament, *Modification of a ray-tracer for Monte Carlo prediction of multiple-scattered radio fields*, Statistical methods in radio wave propagation, W. C. Hoffman, ed., pp. 184–196, Pergamon, London, 1960.

27. V. Ya. Kharanen, *Sound propagation in a medium with random fluctuations of the refractive index*, National Science Foundation Translation NSF-tr-8, U. S. Dept. Commerce, Washington 25, D.C., June, 1953.

28. P. G. Bergmann, *Propagation of radiation in a medium with random inhomogeneities*, Phys. Rev. (2) **70** (1946), 486–492.

29. R. Bellman and R. Kalaba, *Wave branching processes and invariant imbedding*, Proc. Nat. Acad. Sci. U. S. A. **47** (1961), 1507–1509.

30. H. Bremmer, *Scattering by a perturbed continuum*, Electromagnetic Wave Theory and Antennas, E. C. Jordan, ed., Pergamon, London, 1963.

31. D. S. Bugnolo, *Transport equation for the spectral density of a multiple-scattered electromagnetic field*, J. Appl. Phys. **31** (1960), 1176–1182.

32. ———, *On the question of multiple scattering in the troposphere*, J. Geophys. Res. **65** (1960), 879–884.

33. ———, *Radio star scintillation and multiple scattering in the ionosphere*, IRE Trans. **AP–9** (1961), 89–96.

34. I. M. Gel'fand and A. M. Yaglom, *Integration in functional space and its applications in quantum physics*, J. Math. and Phys. **1** (1960), 48–69.

35. R. P. Feynman, *An operator calculus having applications in quantum electrodynamics*, Phys. Rev. (2) **84** (1951), 108–128.

36. T. I. Seidman, *A survey of functional integration with applications of the Wiener integral*, Rep. 55 G–1, Lincoln Lab., Massachusetts Institute of Technology, Bedford, Mass., 1961.

37. R. H. Kraichnan, *Dynamics of nonlinear stochastic systems*, J. Mathematical Phys. **2** (1961), 124–148.

38. H. Staras, *Forward scattering of radio waves by anisotropic turbulence*, Proc. IRE **43** (1955), 1374–1380.

39. H. G. Booker, *Radio scattering in the lower ionosphere*, J. Geophys. Res. **64** (1959), 2164–2177.

40. H. T. Friis, A. B. Crawford, and D. C. Hogg, *A reflection theory for propagation beyond the horizon*, Bell System Tech. J. **36** (1957), 627–644.

41. S. A. Bowhill, *The scattering of radio waves by an extended randomly refracting medium*, J. Atmos. Terrest. Phys. **20** (1961), 9–18.

42. ———, *Statistics of a radio wave diffracted by a random ionosphere*, J. Res. Nat. Bureau Standards Sect. D **65D** (1961), 275–292.

43. K. C. Yeh, *Propagation of spherical waves through an ionosphere containing anisotropic irregularities*, J. Res. Nat. Bureau Standards Sect. D **66D** (1962), 621–636.

44. G. K. Batchelor, *The theory of homogeneous turbulence*, Section 4.1, Cambridge Univ. Press, Cambridge, 1956.

45. V. I. Tatarski, *Wave propagation in a turbulent medium*, McGraw-Hill, New York, 1961.

46. R. Bellman, R. Kalaba, and G. M. Wing, *On the principle of invariant imbedding and neutron transport theory*. I. *One-dimensional case*, J. Math. Mech. **7** (1958), 149–162.

47. ———, *Invariant imbedding and neutron transport theory*. IV. *Generalized transport theory*, J. Math. Mech. **8** (1959), 575–584.

48. C. Dolph, *Recent developments in some non-self-adjoint problems of mathematical physics*, Bull. Amer. Math. Soc. **67** (1961), 1–69.

49. A. T. Bharucha-Reid, *On the theory of random equations*, Proc. Sympos. Appl. Math. Vol. 16, pp. 40–69, Amer. Math. Soc., Providence, R. I., 1964.

50. ———, *Über die konvergenz der folgen von verallgemeinerten zufälligan grössen in Orlicz'schen raümen*, Bull. Acad. Polon. Sci. Sér. Sci. Math. Astronom. Phys. **7** (1959), 425–427.

51. ———, *On random operator equations in Banach spaces*, Bull. Acad. Polon. Sci. Sér. Sci. Math. Astronom. Phys. **7** (1959), 561–564.

52. ———, *On random solutions of integral equations in Banach spaces*, Trans. 2nd Prague Conf. Information Theory, Statistical Decision Functions and Random Processes (1959), pp. 27–48, Publ. House Czechoslovak Acad. Sci., Prague, 1960.

BOEING SCIENTIFIC RESEARCH LABORATORIES,
SEATTLE, WASHINGTON

STOCHASTIC EQUATIONS AND WAVE PROPAGATION IN RANDOM MEDIA[1]

BY

JOSEPH B. KELLER

1. **Introduction.** A stochastic equation is a family of equations depending upon a parameter α which ranges over a space A in which a probability density $p(\alpha)$ is defined. The probability density $p(\alpha)$ determines the probability of a given value of α and therefore of the corresponding equation of the family. If for each value of α there is determined a unique solution $u(\alpha)$ of the equation then $u(\alpha)$ is a random variable (or function) and its probability density is also $p(\alpha)$. An example of a stochastic equation is a linear differential equation in which some of the coefficients and the inhomogeneous term are random, i.e., depend upon α. The objective of the theory of stochastic equations is the determination of the probability distribution of u or of various statistical properties of u such as its expectation, its variance and its higher moments.

Wave propagation in a continuous random medium is often governed by a stochastic linear differential equation. The coefficients in the equation characterize the propagation medium. They may be its refractive index $n(x)$, its density $\rho(x)$, its dielectric constant, etc. A random medium is a family of media, each labeled by one value of α, and each with its own index $n(x, \alpha)$, density $\rho(x, \alpha)$, etc. The probability $p(\alpha)$ gives the probability of each member of the family. The inhomogeneous term represents the source of the waves, which may be either random or sure (i.e., not random). A random medium may also consist of a random distribution of discrete scattering objects distributed throughout some fixed medium within which waves can propagate. This latter description is appropriate when matter is viewed on a molecular scale. We shall see that propagation in such a medium can also be analyzed in terms of stochastic equations.

The practical reason for studying stochastic equations is the belief that their solutions represent physical phenomena which could not be satisfactorily investigated in any other way. Let us consider, for example, the propagation of an electromagnetic wave through air. Because the wave travels so fast, it is adequate to assume that the air molecules do not move during the passage of the wave. If the locations of all the molecules were known, one could in principle determine how they scatter the wave. However, the full details of the scattered wave would be too complex to be useful. Furthermore it is out of the question to determine

[1] This research was supported by the Air Force Cambridge Research Laboratories, under Contract No. AF 19(604)3495. Reproduction in whole or in part is permitted for any purpose of the U.S. Government.

the locations of all the molecules. In view of these two difficulties, it is hoped that the observable features of the wave scattering will be determined by the gross features of the molecular distribution. Therefore the actual distribution of molecular positions is replaced by a random medium, i.e., a collection of molecular distributions with a probability associated with each. The mean particle density and some other statistics of the random medium are adjusted to equal the corresponding properties of the actual particle distribution. Then the mean scattered wave and other statistics of the random wave are presumed to equal the corresponding properties of the actual wave. Of course the success of this procedure, like that of all other theories of natural phenomena, can only be judged by comparison of its predictions with observations.

Once the concept of a stochastic equation is understood, it becomes clear that most, if not all, equations which arise in science and engineering may be viewed as stochastic. This is because the various coefficients and parameters entering such equations are subject to random variations due to noise, thermal fluctuations, etc. Consequently all problems involving such equations should be reexamined from the stochastic viewpoint. In most cases the random variations are small and this is fortunate for analytic reasons, since then the random part of the solution can be determined by perturbation or expansion methods. In the next section a general perturbation method will be developed for the determination of the mean solution of a linear stochastic equation. This is a generalization of a method which has been used before **[1]** on the reduced wave equation for a random medium. It can be used to study propagation in many kinds of continuous and discrete media, as we shall see.

When the random variations are not small, perturbation methods become inconvenient and other methods of analysis must be sought. One such method, considered in §5, is that of direct determination of equations satisfied by the various moments of the solution. One finds that the equation for a moment of any order involves moments of higher order. Therefore an infinite system of equations must be considered for the simultaneous determination of all moments. These may be called the hierarchy equations, in analogy with the similar equations in statistical mechanics. One method of obtaining finite sets of equations is by assuming that some moment can be expressed in a particular way in terms of moments of lower order. Such a closure procedure is the basis for most of the so-called "dishonest" **[1]** methods of analyzing stochastic equations. Boltzmann's molecular chaos assumption in the kinetic theory of gases, Kirkwood's superposition approximation in the kinetic theory of liquids, Millionstchikov's quasinormality approximation in the theory of isotropic turbulence, the effective field approximation in the theory of multiple scattering by discrete scatterers, used by L. Foldy **[2]**, M. Lax **[3]** and V. Twersky **[4]**, and the local independence hypothesis of R. C. Bourret **[5]** and W. S. Ament **[6]** are all closure assumptions of this type. We shall see that the latter two approximations follow from the perturbation analysis of §2, up to terms of a certain order. Thus to the appropriate order they can be deduced. Therefore postulating them for large random variations amounts to using a perturbation expansion for large values of the expansion parameter. Although apparently unjustified, this procedure often yields accurate results. Hierarchy equations and closure approximations in the theory of turbulence have been discussed and analyzed by R. H. Kraichnan [7].

The hierarchy equations can be combined into a single functional differential equation for the generating functional of the moments of the solution and the random coefficients. This procedure is illustrated in §5. It was introduced into statistical mechanics in 1947 by N. N. Bogolyubov [**8**] and into the theory of turbulence by E. Hopf [**9**] in 1952. Methods for solving Bogolyubov's equation have been given by B. Zumino [**10**] and by R. M. Lewis and J. B. Keller [**11**], and for Hopf's equation by R. M. Lewis and R. H. Kraichnan [**12**]. These methods all involve expansions with respect to parameters.

An apparently quite independent description of wave propagation in a random medium is provided by the theory of radiative transfer, which is also called transport theory. The concept of a wave does not occur in it, nor do the related notions of phase and interference. In §6 we shall show how this theory can be deduced from a stochastic reduced wave equation when appropriate conditions are satisfied.

2. **Perturbation theory of linear stochastic equations.** Let us consider a linear operator M which transforms elements of some linear space into itself. Suppose $M = M(\alpha)$ depends upon a parameter α which ranges over a set A (measure space) and that $p(\alpha)$ is a probability density in A. Then $M(\alpha)$ is a stochastic operator. If g is a given element of the linear space and u is an unknown element, we may consider the following stochastic equation for u,

$$M(\alpha)u = g. \tag{1}$$

If this equation has a unique solution $u(\alpha)$ for each α, the solution depends upon α. Since $p(\alpha)$ is the probability density of α, it determines the probability density of $u(\alpha)$, and therefore $u(\alpha)$ is a random solution of (1). We shall attempt to obtain an equation for $\langle u \rangle$, the expected value of $u(\alpha)$, where the expected value of any function $f(\alpha)$ is defined by

$$\langle f \rangle = \int_A f(\alpha)p(\alpha)\, d\alpha. \tag{2}$$

To make this problem tractable, and at the same time to cover a large variety of practical cases, we shall assume that $M(\alpha, \varepsilon)$ depends upon a small parameter ε and that for $\varepsilon = 0$, M reduces to a sure (nonstochastic) operator L. Upon expanding $M(\alpha, \varepsilon)$ in powers of ε we may rewrite (1) in the form

$$[L + \varepsilon L_1(\alpha) + \varepsilon^2 L_2(\alpha) + O(\varepsilon^3)]u(\alpha, \varepsilon) = g. \tag{3}$$

The stochastic operators $L_1(\alpha)$ and $L_2(\alpha)$ represent stochastic perturbations of the sure operator L. We shall denote by u_0 a particular solution of the sure equation obtained by setting $\varepsilon = 0$ in (3)

$$Lu_0 = g. \tag{4}$$

Now assuming that L^{-1} is defined, we can rewrite (3) in the form

$$u = u_0 - L^{-1}(\varepsilon L_1 + \varepsilon^2 L_2)u + O(\varepsilon^3). \tag{5}$$

To obtain the solution of (5) we can employ the method of iterations or successive substitutions which yields

$$u = u_0 - \varepsilon L^{-1}L_1 u_0 + \varepsilon^2 L^{-1}(L_1 L^{-1} L_1 - L_2)u_0 + O(\varepsilon^3). \tag{6}$$

We now take the expectation value of (6) and obtain

$$\langle u\rangle = u_0 - \varepsilon L^{-1}\langle L_1\rangle u_0 + \varepsilon^2 L^{-1}(\langle L_1 L^{-1} L_1\rangle - \langle L_2\rangle)u_0 + O(\varepsilon^3). \tag{7}$$

To obtain an equation for $\langle u\rangle$ we shall eliminate u_0 from (7) by first observing from (7) that

$$\begin{aligned} u_0 &= \langle u\rangle + \varepsilon L^{-1}\langle L_1\rangle u_0 + O(\varepsilon^2) \\ &= \langle u\rangle + \varepsilon L^{-1}\langle L_1\rangle\langle u\rangle + O(\varepsilon^2). \end{aligned} \tag{8}$$

We now use (8) in (7) and find an equation for $\langle u\rangle$,

$$\begin{aligned} \langle u\rangle &= u_0 - \varepsilon L^{-1}\langle L_1\rangle\langle u\rangle \\ &\quad + \varepsilon^2 L^{-1}[\langle L_1 L^{-1} L_1\rangle - \langle L_1\rangle L^{-1}\langle L_1\rangle - \langle L_2\rangle]\langle u\rangle + O(\varepsilon^3). \end{aligned} \tag{9}$$

Upon multiplying (9) by L we obtain another form of equation for $\langle u\rangle$ which is

$$\{L + \varepsilon\langle L_1\rangle + \varepsilon^2[\langle L_1\rangle L^{-1}\langle L_1\rangle - \langle L_1 L^{-1} L_1\rangle + \langle L_2\rangle]\}\langle u\rangle = g + O(\varepsilon^3). \tag{10}$$

This equation simplifies, when $\langle L_1\rangle = 0$, to

$$\{L + \varepsilon^2[\langle L_2\rangle - \langle L_1 L^{-1} L_1\rangle]\}\langle u\rangle = g + O(\varepsilon^3). \tag{11}$$

By omitting the $O(\varepsilon^3)$ term in (9), (10) or (11) we obtain an explicit equation for $\langle u\rangle$, which is what we were seeking.

Let us now consider the case in which $u = u(x)$ is an n component vector function of a vector variable x. Then the operators L, L_1 and L_2 are nth order matrices, each element of which is an operator which may be a differential or integral operator. The inverse operator L^{-1} is also an nth order matrix which we shall represent as an integral operator. The kernel $G(x, x')$ is called the Green's matrix and is defined by the equation

$$LG(x, x') = I\delta(x - x'). \tag{12}$$

In (12) $\delta(x - x')$ denotes the Dirac delta function and I is the nth order unit matrix. With the aid of G, L^{-1} can be written as the integral operator

$$L^{-1}f(x) = \int G(x, x')f(x')\,dx'. \tag{13}$$

Now (10) can be written in the following form

$$L(x)\langle u(x)\rangle + \varepsilon\langle L_1(x)\rangle\langle u(x)\rangle + \varepsilon^2\Big[\langle L_1(x)\rangle \int G(x, x')\langle L_1(x')\rangle\langle u(x')\rangle\, dx' \tag{14}$$
$$- \Big\langle L_1(x) \int G(x, x')L_1(x')\langle u(x')\rangle\, dx' \Big\rangle + \langle L_2(x)\rangle\langle u(x)\rangle\Big] = g(x) + O(\varepsilon^3).$$

In (14) the explicit dependence of the operators upon x has been indicated. When $\langle L_1(x)\rangle = 0$, (14) becomes

$$L(x)\langle u(x)\rangle + \varepsilon^2\Big[\langle L_2(x)\rangle\langle u(x)\rangle - \Big\langle L_1(x) \int G(x, x')L_1(x')\langle u(x')\rangle\, dx' \Big\rangle\Big] = g(x) + O(\varepsilon^3). \tag{15}$$

Equations (14) and (15) become equations for $\langle u(x)\rangle$ when the $O(\varepsilon^3)$ terms are omitted. The resulting equations are the main results of this section.

Before applying our results to special cases, let us consider an alternative "dishonest" derivation of (11). We shall set $L_2 = 0$ and assume that $\langle L_1\rangle = 0$. Then upon taking expectation values in (3) we obtain

$$L\langle u\rangle + \varepsilon\langle L_1 u\rangle + O(\varepsilon^3) = g. \tag{16}$$

To determine $\langle L_1 u\rangle$ we multiply (15) by L_1 and take expectations to obtain

$$\langle L_1 u\rangle = -\varepsilon\langle L_1 L^{-1} L_1 u\rangle + O(\varepsilon^3). \tag{17}$$

In deriving (17) we used the hypothesis that $\langle L_1\rangle = 0$. Now we assume that the expectation on the right side of (17) splits into a product as follows:

$$\langle L_1 L^{-1} L u\rangle = \langle L_1 L^{-1} L_1\rangle\langle u\rangle. \tag{18}$$

When (18) is used in (17) and the result substituted into (16), (16) becomes

$$L\langle u\rangle - \varepsilon\langle L_1 L^{-1} L_1\rangle\langle u\rangle = g + O(\varepsilon^3). \tag{19}$$

This is just our result (11) when $L_2 = 0$. This derivation is essentially that of R. C. Bourret [5] who called (18) the assumption of local independence. Practically the same derivation was given by W. S. Ament [6] for the special case of Maxwell's equations for an electromagnetic wave in a random medium. Our derivation of (11) avoids the assumption (18) by effectively proving that it is correct within $O(\varepsilon)$, and this is all that is needed in the derivation when $L_2 = 0$.

3. **Applications to wave propagation in continuous media.** Let us consider a scalar function $u(x, t)$ which satisfies the wave equation in a medium having a random propagation speed $c[1 + \varepsilon\mu(x, t, \alpha)]^{-1}$. Then the wave equation is

$$\Delta u - c^{-2}[1 + 2\varepsilon\mu + \varepsilon^2\mu^2]u_{tt} = 0. \tag{1}$$

Upon comparing this equation with (2.3) we see that $g = 0$ while L, L_1 and L_2 are given by

$$L = \Delta - c^{-2}\partial_t^2, \tag{2}$$

$$L_1 = -2c^{-2}\mu\partial_t^2, \tag{3}$$

$$L_2 = -c^{-2}\mu^2\partial_t^2. \tag{4}$$

If $\langle\mu(x, t)\rangle = 0$ then $\langle L_1\rangle = 0$ and (2.11) applies to the mean wave, which is also called the "coherent" wave. In it L^{-1} occurs. If x denotes a point in three-dimensional space, then L^{-1} is given by

$$L^{-1}f(x, t) = \frac{-1}{4\pi}\int r^{-1}f(y, t - c^{-1}r)\,dy, \qquad r = |x - y|. \tag{5}$$

This choice of L^{-1} is such that $L^{-1}f$ tends to zero as t tends to $-\infty$ provided that f vanishes sufficiently rapidly at $t = -\infty$.

The term in (2.11) involving L^{-1} is

$$\begin{aligned}\langle L_1L^{-1}L_1\rangle\langle u(x, t)\rangle &= \Big\langle -2c^{-2}\mu(x, t)\,\partial_t^2\frac{(-1)}{4\pi}\int r^{-1}[-2c^{-2}\mu(y, t - c^{-1}r) \\ &\qquad \times \partial_t^2\langle u(y, t - c^{-1}r)\rangle]\,dy\Big\rangle \\ &= \frac{-1}{\pi c^4}\Big\langle \mu(x, t)\int r^{-1}[\mu_{tt}(y, t - c^{-1}r)\langle u(y, t - c^{-1}r)\rangle_{tt} \\ &\qquad + 2\mu_t(y, t - c^{-1}r)\langle u(y, t - c^{-1}r)\rangle_{ttt} \\ &\qquad + \mu(y, t - c^{-1}r)\langle u(y, t - c^{-1}r)\rangle_{tttt}]\,dy\Big\rangle.\end{aligned} \tag{6}$$

If the factor $\mu(x, t)$ is taken under the integral sign in (6), the expectation value of each term of the integrand can be expressed in terms of the correlation function R defined by

$$\langle\mu(x, t)\mu(y, s)\rangle = R(|x - y|, |t - s|). \tag{7}$$

In (7) we have written R as a function of $|x - y|$ and $|t - s|$ which we assume to be the case. This is appropriate when the medium is statistically homogeneous and isotropic in space and stationary in time. When (7) is used in (6) and the result inserted into (2.11), the final equation is

$$\begin{aligned}&[\Delta - c^{-2}(1 + \varepsilon^2\langle\mu^2\rangle)\,\partial_t^2]\langle u(x, t)\rangle + \frac{\varepsilon^2}{\pi c^4}\int r^{-1}[R_{\tau\tau}(r, r/c)\langle u(y, t - c^{-1}r)\rangle_{tt} \\ &\quad - 2R_\tau(r, r/c)\langle u(y, t - c^{-1}r)\rangle_{ttt} + R(r, r/c)\langle u(y, t - c^{-1}r)\rangle_{tttt}]\,dy = 0.\end{aligned} \tag{8}$$

In (8) R_τ denotes the derivative of R with respect to its second argument and the $O(\varepsilon^3)$ term has been omitted. It is to be noted that from (7), $\langle\mu^2\rangle = R(0, 0)$. If the medium is not statistically isotropic then R depends upon the vector $x - y$ rather than just its length. In this case (8) still applies if the first argument of R

is understood to denote this vector. R. C. Bourret [5] derived the special form of (8) which applies when $\mu(x)$ is independent of t so that $R_\tau = R_{\tau\tau} = 0$, but he omitted the term $-c^{-2}\langle\mu^2\rangle\,\partial_t^2\langle u\rangle$.

Let us now apply (8) to a coherent wave $\langle u\rangle$ which is time harmonic with angular frequency ω

(9) $$\langle u(x, t)\rangle = e^{-i\omega t}v(x).$$

If we introduce k_0 defined by $k_0 = \omega/c$, the resulting equation for $v(x)$ becomes

(10) $$[\Delta + k_0^2(1 + \varepsilon^2\langle\mu^2\rangle)]v(x) + \frac{\varepsilon^2 k_0^2}{\pi c^2}\int r^{-1}\, e^{ik_0 r}[\omega^2 R(r, r/c) - i\omega R_\tau(r, r/c) - R_{\tau\tau}(r, r/c)]v(y)\, dy = 0.$$

W. C. Meecham [13] and F. C. Karal and J. B. Keller [14] have derived the special form of (10) in which $R_\tau = R_{\tau\tau} = 0$ by applying the present method to the reduced wave equation for a time independent random medium. (Meecham did not include the term in $\varepsilon^2\mu^2$ in his original equation, so $\varepsilon^2\langle\mu^2\rangle$ does not occur in his result.)

An important consequence of (10) is the effective propagation constant k of the random medium. We may find it by considering a plane wave solution with propagation vector $\mathbf{k}$, with $k = |\mathbf{k}|$. Thus let

(11) $$v(x) = e^{i\mathbf{k}\cdot\mathbf{x}}.$$

To evaluate the volume integral in (10) we may first integrate over the surface of a sphere of radius r centered at x. This integral can be evaluated by using a mean value theorem which applies to any solution v of the reduced wave equation

(12) $$(\Delta + k^2)v = 0.$$

It yields

(13) $$\int v(\mathbf{x} + \mathbf{r})\, dS = \frac{4\pi r}{k}\sin kr \cdot v(x).$$

Upon inserting (11) into (10) and using (13), we obtain

(14) $$k^2 = k_0^2(1 + \varepsilon^2\langle\mu^2\rangle) + \frac{4\varepsilon^2 k_0^2}{kc^2}\int_0^\infty e^{ik_0 r}\sin kr[\omega^2 R(r, r/c) - i\omega R_\tau(r, r/c) - R_{\tau\tau}(r, r/c)]\, dr.$$

This is an equation for k. For the special case in which $R_\tau = R_{\tau\tau} = 0$, it was obtained previously [13; 14]. Any solution v of (10) also satisfies (12) with k determined by (14) as we can see from the above derivation of (14).

We can solve (14) for k when ε is small by replacing k by k_0 on the right side. When $R_\tau = R_{\tau\tau} = 0$, so that R depends only upon its first argument, this procedure yields the following known result [1; 13; 14]

(15) $$(k/k_0)^2 = 1 + \varepsilon^2\langle\mu^2\rangle - 2i\varepsilon^2 k_0\int_0^\infty (e^{2ik_0 r} - 1)R(r)\, dr.$$

The imaginary part of k is the attenuation coefficient for the coherent wave. We shall now prove from (15) that the attenuation coefficient is positive and also that $\text{Re}\, k > (1 + \varepsilon^2\langle\mu^2\rangle)\, \text{Re}\, k_0$, which shows that the phase velocity of the coherent wave is less when $\varepsilon \neq 0$ than when $\varepsilon = 0$. This is in accordance with expectations, since the scattering of the wave should increase the distance which it travels in going from one point to another, and therefore decrease its effective velocity. Our demonstration is essentially that of W. C. Meecham [13].

To prove these things we introduce $\rho(s)$, the three-dimensional Fourier transform of $R(r)$, and utilize (13) to rewrite it as follows:

$$\rho(s) = \int e^{i\mathbf{s}\cdot\mathbf{r}} R(r)\, d\mathbf{r} = \int_0^\infty \frac{4\pi r}{s} \sin sr R(r)\, ds. \tag{16}$$

Since $\rho(s)$ is the Fourier transform of a correlation function, $\rho(s) > 0$. The inverse Fourier sine transform yields

$$rR(r) = \frac{1}{2\pi^2} \int_0^\infty s\rho(s) \sin sr\, ds. \tag{17}$$

Upon using (17) in the integral in (15), that integral becomes

$$\begin{aligned} \int_0^\infty (e^{2ik_0r} - 1)R(r)\, dr &= \frac{1}{2\pi^2} \int_0^\infty \int_0^\infty (e^{2ik_0r} - 1)r^{-1}s\rho(s) \sin sr\, ds\, dr \\ &= -\frac{1}{4\pi} \int_0^{2k_0} s\rho(s)\, ds \\ &\quad + \frac{i}{4\pi^2} \int_0^\infty s\rho(s) \log |(s + 2k_0)/(s - 2k_0)|\, ds. \end{aligned} \tag{18}$$

In (18) we have made use of known Fourier sine transforms. Now (15) and (18) yield

$$\begin{aligned} k = k_0 + k_0\varepsilon^2\langle\mu^2\rangle &+ \frac{\varepsilon^2 k_0^2}{4\pi^2} \int_0^\infty s\rho(s) \log |(s + 2k_0)/(s - 2k_0)|\, ds \\ &+ \frac{i\varepsilon^2 k_0^2}{4\pi} \int_0^{2k_0} s\rho(s)\, ds. \end{aligned} \tag{19}$$

Both integrals in (19) are positive, which proves the statements in the preceding paragraph. It is also of interest to note from (19) that only those Fourier components of the correlation with $s < 2k_0$ contribute to the attenuation. Thus the long wavelength components of the correlation attenuate the wave while the short wavelength ones merely scatter it and slow it down.

It is instructive to consider another derivation of (15) which is of quite general applicability and is based upon physical considerations. Let us consider a time harmonic wave $u_0(x) = e^{ik_0x}$ incident along the x-axis upon a slab of scattering material lying between the planes $x = 0$ and $x = \delta x$. Let the wave scattered by unit volume of the scattering material be $U_s(x) = f(\theta)r^{-1} e^{ik_0r}$ at large distances r

from the scattering material, where θ is the polar coordinate of x with the x-axis as polar axis. Then the total field $u(x) = u_0(x) + u_s(x)$ is given by

$$u(x) = e^{ik_0x} + \int_0^{\delta x}\int_0^{\infty} f(\theta)r^{-1}\, e^{ik_0r} 2\pi\rho\, d\rho\, dx'. \tag{20}$$

Here $r^2 = \rho^2 + (x-x')^2$. If $k_0\delta x << 1$ we may set $x' = 0$ in (20) and then the x' integration merely yields multiplication by δx. Now $\rho d\rho = rdr$ and $\theta = \cos^{-1}(x/r)$ so (20) becomes for $x > 0$,

$$\begin{aligned} u(x) &= e^{ik_0x} + 2\pi\delta x \int_x^{\infty} f[\cos^{-1}(x/r)]\, e^{ik_0r}\, dr \\ &\approx e^{ik_0x} - \frac{2\pi\delta x}{ik_0} f(0)\, e^{ik_0x}. \end{aligned} \tag{21}$$

The last form of (21) is obtained by integration by parts and then neglecting the contribution from infinity, which is valid if k_0 has a positive imaginary part, and neglecting the remaining integral. Actually the last form of (21) is a solution of the reduced wave equation, and it is exactly correct when the exact form of $U_s(x)$ is used rather than the far field form.

When δx is small we may rewrite (21) at $x = \delta x$ in the form

$$u(x) = e^{i[k_0 + 2\pi f(0)/k_0]\delta x}. \tag{22}$$

Thus the scattering material behaves as if it had an effective propagation constant k given by

$$k = k_0 + 2\pi f(0)/k_0. \tag{23}$$

Upon squaring both sides of this equation, and assuming that $f(0)$ is small, we obtain

$$k^2 = k_0^2 + 2\pi f(0). \tag{24}$$

Equation (23) was essentially obtained by Rayleigh **[15]** and (24) by F. Reiche **[16]**, L. Foldy **[2]**, and M. Lax **[3]** for discrete scatterers of various types. The quantity $f(0)$ is called the forward scattering amplitude per unit volume. From (23) we have $\operatorname{Im} k = (2\pi/k_0) \operatorname{Im} f(0)$. The right side of this relation is just the total energy scattered by unit volume of scatterer, according to the so-called cross section theorem. Thus the attenuation coefficient is equal to this energy. Direct calculations of the scattered energy have yielded the expression for Im k contained in (15). That calculation and relevant references are given by L. A. Chernov **[15]**.

Let us apply the preceding considerations to the time harmonic coherent wave $\langle u(x, t)\rangle = e^{-i\omega t}v(x)$. The coherent scattered wave, defined to be $\langle u\rangle - u_0$, can be found from (2.9). When $\langle L_1\rangle = 0$ it is given by

$$\langle u\rangle - u_0 = \varepsilon^2 L^{-1}[\langle L_1 L^{-1} L_1\rangle - \langle L_2\rangle]\langle u\rangle + O(\varepsilon^3). \tag{25}$$

The quantity $\langle L_1 L^{-1} L_1\rangle\langle u\rangle$ has been computed in (6) and specialized to a statistically homogeneous isotropic medium in (8), where it is minus the term involving the integral. It is further specialized to a time harmonic wave in (10) and is again the integral term multiplied by $-e^{-i\omega t}$. The term $\langle L_2\rangle\langle u\rangle$, also given in (10), is $k_0^2\langle\mu^2\rangle v(x)\, e^{-i\omega t}$. Thus the right side of (25) is L^{-1} applied to $-e^{-i\omega t}$ times the ε^2 term in (10). When $v(x) = e^{i\mathbf{k}\cdot\mathbf{x}}$ it is L^{-1} applied to $-e^{-i\omega t+i\mathbf{k}\cdot\mathbf{x}}$ times the ε^2 term in (14), and that term is just a constant which we shall denote by α. Thus (25) becomes

$$\langle u\rangle - u_0 = -\alpha L^{-1}\, e^{-i\omega t+i\mathbf{k}\cdot\mathbf{x}} = \frac{\alpha e^{-i\omega t}}{4\pi}\int_V r^{-1}\, e^{i\mathbf{k}\cdot\mathbf{y}+ik_0 r}\, dy. \tag{26}$$

Here V is the scattering volume. If we set $k = k_0$ in the integral, and evaluate it at a point x far from V in the forward direction (i.e., in the direction of $\mathbf{k}$) we find that the exponent is constant. If $y = 0$ is a point in V and $r = |x|$ then (26) becomes

$$\langle u(x, t)\rangle - u_0(x, t) = \frac{\alpha V}{4\pi r}\, e^{-i\omega t+ikr}. \tag{27}$$

Thus the forward scattering amplitude per unit volume is $f(0) = \alpha/4\pi$. When α, the coefficient of ε^2, is replaced by $4\pi f(0)$ in (14), (14) becomes identical with (24). Thus (24), which was obtained by a physical argument, also follows from our formal result (14). In the case in which $R_\tau = R_{\tau\tau} = 0$, this was shown by W. C. Meecham **[13]**.

It should be observed that the solution of (14) given by (15) becomes infinite, and is therefore not valid when the correlation function $R(r)$ is a constant independent of r. This is the case in which the wavelength is small compared to the correlation length, defined as the distance beyond which the correlation function is practically zero. In this case if $R_\tau = R_{\tau\tau} = 0$ and $R(r) = \langle\mu^2\rangle$, (14) becomes

$$k^2 = k_0^2(1 + \varepsilon^2\langle\mu^2\rangle) + 2\varepsilon^2\langle\mu^2\rangle k_0^4 k^{-1}\left[\frac{1}{k_0 + k} - \frac{1}{k_0 - k}\right]. \tag{28}$$

The solution of (28) for k is

$$k = k_0(1 + \varepsilon\sqrt{\langle\mu^2\rangle}) + O(\varepsilon^2). \tag{29}$$

We see from (29) that the correction to k_0 is of order ε when the correlation length is long compared to the wavelength, while from (15) it is of order ε^2 when the correlation length is not long compared to the wavelength. The result (29) is also given by F. C. Karal and J. B. Keller **[14]**, who give similar results for other types of waves.

The method of §2, which we have employed in this section, has been applied to the equations of elastic wave propagation and to Maxwell's equations by F. C. Karal and J. B. Keller **[14]**. It has also been applied under less general conditions to the wave equation and to Maxwell's equations by R. C. Bourret **[5]**, as well as to various other equations.

4. **Wave propagation in media of discrete scatterers.** Let us now consider wave propagation in a homogeneous medium containing a random distribution of discrete scatterers. If the material constituting the individual scatterers differs very little from the surrounding medium, the present case can be treated by specializing the preceding analysis. However, if the individual scatterers are quite different from the surrounding medium, that analysis does not suffice in its present form. Therefore we shall give a modification of it which is applicable then provided a suitably defined collision operator associated with each scatterer is small.

We begin by assuming that the equation for the field u is of the form

$$\left(L - \sum_i V_i\right) u = 0. \tag{1}$$

Here the operator V_i represents the effect of the ith scatterer. Let u_0 denote a particular solution of the equation which applies when no scatterers are present, namely

$$Lu_0 = 0. \tag{2}$$

Now we may rewrite (1) for a particular solution in the form

$$u = u_0 + L^{-1} \sum_i V_i u. \tag{3}$$

Let us define u^i by

$$u^i = u - L^{-1} V_i u. \tag{4}$$

Then u^i represents the field incident upon the ith scatterer. In terms of u^i we define the ith transition operator T_i' by

$$T_i' u^i = V_i u. \tag{5}$$

From (4) and (5) T_i' is given by

$$T_i' = V_i(1 - L^{-1}V_i)^{-1} = V_i(L - V_i)^{-1}L. \tag{6}$$

We shall henceforth assume that T_i' is known since it depends only upon scattering by one scatterer, and shall continue our analysis in terms of it.

By using (5) and (4) we see that

$$u^i = (1 + L^{-1}T_i')^{-1}u. \tag{7}$$

Now (7) and (5) permit us to write (3) in the form

$$u = u_0 + L^{-1} \sum_i T_i'(1 + L^{-1}T_i')^{-1}u. \tag{8}$$

Upon applying L to (8) it becomes

$$\left[L - \sum_i T_i'(1 + L^{-1}T_i')^{-1}\right] u = 0. \tag{9}$$

To make explicit our hypothesis that T_i' is small we shall write $T_i' = \varepsilon T_i$. Upon expanding the quantity $(1 + \varepsilon L^{-1}T_i)^{-1}$ in powers of ε, we may write (9) in the form

$$\left[L - \varepsilon \sum_i T_i' + \varepsilon^2 \sum_i T_i L^{-1} T_i + O(\varepsilon^3)\right] u = 0. \tag{10}$$

This is the form of the equation for u which we sought.

We now observe that (10) is of the form (2.3) with L_1 and L_2 given by

$$L_1 = -\sum_i T_i, \tag{11}$$

$$L_2 = \sum_i T_i L^{-1} T_i. \tag{12}$$

Thus the analysis and results of §2 apply to (10), and $\langle u \rangle$ satisfies (2.10). When the T_i all have the same mean and there are N of them, we have from (11) and (12)

$$\langle L_1 \rangle = -N\langle T_1 \rangle, \tag{13}$$

$$\langle L_2 \rangle = N\langle T_1 L^{-1} T_1 \rangle, \tag{14}$$

$$\langle L_1 \rangle L^{-1} \langle L_1 \rangle = N^2 \langle T_1 \rangle L^{-1} \langle T_1 \rangle. \tag{15}$$

If $\langle T_i L^{-1} T_j \rangle$ is independent of i and j when $i \neq j$ and independent of i when $i = j$ then we also have

$$\langle L_1 L^{-1} L_1 \rangle = \sum_{i,j} \langle T_i L^{-1} T_j \rangle = N\langle T_1 L^{-1} T_1 \rangle + N(N-1)\langle T_1 L^{-1} T_2 \rangle. \tag{16}$$

Now (2.10) becomes

$$\{L - \varepsilon N\langle T_1 \rangle - (\varepsilon N)^2[(1 - N^{-1})\langle T_1 L^{-1} T_2 \rangle - \langle T_1 \rangle L^{-1} \langle T_1 \rangle]\}\langle u \rangle = O(\varepsilon^3). \tag{17}$$

This is the equation for $\langle u \rangle$ which we shall utilize.

Let us now assume that the ith scatterer, represented by the transition operator T_i, is characterized by a position x_i and an internal coordinate or label f_i. Then we may write $T = T(x_i, f_i)$. Let us further assume that each f_i is independent of all other variables so the mean of T_i with respect to f_i is a function of x_i only which we denote by $T(x_i)$. In addition let each x_i be uniformly distributed over a region of volume v which contains the N scatterers. Then if we let N and v become infinite with $N/v = \rho$ remaining constant, and drop the $O(\varepsilon^3)$ term, (17) becomes

$$\begin{aligned} \Big\{L - \varepsilon\rho \int T_1(x)\,dx - \varepsilon^2\rho^2 \Big[\iint T(x_1)L^{-1}T(x_2)F(x_1, x_2)\,dx_1\,dx_2 \\ - \int T(x)\,dx L^{-1} \int T(x)\,dx\Big]\Big\}\langle u \rangle = 0. \end{aligned} \tag{18}$$

In (18) $F(x_1, x_2)$ denotes v^2 times the probability density of scatterer 1 being at x_1 and scatterer 2 at x_2. We shall assume that $F(x_1, x_2)$ depends only upon $r = x_1 - x_2$ and define the pair correlation function $g(r)$ by $g(r) = f(r) - 1$. When $g(\mathbf{r}) = g(r)$, g is called the radial distribution function.

As an example of the use of (18) let us consider the case in which u is a scalar and $L = \Delta + k_0^2$. Then the Green's function of L is $G(|x - x'|) = G(r) = -e^{ik_0 r}/4\pi r$. Let us assume that the scatterers are small isotropic scatterers so that the wave scattered by a scatterer at x_1 is $L^{-1}(x)T(x_1, f_1)u = -4\pi f_1 G(|x - x_1|)u(x_1)$, a spherical wave emanating from x_1. Upon applying $L(x)$ to this equation we find that T is given by $T(x_1, f_1) = -4\pi f_1 \delta(x - x_1)$. Let us denote the mean value of f_1 by f. Then (18) becomes

$$(19)\quad (\Delta + k_0^2 + 4\pi\varepsilon\rho f)\langle u\rangle - (4\pi\varepsilon\rho f)^2 \left[\int G(|x - x'|)F(x - x')\langle u(x')\rangle\, dx' - \int G(|x - x'|)\langle u(x')\rangle\, dx'\right] = 0.$$

We now assume that $\langle u(x)\rangle$ satisfies (3.12) or is a plane wave with propagation constant k, that $F(\mathbf{r}) = F(r)$ and then use (3.13) to simplify the integral in (19). Then (19) yields the following equation for k^2

$$(20)\quad k^2 = k_0^2 + 4\pi\varepsilon\rho f + (4\pi\varepsilon\rho f)^2 k^{-1} \int_0^\infty e^{ik_0 r} g(r) \sin kr\, dr.$$

The solution of (20) valid to order ε^2 is

$$(21)\quad k^2 = k_0^2 + 4\pi\varepsilon\rho f + (4\pi\varepsilon\rho f)^2 k_0^{-1} \int_0^\infty e^{ik_0 r} g(r) \sin k_0 r\, dr.$$

Let us compare this result with that obtained from a random continuous medium for which u satisfies

$$(22)\quad [\Delta + k_0^2 + \varepsilon\mu(x)k_0^2]u = 0.$$

From (22) we see that $L = \Delta + k_0^2$, $L_1 = \mu k_0^2$, $\langle L_1\rangle = k_0^2\langle\mu\rangle$, and $L_2 = 0$. By using these values in (2.14) and assuming that $\langle\mu\rangle$ is a constant, we obtain

$$(23)\quad (\Delta + k_0^2 + \varepsilon k_0^2\langle\mu\rangle)\langle u\rangle + \varepsilon^2 k_0^4 \langle\mu\rangle^2 \int G(x - x')\langle u(x')\rangle\, dx' - \varepsilon^2 k_0^4 \int G(x - x')\langle\mu(x)\mu(x')\rangle\langle u(x')\rangle\, dx' = 0.$$

We now assume that the correlation function $\langle\mu(x)\mu(x')\rangle$ is a function only of $r = |x - x'|$ and in terms of it we define $g_c(r)$ by

$$(24)\quad g_c(r) = \frac{\langle\mu(x)\mu(x')\rangle}{\langle\mu\rangle^2} - 1.$$

Then if $\langle u(x)\rangle$ is a plane wave or satisfies (3.12) with propagation constant k, we can simplify the integrals in (23) by using (3.13). In this way from (23) we obtain for k the equation

$$(25)\quad k^2 = k_0^2 + \varepsilon k_0^2\langle\mu\rangle + (\varepsilon k_0^2\langle\mu\rangle)^2 k^{-1} \int_0^\infty e^{ik_0 r} g_c(r) \sin kr\, dr.$$

Upon comparing (25) with (20) we see that they become identical if $\langle\mu\rangle = 4\pi\rho f/k_0^2$ and if $g(r) = g_c(r)$.

We may interpret this result by noting that the discrete random medium can be described as a continuous medium with refractive index $n = k/k_0$, where k is given by (20) or (21). This description is appropriate when considering the mean wave $\langle u\rangle$ which satisfies the equation $(\Delta + k_0^2 n^2)\langle u\rangle = 0$. In this description the effective refractive index n is a constant which is given up to order ε^2 by using (21) for k. Alternatively we could use only the terms up to order ε in (21) and define a different equivalent continuous medium with refractive index $1 + \varepsilon\mu/2 = (k_0^2 + 4\pi\varepsilon\rho f)^{1/2}/k_0 = 1 + 2\pi\varepsilon\rho f k_0^{-2}$ so that $\mu = 4\pi\rho f k_0^{-2}$. Then if we let the density of scatterers be a random function of position, $\rho = \rho(x)$, it follows that $\mu = \mu(x)$, so the refractive index is also a random function. Then the mean wave in this medium has a propagation constant given by (25) and its effective refractive index is the constant k/k_0. As we have seen, this effective index is the same as the constant n obtained directly from the discrete case, provided $g(r) = g_c(r)$. Now $g_c(r) = \langle\rho(x)\rho(x')\rangle\langle\rho\rangle^{-2} - 1$. If $\rho(x)$ denotes the probable density at x, this expression is the same as $g(r)$.

To consider more general scatterers let us return to (18) and assume that $T(x)$ differs from the operator $T(0)$ by a translation, which we express by

$$T(x) = e^{-\mathbf{x}\cdot\nabla}T(0)\, e^{\mathbf{x}\cdot\nabla}. \tag{26}$$

Let us also assume that L is independent of x. Then the operator in (18) is translationally invariant so (18) has plane wave solutions. To find them we may assume that $\langle u\rangle$ is a plane wave and insert it into (18). When u is a scalar the result can be expressed in terms of "matrix elements" of the operator in (18). For any operator such as L they are defined by

$$L_{k'k} = \lim_{v\to\infty} \frac{1}{v}\int_v e^{-i\mathbf{k}'\cdot\mathbf{x}} L\, e^{i\mathbf{k}\cdot\mathbf{x}}\, dx. \tag{27}$$

However, for $T(0)$ we define them by

$$T_{k'k}(0) = \int e^{-i\mathbf{k}'\cdot\mathbf{x}} T(0)\, e^{i\mathbf{k}\cdot\mathbf{x}}\, dx. \tag{28}$$

Now if (18) has a plane wave solution $e^{i\mathbf{k}\cdot\mathbf{x}}$ then it follows from (18), (27) and (28) that k must satisfy the equation

$$\begin{aligned} L_{kk} - \varepsilon\rho T_{kk}(0) - \varepsilon^2\rho^2 \Big[\int T(x_1)L^{-1}T(x_2)F(x_1, x_2)\, dx_1\, dx_2 & \\ - \int T(x)\, dx L^{-1} \int T(x)\, dx \Big]_{kk} &= 0. \end{aligned} \tag{29}$$

If we use the facts that L^{-1} is a diagonal matrix and that $F(x_1, x_2) = F(x_1 - x_2)$ we may evaluate the last matrix element in (29) by using the Fourier integral, or equivalently the plane wave representation of the operators. The result after some calculation is that (29) becomes the following equation for k:

$$(30)\qquad L_{kk} - \varepsilon\rho T_{kk}(0) + \varepsilon^2\rho^2 \frac{1}{(2\pi)^3}\int T_{ks}(0)L_{ss}^{-1}T_{sk}(0)\int e^{i(\mathbf{s}-\mathbf{k})\cdot\mathbf{r}}g(\mathbf{r})\,d\mathbf{r}\,d\mathbf{s} = 0.$$

The equation (30) for k may be rewritten in terms of the operator $f = -T(0)/4\pi$ and becomes

$$(31)\qquad L_{kk} + 4\pi\varepsilon\rho f_{kk} + \frac{2}{\pi}(\varepsilon\rho)^2\int f_{ks}L_{ss}^{-1}f_{sk}\int e^{i(\mathbf{s}-\mathbf{k})\cdot\mathbf{r}}g(\mathbf{r})\,d\mathbf{r}\,d\mathbf{s} = 0.$$

This result is identical with that of M. Lax [**3b**] which is obtained from his equations (3.19) and (4.10) provided his factor $c = (1 - J)^{-1}$ is expanded in the form $c \approx 1 + J$, which is appropriate for weak scatterers. His method of derivation, which differs from ours, involves an assumption which will be considered later. We note that the last integrand in (30) involves only the $\mathbf{s} - \mathbf{k}$ Fourier component of the pair correlation function $g(\mathbf{r})$. This is the component of $g(\mathbf{r})$ which yields first order Bragg reflection of a wave with the propagation vector $\mathbf{k}$ into one with the propagation vector $\mathbf{s}$. It also involves only those double scattering processes which lead from a wave with the propagation vector $\mathbf{k}$ into one with the same propagation vector, i.e., which combine to yield forward scattering without change of wavelength. When we specialize (30) to the case in which $L = \Delta + k_0^2$, $g(\mathbf{r}) = g(r)$ and $T(0) = -4\pi f\delta(x)$ we obtain the previous result (19), which provides a check on our calculations.

Let us now see how our original equation (17) simplifies when all V_i are small. To this end we shall indicate that V_i is small by replacing V_i by εV_i in (6), from which it then follows that

$$(32)\qquad T_i = V_i + \varepsilon V_i L^{-1} V_i + O(\varepsilon^2).$$

When (32) is used in (17), (17) becomes

$$(33)\qquad \{L - \varepsilon N\langle V_1\rangle - (\varepsilon N)^2[(1 - N^{-1})\langle V_1L^{-1}V_2\rangle - \langle V_1\rangle L^{-1}\langle V_1\rangle + N^{-1}\langle V_1L^{-1}V_1\rangle]\}\langle u\rangle = O(\varepsilon^3).$$

This equation also follows directly from (1) in which $L_1 = \sum_i V_i$ and $L_2 = 0$. When these expressions are used in (2.10) and $\langle V_i\rangle$ is independent of i while $\langle V_iL^{-1}V_j\rangle$ is independent of i and j for $i \neq j$ and is independent of i for $i = j$, (33) follows at once. This shows that our original analysis applies directly when the scatterers are "weak." If N is large the terms in N^{-1} can be omitted and (33) simplifies to

$$(34)\qquad \{L - \varepsilon N\langle V_1\rangle - (\varepsilon N)^2(\langle V_1L^{-1}V_2\rangle - \langle V_1\rangle L^{-1}\langle V_1\rangle)\}\langle u\rangle = O(\varepsilon^3).$$

If the N^{-1} term is omitted in (17), then (17) has the same form as (34) with T_i replacing V_i. Thus results deduced for weak scatterers from (34) can be converted into results valid for strong scatterers by replacing V_i by T_i in them.

A "dishonest" derivation of (17), which does not yield the ε^2 term, has been used in special cases by L. Foldy [2] and V. Twersky [4], and in a general form by M. Lax [3]. It is based upon a set of equations for the u^i which are derived by first subtracting $L^{-1}V_j u$ from each side of (3) to yield

(35) $$u - L^{-1}V_j u = u_0 + L^{-1}\sum_{i\neq j} V_i u.$$

From (4) the left side of (35) is u^j while the right side can be expressed in terms of the u^i with the aid of (5). Then (35) becomes

(36) $$u^j = u_0 + L^{-1}\sum_{i\neq j} T_i' u^i.$$

There is one equation of the form (36) for each j and these N equations determine the u^j self-consistently. It is easy to show that when the u^i satisfy the set (36), a solution of (3) is

(37) $$u = u_0 + L^{-1}\sum_i T_i' u^i.$$

Upon taking the expectation value of (37) we obtain

(38) $$\langle u\rangle = u_0 = L^{-1}\sum_i \int T_i' \langle u^i\rangle_i \, dp(V_i).$$

Here $\langle u^i\rangle_i$ denotes the conditional expectation of u^i with V_i fixed, i.e., the expectation with respect to the conditional probability distribution of all the V_j with $j \neq i$ and $dp(V_i)$ denotes the probability distribution of V_i. To determine $\langle u^i\rangle_i$ we take the expectation of (36) keeping V_j fixed. This yields

(39) $$\langle u^j\rangle_j = u_0 + L^{-1}\sum_{i\neq j} \int T_i' \langle u^i\rangle_{ij} \, dp(V_i | V_j).$$

Here $\langle u^i\rangle_{ij}$ is the conditional expectation of u^i with V_i and V_j fixed and $dp(V_i | V_j)$ is the conditional distribution of V_i with V_j fixed. We see that (39) involves $\langle u^i\rangle_{ij}$ and to determine it we could take the expectation of (36) with V_i and V_j fixed but this would introduce new conditional expectations. Equations (38) and (39) are the first two in a sequence of equations for successive conditional expectations called the hierarchy equations.

In order to avoid solving the hierarchy equations Foldy and Twersky assume that the "effective" field $\langle u^i\rangle_i$ incident upon scatterer i is the same as the average field $\langle u\rangle$. Lax introduces a factor c and writes

(40) $$\langle u^i\rangle_i = c\langle u\rangle.$$

Then (38) becomes

(41) $$\langle u\rangle = u_0 + L^{-1}cN\langle T_1'\rangle\langle u\rangle.$$

Upon applying L to (41) it becomes

(42) $$[L - cN\langle T_1'\rangle]\langle u\rangle = 0.$$

When $c = 1$ this is the same as (17), except for the ε^2 terms and this completes the derivation. Lax [3b] has also used (39), assuming that $\langle u^i \rangle_{ij} = \langle u^i \rangle_i$ together with a variational procedure to obtain an expression for c. When his value of c is used in (42) it leads to (31), as pointed out below (31). Lax [3] has concluded from (31) that in (42) T_1' should be the scattering operator appropriate to scattering in the "new" medium governed by (42). Twersky [4] instead takes T_1' to be the scattering operator which results when an incident wave appropriate to the new medium is scattered into the original medium. Both of these choices as well as the effective field hypothesis (40) are unproved. Our derivation of (17) confirms the result (42) of the effective field hypothesis with $\varepsilon = 1$ through terms of order ε, but it does not confirm the hypothesis itself. Our result (31) confirms Lax's calculation of c to order ε^2.

To examine the validity of the hypothesis (40) with $c = 1$, we proceed as follows. Let us use (5) in (4) and then take the expectation of the resulting equation with V_i fixed. We obtain

$$\langle u^i \rangle_i = \langle u \rangle_i - L^{-1} T_i' \langle u^i \rangle_i. \tag{43}$$

Solving (43) for $\langle u^i \rangle_i$ yields

$$\langle u^i \rangle_i = (1 + L^{-1} T_i')^{-1} \langle u \rangle_i. \tag{44}$$

Upon setting $T_i' = \varepsilon T_i$ and expanding, we obtain from (44)

$$\langle u^i \rangle_i = [L - \varepsilon L^{-1} T_i + \varepsilon^2 L^{-1} T_i L^{-1} T_i + O(\varepsilon^3)] \langle u \rangle_i. \tag{45}$$

Performing the same expansion in (8) and solving by iterations yields

$$u = u_0 + \varepsilon L^{-1} \sum_j T_j u_0 + \varepsilon^2 L^{-1} \sum_{j \neq k}\sum T_j L^{-1} T_k u_0 + O(\varepsilon^3). \tag{46}$$

The mean of (46) is

$$\langle u \rangle = u_0 + \varepsilon N L^{-1} \langle T_1 \rangle u_0 + \varepsilon^2 N(N-1) L^{-1} \langle T_1 L^{-1} T_2 \rangle u_0 + O(\varepsilon^3). \tag{47}$$

The mean of (46) with T_i fixed, and $i \neq 1, 2$ for notational convenience, is

$$\begin{aligned} \langle u \rangle_i = u_0 &+ \varepsilon[(N-1) L^{-1} \langle T_1 \rangle_i + L^{-1} T_i] u_0 + \varepsilon^2 (N-1)[(N-2) L^{-1} \langle T_1 L^{-1} T_2 \rangle_i \\ &- L^{-1} \langle T_1 L^{-1} T_1 \rangle_i + L^{-1} \langle T_1 \rangle_i L^{-1} T_i + L^{-1} T_i L^{-1} \langle T_1 \rangle_i] u_0 + O(\varepsilon^3). \end{aligned} \tag{48}$$

Now (45) and (48) yield

$$\begin{aligned} \langle u^i \rangle_i &= \langle u_i \rangle - \varepsilon^2 (N-1) L^{-1} T_i L^{-1} \langle T_1 \rangle_i u_0 + O(\varepsilon^3) \\ &= u_0 + \varepsilon[(N-1) L^{-1} \langle T_1 \rangle_i + L^{-1} T_i] u_0 + \varepsilon^2 (N-1)[(N-2) L^{-1} \langle T_1 L^{-1} T_2 \rangle_i \\ &\quad - L^{-1} \langle T_1 L^{-1} T_1 \rangle_i + L^{-1} \langle T_1 \rangle_i L^{-1} T_i] u_0 + O(\varepsilon^3). \end{aligned} \tag{49}$$

To test the effective field hypothesis (40) with $c = 1$ we must compare (49) with (47). To do so we form the difference

$$\begin{aligned} \langle u^i \rangle_i - \langle u \rangle = \varepsilon N L^{-1} &[(1 - N^{-1}) \langle T_1 \rangle_i - \langle T_1 \rangle + N^{-1} T_i] u_0 \\ &+ \varepsilon^2 N(N-1) L^{-1} [(1 - 2N^{-1}) \langle T_1 L^{-1} T_2 \rangle_i - \langle T_1 L^{-1} T_2 \rangle \\ &- N^{-1} \langle T_1 L^{-1} T_1 \rangle_i + N^{-1} \langle T_1 \rangle_i L^{-1} T_i] u_0 + O(\varepsilon^3). \end{aligned} \tag{50}$$

Even if the terms in N^{-1} are dropped from (50) when N is large, the difference between $\langle u^i \rangle_i$ and $\langle u \rangle$ is still $O(\varepsilon)$. This order of difference leads to a result (42) which is correct through terms of order ε when $c = 1$, but fails to yield the ε^2 terms correctly. The intuitive argument for (40) is that keeping V_i fixed affects only $(1/N)$th of the scattered field, which is negligible for large N. This only pertains to the terms in (50) proportional to N^{-1} but it fails to account for the effect of keeping V_i fixed upon the distribution of the other scatterers, which affects the mean fields scattered by them. That effect is responsible for the terms $\varepsilon N(\langle T_1 \rangle_i - \langle T_1 \rangle)$, which would vanish if the scatterers were independently distributed. In that case the ε^2 term in (17) is proportional to N rather than to N^2, so that the effective field hypothesis then yields a result which is practically correct through terms of order ε^2.

One might also be led to believe the hypothesis in the case of independently identically distributed scatterers on the basis of its self-consistency, which we shall now demonstrate. By this we mean that the assumption $\langle u^i \rangle_{ij} = \langle u^i \rangle_i$ implies $\langle u^i \rangle_i = \langle u \rangle$ when N is large. To show this we first note that $\langle u^i \rangle_i = \langle u^1 \rangle_1$ by symmetry, and that $dp(V_i | V_j) = dp(V_i)$ by independence. Therefore the second hierarchy equation (39) can be written as

$$\begin{aligned} \langle u^1 \rangle_1 &= u_0 + L^{-1} \sum_{i \neq j} \int T_i' \langle u^i \rangle_i \, dp(V_i) \\ &= u_0 + (N-1) L^{-1} \int T_1' \langle u^1 \rangle_1 \, dp(V_1). \end{aligned} \tag{51}$$

From (38) we have

$$L^{-1} \int T_1' \langle u^1 \rangle_1 \, dp(V_1) + N^{-1}(\langle u \rangle - u_0). \tag{52}$$

Therefore (51) becomes

$$\langle u^1 \rangle_1 = \langle u \rangle - N^{-1}(\langle u \rangle - u_0). \tag{53}$$

For large N this is just (40) with $c = 1$, proving the asserted self-consistency.

Before concluding the present discussion, we shall consider an exact consequence of the second hierarchy equation (39), based on a consideration applicable to all hierarchy equations. In our previous analysis of (39) we noted that it contained both $\langle u^i \rangle_i$ and $\langle u^i \rangle_{ij}$ and we eliminated the latter by making a hypothesis. Instead we shall now eliminate the former, which can be done exactly since by definition

$$\langle u^i \rangle_i = \int \langle u^i \rangle_{ij} \, dp(V_j | V_i). \tag{54}$$

By using (54), and noting that $\int u_0 \, dp(V_i | V_j) = u_0$, we can write (39) as an equation for $\langle u^i \rangle_{ij}$

$$\int \langle u^j \rangle_{ji} \, dp(V_i | V_j) = \int u_0 \, dp(V_i | V_j) + L^{-1} \sum_{i \neq j} \int T_i' \langle u^i \rangle_{ij} \, dp(V_i | V_j). \tag{55}$$

If the V_i are symmetrically distributed it follows that $\langle u^i \rangle_{ij} = \langle u^1 \rangle_{12}$ and (55) can be written as

$$\int [\langle u^2 \rangle_{21} - u_0 - (N-1)L^{-1}T_1' \langle u^1 \rangle_{12}] \, dp(V_1 | V_2) = 0. \tag{56}$$

From (56) it follows that

$$\langle u^2 \rangle_{21} - u_0 - (N-1)L^{-1}T_1' \langle u^1 \rangle_{12} = w_{12}. \tag{57}$$

Here w_{12} is some function which satisfies the equation

$$\int w_{12} \, dp(V_1 | V_2) = 0. \tag{58}$$

Since (57) involves both $\langle u^2 \rangle_{21}$ and $\langle u^1 \rangle_{12}$ we rewrite it with 1 and 2 interchanged

$$\langle u^1 \rangle_{12} - u_0 - (N-1)L^{-1}T_2' \langle u^2 \rangle_{21} = w_{21}. \tag{59}$$

We may now solve (57) and (59) for $\langle u^2 \rangle_{21}$, obtaining

$$\langle u^2 \rangle_{21} = [1 - (N-1)^2 L^{-1}T_1' L^{-1}T_2']^{-1}[u_0 + w_{12} + (N-1)L^{-1}T_1'(u_0 + w_{21})]. \tag{60}$$

Now (54) yields $\langle u^1 \rangle_1$ and then (38) yields $\langle u \rangle$ in terms of the random function w_{12}, which is known only to satisfy (58). This interesting expression for $\langle u \rangle$ has not yet been used.

5. Hierarchy equations and equations for generating functionals. When the stochastic quantities in an equation are not small, the perturbation method used in the three preceding sections is not useful and a different method of analysis must be employed. We shall now describe two such methods, namely the method of hierarchy equations, which we have already touched upon, and the method involving a functional equation for a certain generating functional. The perturbation method involves solving the equation first and then averaging the solution while the hierarchy equations result from averaging first and then attempting to solve. In order to solve, it has been necessary to make unverified assumptions about the solution, some of which have been described above. Therefore we shall not discuss further the solution of these equations, but just their derivation. For this purpose we shall employ a simple example.

Let us consider a scalar function $u(x)$ satisfying the stochastic equation

$$L_x u + n(x)u(x) = g(x). \tag{1}$$

Here L_x is a given operator, $g(x)$ is a given function and $n(x)$ is a random function. Therefore $u(x)$ is also random. Upon taking the expectation of (1) in order to get an equation for $\langle u(x) \rangle$ we find

$$L_x \langle u \rangle + \langle n(x)u(x) \rangle = g(x). \tag{2}$$

Since (2) involves $\langle n(x)u(x) \rangle$ we may try to get an equation for this quantity by multiplying (1) by $n(x)$ and averaging. But this leads to $\langle nL_x u \rangle$ rather than $L_x \langle nu \rangle$.

Therefore since $n(x_1)$ commutes with L_x we multiply (1) instead by $n(x_1)$ and average to obtain

$$L_x\langle n(x_1)u(x)\rangle + \langle n(x_1)n(x)u(x)\rangle = \langle n(x_1)\rangle g(x). \tag{3}$$

Once $\langle n(x_1)u(x)\rangle$ is found from (3), we may evaluate it at $x_1 = x$ and use it in (2) to get an equation for $\langle u(x)\rangle$. Since (3) involves a new moment we must obtain another equation for it, etc. If we also try to determine higher moments of u, we are led to the following infinite set of equations

$$\begin{aligned} &L_x\langle u(x)u(x_1)\cdots u(x_j)n(x_{j+1})\cdots n(x_{j+k})\rangle \\ &\quad + \langle n(x)u(x)u(x_1)\cdots u(x_j)n(x_{j+1})\cdots n(x_{j+k})\rangle \\ &\qquad = g(x)\langle u(x_1)\cdots u(x_j)n(x_{j+k})\rangle, \qquad j, k = 0, 1, \cdots. \end{aligned} \tag{4}$$

These equations for the hierarchy of moments are called the hierarchy equations. Such equations have been discussed in the introduction and in the preceding sections.

Whenever an infinite set of moments occurs, it is helpful to seek a function which generates them. Since the moments in (4) are functions, they will be generated by a functional. We shall now show that they are generated by the functional $F[\xi, \eta]$, a functional of the two functions $\xi(x)$ and $\eta(x)$ defined by

$$F[\xi, \eta] = \left\langle \exp\left[\int \{\xi(x')u(x') + \eta(x')n(x')\}\, dx'\right]\right\rangle. \tag{5}$$

Functional differentiation of (5) yields

$$\begin{aligned} \frac{\delta^{j+k}F}{\delta\xi(x_1)\cdots\delta\xi(x_j)\delta\eta(x_{j+1})\cdots\delta\eta(x_{j+k})} &= \Big\langle u(x_1)\cdots u(x_j)n(x_{j+1})\cdots n(x_{j+k}) \\ &\quad\times \exp\left[\int \{\xi(x')u(x') + \eta(x')n(x')\}\, dx'\right]\Big\rangle. \end{aligned} \tag{6}$$

Evaluation of (6) at $\xi(x) \equiv 0$, $\eta(x) \equiv 0$ leads to the desired result

$$\begin{aligned} &\left[\frac{\delta^{j+k}F}{\delta\xi(x_1)\cdots\delta\xi(x_j)\delta\eta(x_{j+1})\cdots\delta\eta(x_{j+k})}\right]_{\xi=\eta=0} \\ &\qquad = \langle u(x_1)\cdots u(x_j)n(x_{j+1})\cdots n(x_{j+k})\rangle. \end{aligned} \tag{7}$$

Thus the functional derivatives of $F[\xi, \eta]$ at $\xi = \eta = 0$ are the moments occurring in the hierarchy equations. In terms of the moments, $F[\xi, \eta]$ can be expressed as a functional Taylor series

$$\begin{aligned} F[\xi, \eta] = \sum_{j,k=0}^{\infty} \frac{1}{j!k!} \int &\langle u(x_1)\cdots u(x_j)n(x_{j+1})\cdots n(x_{j+k})\rangle \xi(x_1)\cdots\xi(x_j) \\ &\cdots \eta(x_{j+1})\cdots\eta(x_{j+k})\, dx_1\cdots dx_{j+k}. \end{aligned} \tag{8}$$

We could also define a generating functional of the form (5) with the integral multiplied by i, which might exist for a larger class of distributions. But then factors of i would occur in many equations so we have omitted the i since our analysis is entirely formal.

From the hierarchy equations (4) and the Taylor series (8) one can deduce an equation satisfied by the functional $F[\xi, \eta]$. However, it is simpler to derive this equation directly from (1) by first noting that

$$\text{(9)} \qquad \begin{aligned} L_x \frac{\delta F}{\delta \xi(x)} + \frac{\delta^2 F}{\delta \xi(x) \delta \eta(x)} &= \left\langle \{L_x u(x) + u(x) n(x)\} \exp \left[\int \{\xi u + \eta n\}\, dx' \right] \right\rangle \\ &= \left\langle g(x) \exp \left[\int \{\xi u + \eta n\}\, dx' \right] \right\rangle. \end{aligned}$$

The last form of (9) follows from (1). Since $g(x)$ is not random it can be taken outside the expectation and (9) becomes

$$\text{(10)} \qquad L_x \frac{\delta F[\xi, \eta]}{\delta \xi(x)} + \frac{\delta F[\xi, \eta]}{\delta \xi(x) \delta \eta(x)} = g(x) F[\xi, \eta].$$

This is a functional differential equation for the generating functional F. By differentiating (10) with respect to $\xi(x_1), \cdots, \xi(x_j), \eta(x_{j+1}) \cdots \eta(x_{j+k})$, then setting $\xi(x) \equiv \eta(x) \equiv 0$ and using (7), the hierarchy equations (4) result. Thus (10) implies those equations, and it also follows from them. We note that when $g(x) \equiv 0$, F does not occur in (10) and it may be considered as an equation for the functional $\delta F / \delta \xi(x)$.

An additional condition on F can be obtained by setting $\xi(x) \equiv 0$ in (5), which yields

$$\text{(11)} \qquad F[0, \eta] = \left\langle \exp \left[\int \eta(x') n(x')\, dx' \right] \right\rangle.$$

Since the distribution of $n(x)$ is supposed to be known, the right side of (11) is known. Thus (11) is a "boundary condition" on F at the boundary $\xi(x) \equiv 0$. Other conditions on F can be obtained from information about u or conditions on u. For example, if $u(x) = 0$ for x on a surface S, then it follows from (5) that

$$\text{(12)} \qquad \frac{\delta F[\xi, \eta]}{\delta \xi(x)} = 0 \quad \text{for } x \text{ on } S.$$

Similarly, vanishing of $u(x)$ at infinity implies the vanishing there of $\delta F / \delta \xi(x)$.

Some methods for solving equations of the type (10) with additional conditions on F of the form (11) or (12) are described in the papers referred to in the introduction. Other possible methods, such as those involving functional integration and functional Fourier transforms, have not been exploited much.

6. **Transport theory of incoherent intensity and flux.** So far we have mainly considered the expected or mean wave. Now we shall examine the variance of the

wave as well as other quadratic quantities involving it. To this end let us consider a time harmonic field $u(x)$ produced by a source distribution $j(x)$ in a medium of refractive index $n(x)$. We assume that u satisfies the equation

$$[\Delta + k^2n^2(x)]u = -j. \tag{1}$$

In this equation the constant k is the propagation constant of the medium. In terms of $u(x)$ two quantities of practical interest, the intensity $I(x)$ and the flux $\mathbf{S}(x)$ are defined by

$$I(x) = u(x)\bar{u}(x). \tag{2}$$

$$\mathbf{S}(x) = \frac{1}{2i}(\bar{u}\nabla u - u\nabla\bar{u}) = \operatorname{Im} \bar{u}\nabla u. \tag{3}$$

Here the overbar denotes the complex conjugate. It follows at once from (1) that I and $\mathbf{S}$ are related by the energy equation

$$\nabla\cdot\mathbf{S} = -I \operatorname{Im} k^2n^2 + \operatorname{Im} u\bar{j}. \tag{4}$$

The first term on the right represents energy absorption by the medium and the second term represents work done by the source.

We shall now assume that u, n and j are random functions and denote the expectation value of any quantity q by $\langle q\rangle$. Then the coherent field u_c and the incoherent field u_i are defined by

$$u_c = \langle u\rangle, \tag{5}$$

$$u_i = u - \langle u\rangle = u - u_c. \tag{6}$$

The coherent intensity and flux I_c and $\mathbf{S}_c$ are defined by

$$I_c = u_c\bar{u}_c, \tag{7}$$

$$\mathbf{S}_c = \operatorname{Im}(\bar{u}_c\nabla u_c). \tag{8}$$

The incoherent intensity and incoherent flux I_i and $\mathbf{S}_i$ are defined by

$$I_i = \langle I\rangle - I_c, \tag{9}$$

$$\mathbf{S}_i = \langle\mathbf{S}\rangle - S_c. \tag{10}$$

From these definitions it follows that $\langle u_i\rangle = 0$, $I_i = \langle\bar{u}_iu_i\rangle$ and $\mathbf{S}_i = \operatorname{Im}\langle\bar{u}_i\nabla u_i\rangle$. The energy equation (4) yields

$$\nabla\cdot\mathbf{S}_c + \nabla\cdot\mathbf{S}_i = -\langle I \operatorname{Im} k^2n^2\rangle + \operatorname{Im}\langle u\bar{j}\rangle. \tag{11}$$

Upon using the above definitions in (1) we find the following equations for u_c and u_i

$$[\Delta + k^2\langle n^2\rangle]u_c = -\langle j\rangle - k^2\langle n^2u_i\rangle, \tag{12}$$

$$[\Delta + k^2n^2]u_i = k^2\langle n^2u_i\rangle + k^2[\langle n^2\rangle - n^2]u_c - j + \langle j\rangle. \tag{13}$$

Equation (12) shows that we may regard $\langle j \rangle$ as the source of u_c and $-k^2\langle n^2 u_i \rangle$ as a negative source or sink. Similarly the right side of (13) shows which terms are sources of u_i. It should be noted that $\langle I \rangle$ is a second moment of u and that $\langle \mathbf{S}(x) \rangle$ can be computed from $\langle \bar{u}(y)u(x) \rangle$, the two point second moment of u, by the relation

$$\mathbf{S}\langle (x) \rangle = \lim_{y \to x} \nabla_x \langle \bar{u}(y)u(x) \rangle. \tag{14}$$

We shall now specialize the foregoing considerations to waves in a uniform nonrandom medium for which $n(x) \equiv 1$. Then (1), (12) and (13) become

$$(\Delta + k^2)u = -j, \tag{15}$$

$$(\Delta + k^2)u_c = -\langle j \rangle, \tag{16}$$

$$(\Delta + k^2)u_i = -j + \langle j \rangle. \tag{17}$$

For k real, the solution of (15) which satisfies the radiation condition is

$$u(x) = \frac{1}{4\pi} \int \frac{e^{ik|x-x'|}}{|x - x'|} j(x')\, dx'. \tag{18}$$

If Im $k > 0$ this is the bounded solution. The bounded or radiating solutions of (16) and (17) are given by (18) with $\langle j \rangle$ and $j - \langle j \rangle$ in place of j, respectively.

From the result of the form (18) for u_i we shall now calculate the incoherent intensity and flux. Upon using the fact that $I_i = \langle \bar{u}_i u \rangle$ and writing the product of two integrals as a double integral we have

$$I_i(x) = \left\langle \frac{1}{(4\pi)^2} \int [j(x') - \langle j(x') \rangle][\bar{j}(x'') - \langle \bar{j}(x'') \rangle] \frac{e^{ik|x-x'| - i\bar{k}|x-x''|}}{|x - x'||x - x''|} dx'\, dx'' \right\rangle. \tag{19}$$

This may be written in terms of $N(x', x'')$ the two point correlation function of the source, which is defined by

$$N(x', x'') = \langle [j(x') - \langle j(x') \rangle][j(x'') - \langle j(x'') \rangle] \rangle. \tag{20}$$

Now (19) becomes

$$I_i(x) = \frac{1}{(4\pi)^2} \int \frac{N(x', x'')}{|x - x'||x - x''|} e^{ik|x-x'| - i\bar{k}|x-x''|}\, dx'\, dx''. \tag{21}$$

Similarly we find

$$\mathbf{S}_i(x) = \frac{1}{(4\pi)^2} \operatorname{Im} \int \frac{N(x', x'')}{|x - x'||x - x''|} \times e^{ik|x-x'| - i\bar{k}|x-x''|} \left(ik - \frac{1}{|x - x'|} \right) \nabla(|x - x'|)\, dx'\, dx''. \tag{22}$$

These results (21) and (22) acquire an interesting form when the source is uncorrelated at distinct points, so that N is given by

$$N(x', x'') = (4\pi)^2 M(x') \delta(x' - x''). \tag{23}$$

Then (21) becomes

$$I_i(x) = \int \frac{M(x')}{|x - x'|^2} e^{-2|x-x'|\operatorname{Im} k}\, dx'. \tag{24}$$

Upon introducing polar coordinates r, ω with their origin at x, (24) may be written as

$$I_i(x) = \int_\Omega I_i(x, \omega)\, d\omega. \tag{25}$$

In (25) ω denotes a point on the unit sphere Ω and $I_i(x, \omega)$ is defined by

$$I_i(x, \omega) = \int_0^\infty M(x - r\omega)\, e^{-2r \operatorname{Im} k}\, dr. \tag{26}$$

Similarly (22) becomes

$$\mathbf{S}_i(x) = (\operatorname{Re} k) \int_\Omega \boldsymbol{\omega} I_i(x, \omega)\, d\omega. \tag{27}$$

The results (25) and (27) may be interpreted in terms of an incoherent field of intensity $I_i(x, \omega)$ and flux $\boldsymbol{\omega} I_i(x, \omega) \operatorname{Re} k$ traveling through x in each direction ω. The intensities and fluxes of these fields add together without interference, so we say they combine incoherently. Each source point on the line $x - r\omega$ contributes to $I_i(x, \omega)$ an amount equal to M at the source point multiplied by the decay factor $e^{-2r \operatorname{Im} k}$, which results from absorption in the medium.

A different way of finding I_i and $\mathbf{S}_i$ is based upon the differential equations satisfied by the moments. Any moment of $u(x)$ satisfies a linear equation with the corresponding moment of $j(x)$ as inhomogeneous term. Thus the moment $\langle u(x_1) \cdots u(x_s) j(x_{s+1}) \cdots j(x_r) \rangle$ satisfies the equation

$$L_1 \cdots L_s \langle u(x_1) \cdots u(x_s) j(x_{s+1}) \cdots j(x_r) \rangle = (-1)^s \langle j(x_1) \cdots j(x_r) \rangle, \tag{28}$$

where $L_s = \Delta_s + k^2$ and Δ_s is the Laplacian with respect to x_s. The set of equations (28) for all the moments of u and j may be called the hierarchy equations. In the present case they are uncoupled in the sense that each equation contains only one moment involving u. For nonuniform media the equations are coupled, as we shall see. The bounded or radiating solution of (28) is the multiple integral

$$\langle u(x_1) \cdots u(x_s) j(x_{s+1}) \cdots j(x_r) \rangle = \frac{1}{(4\pi)^s} \int \frac{e^{ik(|x-x_1| + \cdots + |x-x_s|)}}{|x - x_1| \cdots |x - x_s|} \times \langle j(x_1) \cdots j(x_s) \rangle\, dx_1 \cdots dx_s. \tag{29}$$

This result can also be obtained by multiplying together the solutions (18) for u and the factors j and then averaging. Similar considerations apply to the solution of any linear equation in which the inhomogeneous term and the initial and/or boundary data are random while the linear operator (e.g., coefficients, etc.) is "sure."

Let us now try to obtain equations for the intensity and flux in a random medium with a nonrandom source. To this end we assume that the random inhomogeneity in the medium is small and write $n(x) = 1 + \varepsilon\mu(x)$. Then since $\langle j\rangle = j$, we obtain from (13) the following equation for u_i, in which terms through order ε are shown explicitly

$$(\Delta + k^2)u_i = 2\varepsilon k^2[\langle\mu u_i\rangle - \mu u_i + (\langle\mu\rangle - \mu)u_c] + O(\varepsilon^2). \tag{30}$$

From (30) we see that u_i is $O(\varepsilon)$ so (30) may be further simplified to

$$(\Delta + k^2)u_i = 2\varepsilon k^2(\langle\mu\rangle - \mu)u_c + O(\varepsilon^2). \tag{31}$$

The solution of (31) is

$$u_i(x) = 2\varepsilon k^2 \int G(x, x')[\langle\mu(x')\rangle - \mu(x')]u_c(x')\, dx' + O(\varepsilon^2). \tag{32}$$

We now multiply (32) by its complex conjugate and take the mean of the result, obtaining

$$\begin{aligned} I_i(x) = 4\varepsilon^2k^2 \int & G(x, x')G(x, x'')\,\langle[\langle\mu(x')\rangle - \mu(x')][\langle\mu(x'')\rangle - \mu(x'')]\rangle \\ & \times u_c(x')u_c(x'')\, dx'\, dx'' + O(\varepsilon^3). \end{aligned} \tag{33}$$

The correlation function $R(x', x'')$ is defined to be the mean value in the integrand in (33), so (33) can be rewritten as

$$I_i(x) = 4\varepsilon^2k^2 \int G(x, x')G(x, x'')u_c(x')u_c(x'')R(x', x'')\, dx'\, dx'' + O(\varepsilon^3). \tag{34}$$

Let us now suppose that the refractive index variations at distinct points are uncorrelated. Then we may write $R(x', x'')$ in the form

$$R(x', x'') = M(x')\delta(x' - x''). \tag{35}$$

Now (34) becomes

$$I_i(x) = \frac{\varepsilon^2k^2}{4\pi^2} \int \frac{M(x')}{|x - x'|^2} I_c(x') \exp[-2|x - x'|\mathrm{Im}\, k]\, dx' + O(\varepsilon^3). \tag{36}$$

This is an explicit expression for I_i in terms of I_c. Since I_i is $O(\varepsilon^2)$ and $\langle I\rangle = I_c + I_i$, we may replace I_c by $\langle I\rangle$ on the right side of (36). If we then add $I_c(x)$ to each side and omit $O(\varepsilon^3)$, (36) becomes

$$\langle I(x)\rangle = I_c(x) + \frac{\varepsilon^2k^2}{4\pi^2} \int \frac{M(x')}{|x - x'|^2} \langle I(x)\rangle\, e^{-2|x-x'|\mathrm{Im}\, k}\, dx'. \tag{37}$$

This is an integral equation for $\langle I(x)\rangle$ with $I_c(x)$ as the inhomogeneous term. The study of the incoherent radiation by means of integral equations such as this is called the transport theory of radiation.

The integral in (37), which is equal to $I_i(x)$, can be written in the form (25) with $I_i(x, \omega)$ defined by

$$I_i(x, \omega) = \frac{\varepsilon^2k^2}{4\pi^2} \int_0^\infty M(x - r\omega)\langle I(x - r\omega)\rangle\, e^{-2r\,\mathrm{Im}\, k}\, dr. \tag{38}$$

The incoherent flux $S_i(x)$ can be computed from (32) in the same way as $I_i(x)$ was. One finds that it can be written in the form (27) with $I_i(x, \omega)$ given by (38).

Similar considerations to those described here have been applied to the incoherent field in media of discrete scatterers. Other work has concerned the solution of boundary value problems by means of the integral equations of transport theory. These and related matters are discussed in works on transport theory.

References

1. J. B. Keller, *Wave propagation in random media*, Proc. Sympos. Appl. Math. Vol. 13, Amer. Math. Soc., Providence, R. I., 1960.

2. L. L. Foldy, *The multiple scattering of waves*, Phys. Rev. (2) **67** (1945), 107.

3a. M. Lax, *Multiple scattering of waves*, Rev. Modern Phys. **23** (1951), 287.

3b. ———, *Multiple scattering of waves*. II, Phys. Rev. (2) **85** (1952), 621.

4a. V. Twersky, *On multiple scattering of waves*, No. EDL–L16, Electronic Defense Labs., Mt. View, Calif., April, 1960.

4b. ———, *On scattering of waves by a slab region of randomly distributed objects*, No. EDL–E26, Electronic Defense Labs., Mt. View, Calif., January, 1958.

4c. ———, *On propagation in random media of discrete scatterers*, Proc. Sympos. Appl. Math. Vol. 17, Amer. Math. Soc., Providence, R. I., 1964.

5a. R. C. Bourret, *Bilocal theory of randomly perturbed fields*, Research Report No. 215, Hughes Research Labs., Malibu, Calif., September, 1961.

5b. ———, *The scattering of sound in a turbulent and thermally random medium by the method of bilocal perturbations*, Research Report No. 193, Hughes Research Labs., Malibu, Calif., February, 1962.

5c. ———, *Stochastically perturbed fields, with applications to wave propagation in random media*, Hughes Research Labs., Malibu, Calif.

6. W. S. Ament, *Wave propagation in suspensions*, Report 5307, U. S. Naval Research Lab., 1952.

7. R. H. Kraichnan, *The closure problem of turbulence theory*, Proc. Sympos. Appl. Math. Vol. 13, Amer. Math. Soc., Providence, R. I., 1960.

8. N. N. Bogolyubov, *Problems of a dynamical theory in statistical physics*, English transl., Providence College, Providence, R. I., 1959.

9. E. Hopf, *Statistical hydromechanics and functional calculus*, J. Rational Mech. Anal. **1** (1952), 87.

10. B. Zumino, *Formal solution of the equations of statistical equilibrium*, Phys. Fluids **2** (1959), 20.

11. R. M. Lewis and J. B. Keller, *Solution of the functional differentiation equation for the statistical equilibrium of a crystal*, Phys. Rev. (2) **121** (1961), 1022.

12. R. M. Lewis and R. H. Kraichnan, *A space-time functional formalism for turbulence*, Comm. Pure Appl. Math. **15** (1962), 397.

13. W. C. Meecham, *On radiation in a randomly inhomogeneous medium*, Space Technology Labs., Inc., Los Angeles 45, Calif., September, 1961.

14. F. C. Karal and J. B. Keller, *Elastic, electromagnetic and other waves in a random medium*, J. Mathematical Phys. (1964) (to appear).

15. Lord Rayleigh, *Transmission of light through an atmosphere containing small particles in suspension*, Philos. Mag. **47** (1899), 375.

16. F. Reiche, *Zur Theorie der Dispersion in Gasen und Dämpfen*, Ann. Physics **50** (1916), 1; 121.

17. L. A. Chernov, *Wave propagation in a random medium*, English transl., McGraw-Hill, New York, 1960.

New York University
New York, New York

STOCHASTIC TRANSFORMATIONS AND FUNCTIONAL EQUATIONS

BY

RICHARD BELLMAN

1. **Introduction.** A large amount of attention devoted to the study of the linear stochastic transformation

$$s_n = s_{n-1} + r_n, \qquad s_0 = 0, \tag{1.1}$$

or

$$s_n = \sum_{i=1}^{n} r_i,$$

where the r_i are independent random variables, has been amply rewarded. It is to be expected, in view of the richness of this special case, that the study of more general stochastic transformations of the form

$$x_{n+1} = g(x_n, r_n), \tag{1.2}$$

will reveal equally interesting phenomena. These transformations arise quite naturally in many branches of mathematical physics, in modern control theory, in mathematical psychology in connection with learning processes, in stochastic approximation, in dynamic programming, and in many other mathematical settings as well.

There are considerable difficulties in obtaining general results. In this paper, we wish to discuss three particular problems. The first leads us to functional equations generalizing those of Abel–Schroder; the second involves a use of quasilinearization, the third arises in connection with the produce of random matrices.

2. **The Abel–Schroder equation.** Let $g(x)$ be a function which is analytic in the neighborhood of the origin

$$g(x) = a_1 x + a_2 x^2 + \cdots, \qquad |x| \leqq c_1. \tag{2.1}$$

We say that the transformation represented by $g(x)$ is *linearized* by $f(x)$ if

$$f(g(x)) = a_1 f(x). \tag{2.2}$$

Does there exist a function $f(x)$, analytic in some neighborhood of the origin, which accomplishes this objective? Of the many paths that can be followed in answer to this question, let us pursue one based upon iteration. Write $g^{(n)}$ for the nth iterate of g,

$$g^{(0)} = x, \qquad g^{(n+1)} = g(g^{(n)}). \tag{2.3}$$

The functions $g^{(n)}$ enjoy the semi-group property

$$g^{(m+n)} = g^{(m)}(g^{(n)}), \tag{2.4}$$

$m, n = 0, 1, 2, \cdots$ Consider the new sequence of functions defined by

$$f_n(x) = g^{(n)}(x)/a_1, \tag{2.5}$$

where a_1 is, as in (2.1), $g'(0)$. Assume that $0 < |a_1| < 1$. Observe that

$$f_{n+1}(x) = g^{(n+1)}/a_1^{n+1} = \frac{f_n(g(x))}{a_1}. \tag{2.6}$$

Hence, if the sequence $\{f_n(x)\}$ converges as $n \to \infty$ to a function $f(x)$, we have

$$f(g(x)) = a_1 f(x). \tag{2.7}$$

Thus, provided $f(x)$ exists, it is a linearizing function. The existence of $f(x)$ and the validity of the preceding formalism can be readily established, in the one-dimensional case, Koenigs **[1]**, the multidimensional case, Bellman **[2]**, where many other references may be found, and in more general cases arising in the theory of branching processes, Harris **[3]**.

3. **Stochastic iteration.** Let us now consider a stochastic version of the foregoing. Let

$$g(x) = g(x, a) = a_1 x + a_2 x^2 + \cdots, \tag{3.1}$$

where the a_i are random variables with a joint distribution $dG(a_1, a_2, \cdots) \equiv dG(a)$.

Let $g_1(x)$ represent the function obtained with the random variables $[a_1^{(1)}, a_2^{(1)}, \cdots]$, $g_2(x)$ the function obtained with set $[a_1^{(2)}, a_2^{(2)}, \cdots]$, and so on. We wish to consider the function

$$h_n(x) = \underset{a^{(i)}}{\exp}\, g_n(g_{n-1}(\cdots g_1(x) \cdots)). \tag{3.2}$$

It is easy to see that

$$h_n(x) = \int h_{n-1}(g(x, a))dG(a), \tag{3.3}$$

$n \geqq 1$, with $h_0(x) = x$, as before.

A particularly interesting case is that where

$$\begin{aligned} g(x, a) = t_1(x) &= b_{11}x + b_{12}x^2 + \cdots, \text{ with probability } p_1 \\ = t_2(x) &= b_{21}x + b_{22}x^2 + \cdots, \text{ with probability } 1 - p_1. \end{aligned} \tag{3.4}$$

Then (3.3) becomes

$$h_n(x) = p_1 h_{n-1}(t_1(x)) + (1 - p_1)h_{n-1}(t_2(x)). \tag{3.5}$$

Proceeding formally, write

$$e_1 = \int a_1 \, dG(a), \tag{3.6}$$

and introduce the functions

$$f_n(x) = \frac{h_n(x)}{e_1^n}. \tag{3.7}$$

We see that

$$f_{n+1}(x) = \frac{1}{e_1} \int f_n(g(x, a))dG(a). \tag{3.8}$$

If $f_n(x)$ converges to $f(x)$ as $n \to \infty$, we have

$$f(x) = \frac{1}{e_1} \int f(g(x, a))dG(a), \tag{3.9}$$

an average linearization.

Following the argument in Koenigs **[1]**, it is easy to show that if $t_1(x)$ and $t_2(x)$ are analytic in some neighborhood of the origin and if $|t_1'(0)|, |t_2'(0)| < 1$, then the sequence $\{f_n(x)\}$ converges uniformly to an analytic function $f(x)$ satisfying (3.9).

Setting

$$f(x) = x + c_2x^2 + \cdots + c_nx^2 + \cdots, \tag{3.10}$$

we can determine the coefficients recurrently from (3.9).

4. **Asymptotic behavior.** Returning to the deterministic case discussed in §2, suppose that we wish to study the asymptotic behavior of $g^{(n)}(x)$ as $n \to \infty$. Since (2.7) holds, we have

$$f(g^{(n)}(x)) = a_1^n f(x), \tag{4.1}$$

and thus

$$g^{(n)}(x) = f^{-1}(a_1^n f(x)). \tag{4.2}$$

This yields a complete asymptotic description as $n \to \infty$, since $f(x)$ is a known function.

It follows that we have a complete description of the asymptotic behavior of the solution of the difference equation

$$u_{n+1} = g(u_n), \qquad u_0 = x, \tag{4.3}$$

provided that $|x|$ is sufficiently small. The multidimensional analogues of these results are valid, but require considerably more effort; cf. **[2]**, where other references may be found. Similar results may be obtained for differential equations **[4]**. These represent extensions of the classical work of Poincaré–Lyapunov concerning the stability of the null solution of nonlinear differential equations **[5]**.

The results of this paper were obtained in the course of attempts to derive similar results for differential and difference equations with stochastic elements. Let us see what the results of §3 yield. From (3.7), we see that if

$$u_{n+1} = g(u_n, a^{(n)}), \qquad u_0 = x, \tag{4.4}$$

then

$$\exp_a(u_n) \sim e_1^n f(x), \tag{4.5}$$

where $f(x)$ is determined by (3.9), and e_1 is as in (3.6).

The multidimensional versions of (4.5) are valid, and one can obtain analogous results for all moments, a topic we shall discuss in more detail below in connection with the product of random matrices.

Observe that (4.5) is very much weaker than (4.2). It is an open question as to whether an analogue of (4.2) exists for stochastic iteration.

5. **Random matrices.** Consider the vector difference equation

$$x_{n+1} = R_n x_n, \qquad x_0 = c, \tag{5.1}$$

where x_n is an N-dimensional vector and R_n is an $N \times N$ matrix whose elements are stochastic variables. Clearly,

$$x_n = R_n R_{n-1} \cdots R_0 c. \tag{5.2}$$

Let us assume at this point that the R_i are independent.

We wish to determine various moments of the components of x_n. First moments are easy. We have

$$E(x_n) = E(R)E(x_{n-1}) = E(R)^n c. \tag{5.3}$$

One way to obtain higher moments is to introduce the Kronecker product of two matrices [6]. To see the way in which this arises, consider the 2×2 case. We have, componentwise,

$$\begin{aligned} u_{n+1} &= r_{11}u_n + r_{12}v_n, \\ v_{n+1} &= r_{21}u_n + r_{22}v_n. \end{aligned} \tag{5.4}$$

Hence,

$$\begin{aligned} u_{n+1}^2 &= r_{11}^2 u_n^2 + 2r_{11}r_{12}u_n v_n + r_{12}^2 v_n^2, \\ u_{n+1}v_{n+1} &= r_{11}r_{21}u_n^2 + \cdots \\ &\cdot \\ &\cdot \\ &\cdot \end{aligned} \tag{5.5}$$

In vector-matrix notation,

$$\begin{pmatrix} u_{n+1}^2 \\ u_{n+1}v_{n+1} \\ v_{n+1}u_{n+1} \\ v_{n+1}^2 \end{pmatrix} = \begin{pmatrix} r_{11}R & r_{12}R \\ & \\ & \\ r_{21}R & r_{22}R \end{pmatrix} \begin{pmatrix} u_n^2 \\ u_n v_n \\ v_n u_n \\ v_n^2 \end{pmatrix} \tag{5.6}$$

The 4×4 matrix $(r_{ij}R)$ is the Kronecker product of R with itself, written $R \otimes R$ or $R^{(2)}$. It plays an important role in the study of the stability of linear systems of difference or differential equations with random coefficients; see Zadeh [7].

Higher Kronecker powers will yield the higher moments; see Bellman [**8**].

6. **Correlation.** In place of the introduction of Kronecker products, we can employ the following procedure which applies in the more complex case of correlation between the R_i. If the R_i are independent, introduce the function

$$f_n(c) = \exp\,(x_n, Bx_n). \tag{6.1}$$

Then

$$f_n(c) = \int f_{n-1}(Rc)dG(R), \tag{6.2}$$

with $f_0(c) = (c, Bc)$. If the R_i are correlated in a Markovian fashion, where the distribution of R_i depends only on the matrix R_{i-1}, we introduce the function

$$f_n(c, S) = \exp\,(x_n, Bx_n), \tag{6.3}$$

where $R_{-1} = S$. Then

$$f_n(c, S) = \int f_{n-1}(Rc, R)dG(R, S), \tag{6.4}$$

with $f_0(c, S) = (c, Bc)$.

Turning to (6.2), we write $f_n(c) = (c, Q_n c)$, a quadratic form in c. We obtain the matrix relation

$$Q_n = \int RQ_{n-1}RdG(R). \tag{6.5}$$

The relations connecting the elements of Q_n with those of Q_{n-1} introduce the Kronecker product in a direct fashion.

7. **Asymptotic behavior.** There is no difficulty in determining the asymptotic behavior of the moments of x_n. However, the study of the distribution of a random variable such as $\log x_{1n}$, where x_{1n} is the first component of x_n, is a matter of considerably greater difficulty. If the R_i are independent, one would expect that $\log x_{1n}$ suitably normalized will behave like a Gaussian variable. Under various assumptions, this is demonstrated by Kesten–Furstenberg [**9**].

8. **Dynamic programming.** A characteristic functional equation in the theory of dynamic programming is

$$f_n(x) = \max_y f_{n-1}(T(x, y)), \qquad f_0(x) = x. \tag{8.1}$$

Suppose that

$$T(x, y) = a_1(y)x + a_2(y)x^2 + \cdots, \tag{8.2}$$

where $|a_1(y)| < 1$ for all y. Let

$$b = \max_y a_1(y). \tag{8.3}$$

Under various conditions which we will not enter into here, it can be shown that

$$\lim_{n\to\infty} \frac{f_n(x)}{b^n} = \phi(x) \tag{8.4}$$

uniformly for $|x| \leqq b_2$ and that

$$b\phi(x) = \max_y \phi(T(x, y)). \tag{8.5}$$

These results have applications in the study of the asymptotic behavior of variational processes.

If we consider stochastic variational processes, we obtain an extension of the foregoing results as well as those obtained above; see also [**10**; **11**].

9. **Quasilinearization.** Let us now briefly indicate a new technique that can be applied to the study of differential equations with random elements. Consider the scalar equation

$$\frac{du}{dt} = g(u, r(t)), \qquad u(0) = c, \tag{9.1}$$

where $r(t)$ is a random function of t and $g(u, r)$ is convex in u for any value of r. An important class of functions of this type is given by

$$\frac{du}{dt} = u^k + r(t), \qquad k > 1. \tag{9.2}$$

Applying the technique of quasilinearization [**12**; **13**], we consider the associated linear equation

$$\frac{dv}{dt} = g(w, r(t)) + (v - w)g_w(w, r(t)), \qquad v(0) = c, \tag{9.3}$$

where w is a random function as yet unspecified. Since

$$g(u, r) = \max_w [g(w, r) + (v - w)g_w(w, r)], \tag{9.4}$$

by virtue of convexity, we see that

$$\frac{du}{dt} = \max_w [g(w, r) + (u - w)g_w(w, r)], \qquad w(0) = c. \tag{9.5}$$

It now follows readily that

$$v(t) \leqq u(t) \tag{9.6}$$

for all choices of w, with equality if $w = u$. Hence,

$$\text{Prob}\,(v(t) \geqq z) \leqq \text{Prob}\,(u(t) \geqq z) \tag{9.7}$$

for all w, and thus

$$\text{Prob}\,(u(t) \geqq z) = \max_w \text{Prob}\,(v(t) \geqq z). \tag{9.8}$$

With suitable choices of w, we can obtain excellent approximations to the left-hand side. A case of particular interest is that where $k = z$.

References

1. M. G. Koenigs, *Nouvelles recherches sur les équations fonctionnelles*, Ann. Sci. Ecole Norm. Sup. **2** (1885), 385–404.

2. R. Bellman, *The iteration of power series in two variables*, Duke Math. J. **19** (1952), 339–347.

3. T. E. Harris, *Branching processes*, Springer, Berlin, 1963.

4. R. Bellman and J. M. Richardson, *On the asymptotic behavior of solutions of nonlinear differential equations*, J. Math. Anal. Appl. **4** (1962), 470–474.

5. ———, *Stability theory of differential equations*, McGraw-Hill, New York, 1954.

6. ———, *Introduction to matrix analysis*, McGraw-Hill, New York, 1960.

7. L. Zadeh, *Time-varying networks*, Proc. IRE. **49** (1961), 1488–1503.

8. R. Bellman, *Limit theorems for noncommutative operations*. I, Duke Math. J. **21** (1954), 491–500.

9. J. Kesten and H. Furstenberg, *Products of random matrices*, Ann. Math. Statist. **31** (1960), 457–469.

10. R. Bellman, *A Markovian decision process*, J. Math. Mech. **6** (1957), 679–684.

11. ———, *Functional equations in the theory of dynamic programming*. XI. *Limit theorems*, Rend. Circ. Mat. Palermo **8** (1959), 1–3.

12. R. Kalaba, *On nonlinear differential equations, the maximum operation and monotone convergence*, J. Math. Mech. **8** (1959), 519–573.

13. R. Bellman, *Functional equations in the theory of dynamic programming*. V. *Positivity and quasilinearity*, Proc. Nat. Acad. Sci. U.S.A. **41** (1955), 743–746.

14. U. Grenander, *Stochastic groups*, Ark. Mat. **4** (1961), 163–183.

15. J. C. Samuels and A. C. Eringen, *On stochastic linear systems*, J. Math. Phys. **38** (1959), 83–103.

16. A. Dvoretsky, *On stochastic approximation*, Proc. 3rd Berkeley Sympos. Math. Statist. and Prob. (1954–1955), Vol. 1, pp. 39–56, Univ. of California Press, Berkeley, Calif., 1956.

17. R. R. Bush and F. Mosteller, *Stochastic models for learning*, Wiley, New York, 1955.

THE RAND CORPORATION,
SANTA MONICA, CALIFORNIA

THE APPLICATION OF STOCHASTIC APPROXIMATION TO THE OPTIMIZATION OF RANDOM CIRCUITS

BY

K. B. GRAY

1. **Problem.** The problem is that of designing a circuit, whose configuration is fixed in advance, to achieve a certain desired output. The circuit input may be stochastic and there may be internal stochastic disturbances. Moreover, many circuit component values cannot (or need not) be deterministically fixed. Instead, we may specify the statistical distribution of the circuit's component values in order that the circuit output will have desired statistical properties.

The problem arises in the real world because circuit components exhibit variations from their design or nominal values. Therefore, it is generally unrealistic to design circuits or systems solely on the basis of design values. Thus, one does not order, say, 10 ohm resistors. Rather, one specifies the distribution of the resistors. Frequently, many of the circuits are going to be used in larger circuits or systems. Hence, one is interested in the statistical aspects of the circuit performance [**1**].

2. **Example.** Let the circuit output $Y_t(\omega)$ be a random function that satisfies the differential equation

$$R(\omega)\frac{dY_t(\omega)}{dt} + \frac{1}{C(\omega)}\,Y_t(\omega) = 0 \tag{2.1}$$

with initial value $Y_0(\omega)$ being a random variable. ω denotes a point in the basic probability space. From here on we will not explicitly exhibit the functional form of the random variables involved. Rather, we use the shortened notation

$$R\frac{dY_t}{dt} + \frac{1}{C}\,Y_t = 0. \tag{2.2}$$

Call R and C the resistance and capacitance, respectively, of the circuit. The circuit output is, of course, the random function

$$Y_t = Y_0\, e^{-t/RC}. \tag{2.3}$$

Suppose we desire to select the distribution of R and C so that in some statistical sense Y_t is close to $e^{-t/10}$ for $0 \leqq t \leqq 5$. That is, a significant difference between Y_t and $e^{-t/10}$ represents a loss.

Let $U(a, b)$ denote the rectangular density over the interval $[a, b]$. Suppose that the densities of R and C are $U(u_1, u_1 + 1/u_2)$ and $U(u_3, u_3 + 1/u_4)$, respectively,

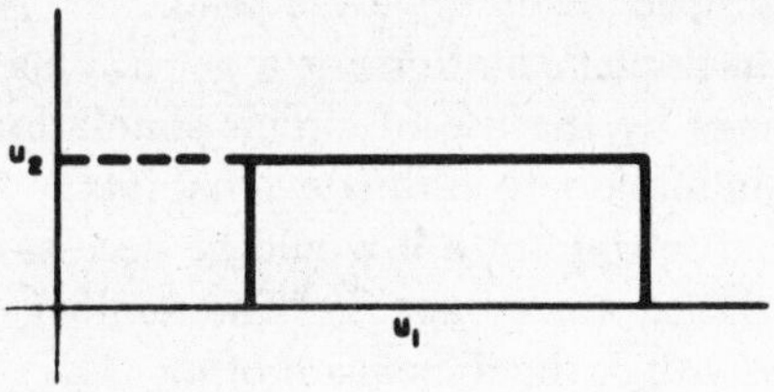

FIGURE 1. Density of R.

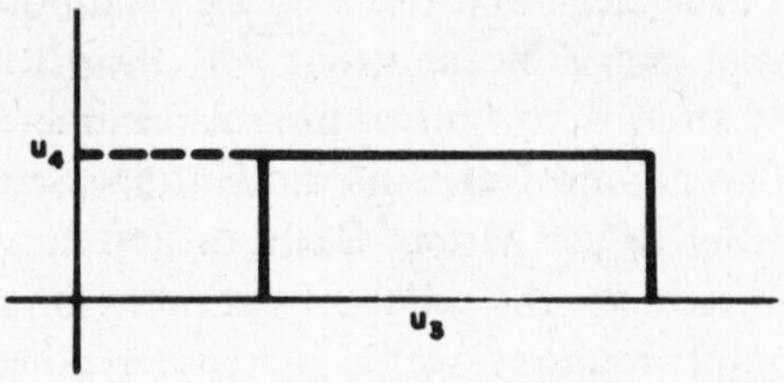

FIGURE 2. Density of C.

with $u_1, u_3 \geqq 0$ and $u_2, u_4 > 0$. Note that u_2 and u_4 measure the dispersion of R and C about their mean values.

Define our loss to be

$$L(Y, \mathbf{u}) = \sum_{t=0}^{5} |Y_t - e^{-t/10}| + d_2 u_2 + d_4 u_4 \tag{2.4}$$

where $d_2, d_4 \leqq 0$ indicate the cost relationship between output errors and the cost of decreasing the dispersion of R and C. We seek to minimize the average loss, or risk,

$$R(\mathbf{u}) = EL(Y, \mathbf{u}) \tag{2.5}$$

subject to a rectangular constraint on the vector $\mathbf{u}$. The constraint is of the form

$$0 < a_i \leqq u_i \leqq b_i < \infty \quad \text{for } i = 1, \cdots, 4. \tag{2.6}$$

3. **Traditional approaches to statistical circuit design.** The simplest approach is to ignore the statistical aspects of the design problem and proceed under the assumption that component values do not vary from their nominal values. The problem is then deterministic. This method may be a fair way to make an initial guess at the optimum setting for the parameter $\mathbf{u}$, but it obviously gives no information about the output tolerances or deviations.

A somewhat more sophisticated design technique is so-called "worst-case" design [2]. This assumes tolerances for all component values. The tolerance for the output is computed by letting the components take their "worst" values. It is generally assumed that the "worst" values lie at the end points of the tolerances. "Worst-case" design frequently results in significant "over-design."

Certain relatively simple circuits, with distribution assumptions about the circuit components and input, allow one to approximate analytically the probability distribution of the output [3; 4]. In order to solve complex problems by this method it is usually necessary to make significantly unrealistic assumptions.

If the parameter $\mathbf{u}$, defining the probability distribution of the component values, is fixed in advance, then one can use Monte Carlo simulation to estimate the probability that the output will be out of tolerance [5]. This technique becomes impractical as a design aid as the dimension of the parameter $\mathbf{u}$ increases.

It is clear that none of the techniques described really solve the problem. An approach is needed that will allow numerical implementation for a general class of circuits to find optimum parameter settings by the use of circuit simulation. The Monte Carlo method utilizes circuit simulation to estimate reliability. In order to use Monte Carlo to find an optimum setting for **u** it would be necessary to estimate the reliability at many points in the parameter space. The number of points required would increase exponentially with q, the dimension of **u**.

A further criticism of the above techniques is that they do not allow sufficiently general criteria of loss. It would seem desirable to consider criteria other than that of being out of tolerance. Also, one should consider the cost of selecting a particular setting for **u**.

4. **Mathematical model of problem.** Let the random variables $X_{\mathbf{u}}^1, X_{\mathbf{u}}^2, \cdots, X_{\mathbf{u}}^p$ represent the various component values of the circuit. The vector $\mathbf{u} = (u_1, u_2, \cdots, u_q)$ determines the distribution of these random variables. Inputs and internal disturbances can be represented as random variables $X_{\mathbf{u}}^1$ whose distributions are independent of **u**. Let the circuit output be

$$Y_{\mathbf{u}} = T[X_{\mathbf{u}}^1, X_{\mathbf{u}}^2, \cdots, X_{\mathbf{u}}^p] \tag{4.1}$$

where T is a scalar valued measurable function and $Y_{\mathbf{u}}$ is a random variable whose distribution depends on **u**.

We say that if the output is $Y_{\mathbf{u}}$ and **u** is the parameter setting, we accrue a loss

$$L(Y_{\mathbf{u}}, \mathbf{u}) = L_1(Y_{\mathbf{u}}) + L_2(\mathbf{u}). \tag{4.2}$$

For example, L_1 could represent the cost of the output being out of tolerance and L_2 the cost of selecting the parameter **u**. In some problems L_2 might reflect the fact that component cost usually increases as the allowable component tolerance decreases.

We consider the problem of minimizing the expected loss

$$R(\mathbf{u}) = EL(Y_{\mathbf{u}}, \mathbf{u}), \tag{4.3}$$

subject to a constraint

$$a_i \leqq u_i \leqq b_i; \qquad i = 1, 2, \cdots, q.$$

If the exact form of the risk function $R(\mathbf{u})$ were known, the problem would be straightforward. However, it is not. Suppose we can, by simulation or some other technique, sample the random variable $L(Y_{\mathbf{u}}, \mathbf{u})$ for prescribed settings of **u**. We propose applying a stochastic steepest ascent method, based on the sample observations of $L(Y_{\mathbf{u}}, \mathbf{u})$, that will converge in a probabilistic sense to the optimum setting for **u**. The Kiefer–Wolfowitz [6; 7; 8] stochastic approximation procedure is such a technique.

5. **Multidimensional Kiefer–Wolfowitz procedure.** The setting of the discussion is R^q, q-dimensional real coordinate space. Let $\mathbf{x} = (x_1, \cdots, x_q) \in R^q$. We define the norm of $\mathbf{x}$ by

$$\|\mathbf{x}\| = \left(\sum_{i=1}^{q} x_i^2\right)^{1/2}. \tag{5.1}$$

The inner product of $\mathbf{x}$ and $\mathbf{y}$, both elements of R^q, is

$$(\mathbf{x}, \mathbf{y}) = \sum_{i=1}^{q} x_i y_i. \tag{5.2}$$

Suppose there is a family $\{Z_{\mathbf{u}}\}$ of random variables $Z_{\mathbf{u}}$ defined for all $\mathbf{u} \in R^q$. We assume that if $\mathbf{u}$ is specified it is possible to sample any of the random variables $Z_{\mathbf{u}}$. Let

$$f(\mathbf{u}) = EZ_{\mathbf{u}} \tag{5.3}$$

be the expected value of $Z_{\mathbf{u}}$. If the scalar-valued function f defined on R^q has a unique maximum at $\boldsymbol{\theta}$ and satisfies various other technical assumptions, then the Kiefer–Wolfowitz (KW) procedure provides a stochastic sequence $\mathbf{X}_n$ that converges to $\boldsymbol{\theta}$ in the sense that $E\|\mathbf{X}_n - \boldsymbol{\theta}\|^2 \to 0$ and $P[\lim \mathbf{X}_n = \boldsymbol{\theta}] = 1$.

DEFINITION 5.1. Let the nonnegative, real sequences $\{b_n\}$ and $\{c_n\}$ defined for $n = 1, 2, 3, \cdots$ satisfy

$$\sum_{n=1}^{\infty} b_n = \infty, \tag{5.4}$$

$$\lim_{n\to\infty} c_n = 0, \tag{5.5}$$

and

$$\sum_{n=1}^{\infty} \frac{b_n^2}{c_n^2} < \infty. \tag{5.6}$$

Let $\mathbf{e}_1 = (1, 0, \cdots, 0)$, $\mathbf{e}_2 = (0, 1, 0, \cdots, 0), \cdots, \mathbf{e}_q = (0, \cdots, 0, 1)$ be an orthonormal basis for R^q. For $c > 0$, define the random vectors

$$\mathbf{Z}_{\mathbf{u},c}^{+} = (Z_{\mathbf{u}+c\mathbf{e}_1}, \cdots, Z_{\mathbf{u}+c\mathbf{e}_q}) \tag{5.7}$$

and

$$\mathbf{Z}_{\mathbf{u},c}^{-} = (Z_{\mathbf{u}-c\mathbf{e}_1}, \cdots, Z_{\mathbf{u}-c\mathbf{e}_q}). \tag{5.8}$$

The expectations of the above random vectors are

$$\mathbf{f}^{+}(\mathbf{u}, c) = (f(\mathbf{u} + c\mathbf{e}_1), \cdots, f(\mathbf{u} + c\mathbf{e}_q)) \tag{5.9}$$

and

$$\mathbf{f}^{-}(\mathbf{u}, c) = (f(\mathbf{u} - c\mathbf{e}_1), \cdots, f(\mathbf{u} - c\mathbf{e}_q)). \tag{5.10}$$

It is assumed that, for any n, all $2qn$ random observations made in n iterations are independent. The KW procedure begins by guessing $\mathbf{X}_1$. The succeeding elements of the stochastic sequence are defined by

$$\mathbf{X}_{n+1} = \mathbf{X}_n + \frac{b_n}{c_n}(\mathbf{Z}^+_{\mathbf{X}_n, c_n} - \mathbf{Z}^-_{\mathbf{X}_n, c_n}), \tag{5.11}$$

for $n = 1, 2, 3, \cdots$.

We shall state a theorem (Theorem 5.2) that gives conditions for convergence of the multidimensional KW procedure. Sacks **[9]** has considered the asymptotic distribution of $\mathbf{X}_n$ as $n \to \infty$. The q-dimensional procedure considered here and discussed by Sacks uses $2q$ sample observations of Z at each iteration. Blum **[10]** gives a procedure that uses $q + 1$ sample observations at each iteration. The Blum procedure does not converge as rapidly as the multidimensional KW procedure. Originally the scalar KW procedure was shown to converge in probability by Kiefer and Wolfowitz **[6]**. Blum **[7]** strengthened the result to almost sure convergence. Dvoretzky **[8]** derived general theorems that yield both almost sure and expected norm squared convergence as special cases.

THEOREM 5.1 (DVORETZKY). *Let $\{\alpha_n\}$ be a nonnegative real sequence, defined for $n = 1, 2, \cdots$, satisfying*

$$\limsup_{n\to\infty} \alpha_n \leqq \alpha; \tag{5.12}$$

suppose that $\gamma_n(\mathbf{r}_1, \cdots, \mathbf{r}_n)$ is a sequence of nonnegative scalar-valued functions, on $\mathbf{r}_1, \cdots, \mathbf{r}_n$, satisfying

$$\sum_{n=1}^{\infty} \gamma_n(\mathbf{r}_1, \cdots, \mathbf{r}_n) = \infty \tag{5.13}$$

uniformly for all sequences $\mathbf{r}_1, \mathbf{r}_2, \cdots$ such that

$$\sup_n \|\mathbf{r}_n\| < L, \tag{5.14}$$

where $L > 0$ is arbitrary. Let $\boldsymbol{\theta} \in R^q$ and suppose $\{\mathbf{T}_n\}$ are measurable vector-valued transformations satisfying

$$\|\mathbf{T}_n(\mathbf{r}_1, \cdots, \mathbf{r}_n) - \boldsymbol{\theta}\| \leqq \max\,[\alpha_n, \|\mathbf{r}_n - \boldsymbol{\theta}\| - \gamma_n] \tag{5.15}$$

for all sequences $\mathbf{r}_1, \mathbf{r}_2, \cdots, \mathbf{r}_n$. Define

$$\mathbf{X}_{n+1}(\omega) = \mathbf{T}_n[\mathbf{X}_1(\omega), \cdots, \mathbf{X}_n(\omega)] + \mathbf{Y}_n(\omega) \tag{5.16}$$

for $n = 1, 2, \cdots$, where ω is a point in the fundamental probability space Ω. Let $\mathbf{X}_1$ and $\mathbf{Y}_n$ be random variables satisfying

$$E\|\mathbf{X}_1\|^2 < \infty, \tag{5.17}$$

$$\sum_{n=1}^{\infty} E\|\mathbf{Y}_n\|^2 < \infty, \tag{5.18}$$

and

(5.19) $$E\{\mathbf{Y}_n | \mathbf{x}_1, \cdots, \mathbf{x}_n\} = 0 \text{ almost surely.}$$

Then,

(5.20) $$\limsup_{n\to\infty} E\|\mathbf{X}_n - \boldsymbol{\theta}\|^2 \leqq \alpha^2$$

and

$$P\left[\limsup_{n\to\infty} \|\mathbf{X}_n - \boldsymbol{\theta}\| \leqq \alpha\right] = 1.$$

PROOF. The theorem is a statement of the relevant results in Dvoretzky's Theorem **[8]**, its extension, and Generalization 3. The multidimensional extension of his results is straightforward.

Armed with Theorem 5.1 we are prepared to prove the convergence of the KW procedure. The method of proof is the same as Dvoretzky's proof for the scalar case. The conditions of Theorem 5.2 are somewhat different from the conditions used by Dvoretzky. His conditions do not allow a convenient multidimensional extension. The conditions of this paper, for the case $q = 1$, are at least as weak as Dvoretzky's.

THEOREM 5.2. *Let*

(5.21) $$E|Z_{\mathbf{u}} - f(\mathbf{u})|^2 \leqq \sigma^2 < \infty$$

for all $\mathbf{u} \in R^q$. *Suppose that for some* $\varepsilon_0 > 0$ *there exist constants* A, B *such that* $0 \leqq \varepsilon \leqq \varepsilon_0 \Rightarrow$ *for all* $\mathbf{u} \in R^q$,

(5.22) $$\|\mathbf{f}^+(\mathbf{u}, \varepsilon) - \mathbf{f}^-(\mathbf{u}, \varepsilon)\| < A\|\mathbf{u} - \boldsymbol{\theta}\| + B.$$

Also, suppose that for arbitrary constants ρ *and* L $(0 < \rho < L)$ *there exists* $\varepsilon_1 > 0$ *such that* $0 < \varepsilon \leqq \varepsilon_1$ *and* $\rho < \|\mathbf{u} - \boldsymbol{\theta}\| < L \Rightarrow$ *for* $1/\sqrt{2} < \kappa$,

(5.23) $$(\mathbf{u} - \boldsymbol{\theta}, \mathbf{f}^+(\mathbf{u}, \varepsilon) - \mathbf{f}^-(\mathbf{u}, \varepsilon)) \leqq -\kappa\|\mathbf{u} - \boldsymbol{\theta}\| \cdot \|\mathbf{f}^+(\mathbf{u}, \varepsilon) - \mathbf{f}^-(\mathbf{u}, \varepsilon)\|,$$

and

(5.24) $$\liminf_{0\neq\delta\to 0} \frac{\|\mathbf{f}^+(\mathbf{u}, \delta) - \mathbf{f}^-(\mathbf{u}, \delta)\|}{2\delta} \geqq \gamma > 0.$$

Then,

(5.25) $$P\left[\lim_{n\to\infty} \mathbf{X}_n = \boldsymbol{\theta}\right] = 1$$

and

(5.26) $$\lim_{n\to\infty} E\|\mathbf{X}_n - \boldsymbol{\theta}\|^2 = 0.$$

PROOF. We apply Theorem 5.1. Let the transformation $\mathbf{T}_n$ be defined by

(5.27) $$\mathbf{T}_n(\mathbf{r}_n) = \mathbf{r}_n + \frac{b_n}{c_n}(\mathbf{f}^+(\mathbf{r}_n, c_n) - \mathbf{f}^-(\mathbf{r}_n, c_n)).$$

Define the random variable $\mathbf{Y}_n$ by

$$\mathbf{Y}_n = \frac{b_n}{c_n}(\mathbf{Z}^+_{\mathbf{r}_n,c_n} - \mathbf{Z}^-_{\mathbf{r}_n,c_n}). \tag{5.28}$$

Then,

$$\mathbf{X}_{n+1} = \mathbf{T}_n[\mathbf{X}_1, \cdots, \mathbf{X}_n] + \mathbf{Y}_n. \tag{5.29}$$

It is obvious from the definitions of $\mathbf{T}_n$ and $\mathbf{Y}_n$ that (5.19) holds. Also,

$$\begin{aligned} E\|\mathbf{Y}_n\|^2 \leqq \frac{b_n^2}{c_n^2}\{E\|\mathbf{Z}^+_{\mathbf{r}_n,c_n} &- \mathbf{f}^+(\mathbf{r}_n, c_n)\|^2 \\ &+ 2E(\mathbf{Z}^+_{\mathbf{r}_n,c_n} - \mathbf{f}^+(\mathbf{r}_n, c_n), \mathbf{Z}^-_{\mathbf{r}_n,c_n} - \mathbf{f}^-(\mathbf{r}_n, c_n)) \\ &+ E\|\mathbf{Z}^-_{\mathbf{r}_n,c_n} - \mathbf{f}^-(\mathbf{r}_n, c_n)\|^2\} \\ \leqq 2\frac{b_n^2}{c_n^2}q\sigma^2, \end{aligned} \tag{5.30}$$

since the expected value of the inner product term is zero and the variance is bounded by (5.21). Hence,

$$\sum_{n=1}^{\infty} E\|\mathbf{Y}_n\|^2 \leqq 2q\sigma^2 \sum_{n=1}^{\infty} \frac{b_n^2}{c_n^2} < \infty, \tag{5.31}$$

by (5.6).

It is clear that (5.17) holds for the KW procedure.

We have yet to verify (5.15). There is no loss of generality by considering the case that $\boldsymbol{\theta} = 0$. Let $\rho > 0$ be arbitrary. Either $\|\mathbf{r}_n\| \leqq \rho$ or $\|\mathbf{r}_n\| > \rho$. Consider the case that $\|\mathbf{r}_n\| \leqq \rho$. Now

$$\begin{aligned} \|\mathbf{T}_n(\mathbf{r}_n)\| &= \left\|\mathbf{r}_n + \frac{b_n}{c_n}(\mathbf{f}^+(\mathbf{r}_n, c_n) - \mathbf{f}^-(\mathbf{r}_n, c_n))\right\| \\ &\leqq \|\mathbf{r}_n\| + \frac{b_n}{c_n}\|\mathbf{f}^+(\mathbf{r}_n, c_n) - \mathbf{f}^-(\mathbf{r}_n, c_n)\|. \end{aligned} \tag{5.32}$$

(5.22) implies that, for n sufficiently large,

$$\|\mathbf{T}_n(\mathbf{r}_n)\| \leqq \rho + \frac{b_n}{c_n}(A\|\mathbf{r}_n\| + B). \tag{5.33}$$

Since $b_n/c_n \to 0$, for n sufficiently large and $\|\mathbf{r}_n\| \leqq \rho$ we have that

$$\|\mathbf{T}_n(\mathbf{r}_n)\| \leqq 2\rho. \tag{5.34}$$

Next, consider the case that $\|\mathbf{r}_n\| > \rho$. Let $L > \rho$ be the arbitrary constant mentioned in Theorem 5.1 and assume that $\rho < \|\mathbf{r}_n\| \leqq L$. Then,

$$\|\mathbf{T}_n(\mathbf{r}_n)\|^2 = \left\|\mathbf{r}_n + \frac{b_n}{c_n}(\mathbf{f}^+(\mathbf{r}_n, c_n) - \mathbf{f}^-(\mathbf{r}_n, c_n))\right\|^2$$

$$= \|\mathbf{r}_n\|^2 + 2\frac{b_n}{c_n}(\mathbf{r}_n, \mathbf{f}^+(\mathbf{r}_n, c_n) - \mathbf{f}^-(\mathbf{r}_n, c_n)) \tag{5.35}$$

$$+ \frac{b_n^2}{c_n^2}\|\mathbf{f}^+(\mathbf{r}_n, c_n) - \mathbf{f}^-(\mathbf{r}_n, c_n)\|^2.$$

By (5.23),

$$\begin{aligned}\|\mathbf{T}_n(\mathbf{r}_n)\|^2 \leqq \|\mathbf{r}_n\|^2 - 2\kappa\frac{b_n}{c_n}\|\mathbf{r}_n\| \cdot \|\mathbf{f}^+(\mathbf{r}_n, c_n) - \mathbf{f}^-(\mathbf{r}_n, c_n)\| \\ + \frac{b_n^2}{c_n^2}\|\mathbf{f}^+(\mathbf{r}_n, c_n) - \mathbf{f}^-(\mathbf{r}_n, c_n)\|^2.\end{aligned} \tag{5.36}$$

Hence,

$$\begin{aligned}\|\mathbf{T}_n(\mathbf{r}_n)\| \leqq \left| \|\mathbf{r}_n\| - \kappa\frac{b_n}{c_n}\|\mathbf{f}^+(\mathbf{r}_n, c_n) - \mathbf{f}^-(\mathbf{r}_n, c_n)\| \right| \\ + \frac{b_n}{c_n}\sqrt{(1-\kappa^2)}\|\mathbf{f}^+(\mathbf{r}_n, c_n) - \mathbf{f}^-(\mathbf{r}_n, c_n)\|.\end{aligned} \tag{5.37}$$

We need

LEMMA 5.1. *For n sufficiently large and* $\rho < \|\mathbf{r}_n\| < L$,

$$\frac{b_n}{c_n}\|\mathbf{f}^+(\mathbf{r}_n, c_n) - \mathbf{f}^-(\mathbf{r}_n, c_n)\| < \|\mathbf{r}_n\|. \tag{5.38}$$

PROOF. By (5.22)

$$\frac{b_n}{c_n}\|\mathbf{f}^+(\mathbf{r}_n, c_n) - \mathbf{f}^-(\mathbf{r}_n, c_n)\| \leqq \frac{b_n}{c_n}(A\|\mathbf{r}_n\| + B), \tag{5.39}$$

for n sufficiently large. Equation (5.6) implies that $b_n/c_n \to 0$. Hence,

$$\frac{b_n}{c_n}(A\|\mathbf{r}_n\| + B) \leqq \frac{b_n}{c_n}(AL + B) < \rho \tag{5.40}$$

for n sufficiently large.

Applying the lemma, we see that we can remove the absolute value signs in (5.37) for n sufficiently large. Thus,

$$\|\mathbf{T}_n(\mathbf{r}_n)\| \leqq \|\mathbf{r}_n\| - (\kappa - \sqrt{(1-\kappa^2)})\frac{b_n}{c_n}\|\mathbf{f}^+(\mathbf{r}_n, c_n) - \mathbf{f}^-(\mathbf{r}_n, c_n)\| \tag{5.41}$$

for n sufficiently large. Now, for $1/\sqrt{2} < \kappa$, $\lambda = \kappa - \sqrt{(1-\kappa^2)} > 0$. Therefore, (5.24) implies that

$$\frac{1}{c_n}\|\mathbf{f}^+(\mathbf{r}_n, c_n) - \mathbf{f}^-(\mathbf{r}_n, c_n)\| \geqq \gamma > 0. \tag{5.42}$$

This together with (5.41) yields

$$\|\mathbf{T}_n(\mathbf{r}_n)\| \leqq \|\mathbf{r}_n\| - \lambda\gamma b_n \tag{5.43}$$

for n sufficiently large and $\rho < \|\mathbf{r}_n\| < L$.

Combining this with (5.34) we have for n sufficiently large and $\|\mathbf{r}_n\| < L$,

$$\|\mathbf{T}_n(\mathbf{r}_n)\| \leqq \max\,[2\rho, \|\mathbf{r}_n\| - \lambda\gamma b_n] \tag{5.44}$$

where $\rho > 0$ is an arbitrary constant. We have thus satisfied the hypotheses of Theorem 5.1. Hence,

$$E\|\mathbf{X}_n - \boldsymbol{\theta}\|^2 \leqq 4\rho^2 \tag{5.45}$$

and

$$P[\|\mathbf{X}_n - \boldsymbol{\theta}\| \leqq 2\rho] = 1,$$

for all $\rho > 0$. Therefore,

$$E\|\mathbf{X}_n - \boldsymbol{\theta}\|^2 \to 0, \quad \text{as } n \to \infty, \tag{5.46}$$

and

$$P[\mathbf{X}_n \to \boldsymbol{\theta}] = 1.$$

This completes the proof of Theorem 5.1.

6. **Kiefer–Wolfowitz procedure over a rectangular subset of R^q.** The multidimensional KW procedure assumes that $z_{\mathbf{u}}$ can be sampled for all $\mathbf{u} \in R^q$, and that the conditions of Theorem 5.2 hold for all $\mathbf{u} \in R^q$. In the application we are concerned with, it is possible to sample $z_{\mathbf{u}}$ only for $\mathbf{u}$ in a certain subset

$$C(\mathbf{a}, \mathbf{b}) = \{\mathbf{x}\colon a_i \leqq x_i \leqq b_i, \quad i = 1, \cdots, q\} \tag{6.1}$$

of R^q. Call the restriction of $\mathbf{u}$ to $C(\mathbf{a}, \mathbf{b})$ a rectangular constraint. We consider a modified multidimensional KW procedure that samples $Z_{\mathbf{u}}$ only for $\mathbf{u} \in C(\mathbf{a}, \mathbf{b})$.

If $f(\mathbf{u})$ has a unique maximum over $C(\mathbf{a}, \mathbf{b})$ at $\boldsymbol{\theta}'$ and satisfies various other technical assumptions, the procedure $\{\mathbf{X}_n'\}$, to be defined, converges almost surely and in mean norm squared.

DEFINITION 6.1. If $\mathbf{x} = (x_1, \cdots, x_q)$, define the vector-valued function $(\mathbf{x})^* = (x_1^*, \cdots, x_q^*)$ by

$$x_i^* = \begin{cases} a_i & \text{if } x_i < a_i, \\ x_i & \text{if } a_i \leqq x_i \leqq b_i, \\ b_i & \text{if } b_i < x_i \end{cases} \tag{6.2}$$

for $i = 1, \cdots, q$.

Using this notation the constrained KW procedure can be conveniently defined so that it stays inside of $C(\mathbf{a}, \mathbf{b})$ and all sampling is done inside of $C(\mathbf{a}, \mathbf{b})$.

DEFINITION 6.2. Let the sequences $\{b_n\}$ and $\{c_n\}$ be as in Definition 5.1. For $c > 0$, define the random variables

$$\begin{aligned} \mathbf{Z}_{\mathbf{u},c}^{+,*} &= (Z_{(\mathbf{u}+c\mathbf{e}_1)*}, \cdots, Z_{(\mathbf{u}+c\mathbf{e}_q)*}), \\ \mathbf{Z}_{\mathbf{u},c}^{-,*} &= (Z_{(\mathbf{u}-c\mathbf{e}_1)*}, \cdots, Z_{(\mathbf{u}-c\mathbf{e}_q)*}). \end{aligned} \tag{6.3}$$

It is assumed that all $2qn$ random observations made in n iterations are independent for all n. The procedure begins by guessing $\mathbf{X}_1' \in C(\mathbf{a}, \mathbf{b})$. The succeeding elements of the sequence are given by the recursive relation

$$\mathbf{X}_{n+1}' = \left(\mathbf{X}_n' + \frac{b_n}{c_n}(\mathbf{Z}_{\mathbf{X}'_n,c_n}^{+,*} - \mathbf{Z}_{\mathbf{X}'_n,c_n}^{-,*})\right)^* \tag{6.4}$$

for $n = 1, 2, \cdots$. Before stating a theorem giving conditions for convergence of $\mathbf{X}_n'$, it is convenient to define the random variable $\mathbf{D}(\mathbf{u}, \varepsilon, \delta) = (D_1, \cdots, D_q)$, for $\varepsilon, \delta > 0$, by defining its components

$$D_i(\mathbf{u}, \varepsilon, \delta) = \begin{cases} \frac{1}{\delta}(a_i - u_i) & \text{if } Z_{(\mathbf{u}+\varepsilon\mathbf{e}_i)*} - Z_{(\mathbf{u}-\varepsilon\mathbf{e}_i)*} < \frac{1}{\delta}(a_i - u_i), \\ Z_{(\mathbf{u}+\varepsilon\mathbf{e}_i)*} - Z_{(\mathbf{u}-\varepsilon\mathbf{e}_i)*} & \text{if } \frac{1}{\delta}(a_i - u_i) \leqq Z_{(\mathbf{u}+\varepsilon\mathbf{e}_i)*} - Z_{(\mathbf{u}-\varepsilon\mathbf{e}_i)} \leqq \frac{1}{\delta}(b_i - u_i), \\ \frac{1}{\delta}(b_i - u_i) & \text{if } \frac{1}{\delta}(b_i - u_i) < Z_{(\mathbf{u}+\varepsilon\mathbf{e}_i)*} - Z_{(\mathbf{u}-\varepsilon\mathbf{e}_i)*}. \end{cases} \tag{6.5}$$

Define the mean of $\mathbf{D}(\mathbf{u}, \varepsilon, \delta)$ to be

$$\mathbf{M}(\mathbf{u}, \varepsilon, \delta) = E\mathbf{D}(\mathbf{u}, \varepsilon, \delta). \tag{6.6}$$

Using this notation we can state the relation of (6.4) in the form

$$\mathbf{X}_{n+1}' = \mathbf{X}_n' + \frac{b_n}{c_n}\mathbf{D}\left(\mathbf{X}_n', c_n, \frac{b_n}{c_n}\right). \tag{6.7}$$

Also, let

$$\begin{aligned} \mathbf{f}^{+,*}(\mathbf{u}, \varepsilon) &= (f[(\mathbf{u} + \varepsilon\mathbf{e}_1)^*], \cdots, f[(\mathbf{u} + \varepsilon\mathbf{e}_q)^*]), \\ \mathbf{f}^{-,*}(\mathbf{u}, \varepsilon) &= (f[(\mathbf{u} - \varepsilon\mathbf{e}_1)^*], \cdots, f[(\mathbf{u} - \varepsilon\mathbf{e}_q)^*]). \end{aligned} \tag{6.7a}$$

THEOREM 6.1. *Let*

$$E|Z_{\mathbf{u}} - f(\mathbf{u})|^2 \leqq \sigma^2 < \infty \tag{6.8}$$

for all $u \in C(\mathbf{a}, \mathbf{b})$, *and suppose that for positive* ε *sufficiently small there exist constants* A *and* B *such that*

$$\|\mathbf{f}^{+,*}(\mathbf{u}, \varepsilon) - f^{-,*}(\mathbf{u}, \varepsilon)\| < A\|\mathbf{u} - \boldsymbol{\theta}'\| + B. \tag{6.9}$$

Assume that for arbitrary $\rho > 0$ *there exists* $\kappa > 1/\sqrt{2}$ *such that if positive* ε *and* δ *are sufficiently small,* $\mathbf{u} \in C(\mathbf{a}, \mathbf{b})$, *and* $\rho < \|\mathbf{u} - \boldsymbol{\theta}'\|$, *it follows that*

$$(\mathbf{u} - \boldsymbol{\theta}', \mathbf{M}(\mathbf{u}, \varepsilon, \delta)) \leqq -\kappa\|\mathbf{u} - \boldsymbol{\theta}'\| \cdot \|\mathbf{M}(\mathbf{u}, \varepsilon, \delta)\|. \tag{6.10}$$

Further, suppose that for arbitrary $\rho > 0$, *there exists* $\varepsilon_0 > 0$ *such that*

$$\inf_{\substack{0<\varepsilon, \delta<\varepsilon_0 \\ \rho<\|\mathbf{u}-\boldsymbol{\theta}'\|}} \frac{\|\mathbf{M}(\mathbf{u}, \varepsilon, \delta)\|}{2\varepsilon} > 0. \tag{6.11}$$

Then,

$$P[\|\mathbf{X}_n' - \boldsymbol{\theta}'\| \to 0] = 1 \tag{6.12}$$

and

$$E\|\mathbf{X}_n' - \boldsymbol{\theta}'\|^2 \to 0. \tag{6.13}$$

PROOF. It is sufficient to modify certain parts of the proof of Theorem 5.2. Let

$$\mathbf{T}_n'(\mathbf{r}_n) = \mathbf{r}_n + \frac{b_n}{c_n}\mathbf{M}\left(\mathbf{r}_n, c_n, \frac{b_n}{c_n}\right) \tag{6.14}$$

and

$$\mathbf{Y}_n' = \frac{b_n}{c_n}\left(\mathbf{D}\left(\mathbf{r}_n, c_n, \frac{b_n}{c_n}\right) - \mathbf{M}\left(\mathbf{r}_n, c_n, \frac{b_n}{c_n}\right)\right).$$

Then

$$\mathbf{X}_{n+1}' = \mathbf{T}_n'(\mathbf{r}_n) + \mathbf{Y}_n', \tag{6.15}$$

where $\mathbf{r}_n$ is a number denoting the value taken by $\mathbf{X}_n'$.

As in the proof of Theorem 5.2, we must verify that the conditions of Theorem 5.1 are satisfied.

Clearly, (5.19) holds.

The following lemma will be used several times in checking that the conditions of Theorem 5.1 hold.

LEMMA 6.1. *For positive* ε, δ *sufficiently small, there exist constants* A', B' *such that*

$$\|\mathbf{M}(\mathbf{u}, \varepsilon, \delta)\| \leqq A'\|\mathbf{u} - \boldsymbol{\theta}'\| + B', \tag{6.16}$$

for all $\mathbf{u} \in C(\mathbf{a}, \mathbf{b})$.

PROOF. Let M_i be a component of $\mathbf{M}(\mathbf{u}, \varepsilon, \delta)$. Since $\mathbf{M}$ is the expected value of $\mathbf{D}$,

$$
\begin{aligned}
|M_i| = \Bigg| & \frac{1}{\delta}(a_i - u_i)P\left[Z_{(\mathbf{u}+\varepsilon\mathbf{e}_i)*} - Z_{(\mathbf{u}-\varepsilon\mathbf{e}_i)*} < \frac{1}{\delta}(a_i - u_i)\right] \\
& + \int_{\{(a_i-u_i)/\delta < Z_{(\mathbf{u}+\varepsilon\mathbf{e}_i)*} - Z_{(\mathbf{u}-\varepsilon\mathbf{e}_i)*} < (b_i-u_i)/\delta\}} (Z_{(\mathbf{u}+\varepsilon\mathbf{e}_i)*} - Z_{(\mathbf{u}-\varepsilon\mathbf{e}_i)*})\,dP \\
& + \frac{1}{\delta}(b_i - u_i)P\left[\frac{1}{\delta}(b_i - u_i) < Z_{(\mathbf{u}+\varepsilon\mathbf{e}_i)*} - Z_{(\mathbf{u}-\varepsilon\mathbf{e}_i)*}\right]\Bigg|
\end{aligned}
\tag{6.17}
$$

$$
\begin{aligned}
& \leqq |f[(\mathbf{u} + \varepsilon\mathbf{e}_i)^*] - f[(\mathbf{u} - \varepsilon\mathbf{e}_i)^*]| \\
& + \int_{\{Z_{(\mathbf{u}+\varepsilon\mathbf{e}_i)*} - Z_{(\mathbf{u}-\varepsilon\mathbf{e}_i)*} < (a_i-u_i)/\delta\}} \left|\frac{1}{\delta}(a_i - u_i) - (Z_{(\mathbf{u}+\varepsilon\mathbf{e}_i)*} - Z_{(\mathbf{u}-\varepsilon\mathbf{e}_i)*})\right| dP \\
& + \int_{\{(b_i-u_i)/\delta < Z_{(\mathbf{u}+\varepsilon\mathbf{e}_i)*} - Z_{(\mathbf{u}-\varepsilon\mathbf{e}_i)*}\}} \left|\frac{1}{\delta}(b_i - u_i) - (Z_{(\mathbf{u}+\varepsilon\mathbf{e}_i)*} - Z_{(\mathbf{u}-\varepsilon\mathbf{e}_i)*})\right| dP.
\end{aligned}
$$

Consider the second term above.

$$
\begin{aligned}
& \int_{\{Z_{(\mathbf{u}+\varepsilon\mathbf{e}_i)*} - Z_{(\mathbf{u}-\varepsilon\mathbf{e}_i)*} < (a\ -u_i)/\delta\}} \left|\frac{1}{\delta}(a_i - u_i) - (Z_{(\mathbf{u}+\varepsilon\mathbf{e}_i)*} - Z_{(\mathbf{u}-\varepsilon\mathbf{e}_i)*})\right| dP \\
& \leqq \frac{1}{\delta}|a_i - u_i| P\left[Z_{(\mathbf{u}+\varepsilon\mathbf{e}_i)*} - Z_{(\mathbf{u}-\varepsilon\mathbf{e}_i)*} < \frac{1}{\delta}(a_i - u_i)\right] + E|Z_{(\mathbf{u}+\varepsilon\mathbf{e}_i)*} - Z_{(\mathbf{u}-\varepsilon\mathbf{e}_i)*}|.
\end{aligned}
\tag{6.18}
$$

The first term above is zero if $a_i = u_i$. If not, then by Loève's Basic Inequality [**11**, p. 157] it is

$$
\leqq \frac{1}{\delta}|a_i - u_i| \frac{E|Z_{(\mathbf{u}+\varepsilon\mathbf{e}_i)*} - Z_{(\mathbf{u}-\varepsilon\mathbf{e}_i)*}|}{|a_i - u_i|/\delta}.
\tag{6.19}
$$

Thus, (6.18) is

$$
\leqq 2E|Z_{(\mathbf{u}+\varepsilon\mathbf{e}_i)*} - Z_{(\mathbf{u}-\varepsilon\mathbf{e}_i)*}|.
\tag{6.20}
$$

Similar reasoning applies to the third term in (6.17). Therefore,

$$
|M_i| \leqq |f[(\mathbf{u} + \varepsilon\mathbf{e}_i)^*] - f[(\mathbf{u} - \varepsilon\mathbf{e}_i)^*]| + 4E|Z_{(\mathbf{u}+\varepsilon\mathbf{e}_i)*} - Z_{(\mathbf{u}-\varepsilon\mathbf{e}_i)*}|.
\tag{6.21}
$$

Thus,

$$
|M_i| \leqq |f[(\mathbf{u} + \varepsilon\mathbf{e}_i)^*] - f[(\mathbf{u} - \varepsilon\mathbf{e}_i)^*]| + C
\tag{6.22}
$$

and

$$
|M_i|^2 \leqq |f[(\mathbf{u} + \varepsilon\mathbf{e}_i)^*] - f[(\mathbf{u} - \varepsilon\mathbf{e}_i)^*]|^2 + C
\tag{6.23}
$$

where all of the C's here are not necessarily equal. Equation (6.23) implies that

$$
\|\mathbf{M}(\mathbf{u}, \varepsilon, \delta)\| \leqq \|\mathbf{f}^{+,*}(\mathbf{u}, \varepsilon) - \mathbf{f}^{-,*}(\mathbf{u}, \varepsilon)\| + C.
\tag{6.24}
$$

Now, (6.9) implies that

$$\|\mathbf{M}(\mathbf{u}, \varepsilon, \delta)\| \leqq A'\|\mathbf{u} - \boldsymbol{\theta}'\| + B' \tag{6.25}$$

for some constants A', B'. This completes the proof of the lemma.

Next we verify condition (5.18) of Dvoretzky's Theorem. By the definition of $\mathbf{Y}_n'$,

$$E\|\mathbf{Y}_n'\|^2 = \frac{b_n^2}{c_n^2} E\left\| \mathbf{D}\left(\mathbf{r}_n, c_n, \frac{b_n}{c_n}\right) - \mathbf{M}\left(\mathbf{r}_n, c_n, \frac{b_n}{c_n}\right)\right\|^2. \tag{6.26}$$

Since $\sum b_n^2/c_n^2 < \infty$, it is sufficient to show that $E\|\mathbf{D} - \mathbf{M}\|^2$ is uniformly bounded for n sufficiently large. Now, let $r_{n,i}$ denote the ith component of $\mathbf{r}_n$. Then,

$$\begin{aligned} E|D_i - M_i|^2 \leqq & \left|\frac{c_n}{b_n}(a_i - r_{n,i}) - M_i\right|^2 P\left[Z_{(\mathbf{r}_n+c_n\mathbf{e}_i)^*} - Z_{(\mathbf{r}_n-c_n\mathbf{e}_i)^*} < \frac{1}{\delta}(a_i - r_{n,i})\right] \\ & + \int_{\{(a_i-r_{n,i})\leq b_n(Z_{(\mathbf{r}_n+c_n\mathbf{e}_i)^*}-Z_{(\mathbf{r}_n-c_n\mathbf{e}_i)^*})/c_n\leq(b_i-r_{n,i})\}} |Z_{(\mathbf{r}_n+c_n\mathbf{e}_i)^*} - Z_{(\mathbf{r}_n-c_n\mathbf{e}_i)^*} - M_i|^2 \\ & + \left|\frac{c_n}{b_n}(b_i - r_{n,i}) - M_i\right|^2 P\left[\frac{c_n}{b_n}(b_i - r_{n,i}) < Z_{(\mathbf{r}_n+c_n\mathbf{e}_i)^*} - Z_{(\mathbf{r}_n-c_n\mathbf{e}_i)^*}\right]. \end{aligned} \tag{6.27}$$

Condition (6.9) and Lemma 6.1 together with the fact that $\|\mathbf{u}\|$ is bounded ($\mathbf{u} \in C(\mathbf{a}, \mathbf{b})$) yield that the middle term above is bounded.

Consider the first term of (6.27). It is

$$\begin{aligned} \leqq & \frac{c_n^2}{b_n^2}|a_i - r_{n,i}|^2 P\left[Z_{(\mathbf{r}_n+c_n\mathbf{e}_i)^*} - Z_{(\mathbf{r}_n-c_n\mathbf{e}_i)^*} < \frac{c_n}{b_n}(a_i - r_{n,i})\right] \\ & + |M_i|^2 P\left[Z_{(\mathbf{r}_n+c_n\mathbf{e}_i)^*} - Z_{(\mathbf{r}_n-c_n\mathbf{e}_i)^*} < \frac{c_n}{b_n}(a_i - r_{n,i})\right]. \end{aligned} \tag{6.28}$$

The first term of (6.28) is bounded by argument used in the proof of Lemma 6.1. The second term is bounded by the lemma. Thus

$$E\|\mathbf{Y}_n'\|^2 \leqq \frac{b_n^2}{c_n^2}\text{const} \tag{6.29}$$

and, hence,

$$E(\textstyle\sum\|\mathbf{Y}_n'\|^2) \leqq \text{const} \sum \frac{b_n^2}{c_n^2} < \infty. \tag{6.30}$$

This completes the verification of (5.18) of Theorem 5.1.

The remainder of the proof of the theorem is a straightforward modification of the proof of Theorem 5.2.

7. **Application to circuit design.** In §4 a model was indicated for a class of circuit design problems. We wished to minimize the risk

$$R(\mathbf{u}) = EL(Y_\mathbf{u}, \mathbf{u}) = EL_1(Y_\mathbf{u}) + L_2(\mathbf{u}) \tag{7.1}$$

subject to a rectangular constraint

$$\mathbf{u} \in C(\mathbf{a}, \mathbf{b}). \tag{7.2}$$

By considering the equivalent problem of maximizing

$$-R(\mathbf{u}) = E[-L(Y_{\mathbf{u}}, \mathbf{u})], \tag{7.3}$$

we can apply the techniques of §§5 and 6.

In order to implement these techniques, we must have available a means of sampling the random variable

$$Z_{\mathbf{u}} = -L(Y_{\mathbf{u}}, \mathbf{u}) \tag{7.4}$$

for any parameter setting $\mathbf{u} \in C(\mathbf{a}, \mathbf{b})$. This can be accomplished by computer simulation. Thus, for the example of §2 it would be sufficient to generate random variables R and C whose uniform distributions are determined by the four components of $\mathbf{u}$. Using the relations of (7.3) and (7.4) it would be possible to make random observations of $Z_{\mathbf{u}} = -L(Y_{\mathbf{u}}, \mathbf{u})$.

Consider the application of the technique to a practical problem. The first task is to define the loss function L_1, giving the contribution to the total loss resulting from an output $Y_{\mathbf{u}}$. L_2 reflects the cost of selecting the parameter setting $\mathbf{u}$.

Next, one could use the design values and possibly some "worst-case" analysis for a first guess $\mathbf{X}_1'$ at the optimum parameter setting $\boldsymbol{\theta}'$. Also, one faces the problem of defining a suitable constraint for the problem. This would likely be governed by such considerations as the availability and the cost of components with different distributions on their values.

Frequently, for a realistically defined loss function $L(Y_{\mathbf{u}}, \mathbf{u})$, the function $-R(\mathbf{u})$ to be maximized has more than one *local* maximum, although it may satisfy the conditions of Theorem 6.1 locally for various points. The problem, of course, is that generally $L(Y_{\mathbf{u}}, \mathbf{u})$ is defined explicitly and the form of the function $-R(\mathbf{u})$ is unknown. Thus, in order for stochastic approximation to be useful, the technique must be used experimentally. That is, one may suspect that within $C(\mathbf{a}, \mathbf{b})$ there is more than one local maximum. But, he may also suspect that the conditions of §6 are satisfied locally. Suppose the modified KW procedure is applied blindly starting at the best guess $\mathbf{X}_1'$ that one's intuition will yield. Possibly several independent KW sequences will converge to, say, two or three points. If, no matter where in $C(\mathbf{a}, \mathbf{b})$ the process is started, it invariably converges to these points, then one would suspect that these were the only local maxima in $C(\mathbf{a}, \mathbf{b})$. Monte Carlo estimation could then be used at the local maxima to find which was a maximum for $C(\mathbf{a}, \mathbf{b})$.

The point of the above discussion is that in practice it may be difficult, or impossible, to verify the assumptions of §6, but the technique may still be a useful tool for searching for a maximum of $-R(\mathbf{u})$.

References

1. J. R. Rosenblatt, *On prediction of system performance from information on component performance*, Proc. Western Joint Computer Conf., I.R.E., February, 1957.

2. W. D. Ashcroft and W. Hochwald, *Design by worst-case analysis: A systematic method to approach specified reliability requirements*, IRE Trans. **RQC–10** (1961), 15–21.

3. J. W. Tukey, *The propagation of errors, fluctuations and tolerances. Basic generalized formulas*, Princeton Univ. Tech. Rep. No. 10, AD 155 082, Princeton University, Princeton, N. J.

4. H. J. Gray, Jr., *An application of piecewise approximations to reliability and statistical design*, Proc. IRE **47** (1959), 1226–1231.

5. S. I. Firstman, *Reliability estimating by the use of random sampling simulation*, Rep. No. P–1521, The RAND Corp., Santa Monica, Calif., 1958.

6. J. Kiefer and J. Wolfowitz, *Stochastic estimation of the maximum of a regression function*, Ann. Math. Statist. **23** (1952), 462–466.

7. J. R. Blum, *Approximation methods which converge with probability one*, Ann. Math. Statist. **25** (1954), 382–386.

8. A. Dvoretzky, *On stochastic approximation*, Proc. 3rd Berkeley Sympos. Math. Statist. and Prob., Vol. I, pp. 39–55, Univ. of California Press, Berkeley, Calif., 1956.

9. J. Sacks, *Asymptotic distribution of stochastic approximation procedures*, Ann. Math. Statist. **29** (1958), 373–405.

10. J. R. Blum, *Multidimensional stochastic approximation procedures*, Ann. Math. Statist. **25** (1954), 737–744.

11. M. Loève, *Probability theory*, Van Nostrand, New York, 1955.

Hughes Research Laboratories,
Malibu, California

RANDOM WALKS ON LATTICES

BY

ELLIOTT W. MONTROLL

The theory of random walks on periodic space lattices has been dealt with sporadically since the turn of the century. In all university courses on the theory of probability or statistical mechanics the lecturer finds an excuse for discussing the one dimensional (1 D) lattice walk by a walker who with every step has a probability p of going to the right and $q = 1 - p$ of going to the left. In keeping with tradition this problem will also be treated here even though the emphasis will be on walks on lattices in higher dimensional spaces.

The century opened with the classic paper of Bachelier **[1]**[1] which presented a random walk model of the stock market. It was there shown that if a large number of stocks is normalized to the same value, the dispersion of the prices of the stocks from their mean value grows as the square root of the time just as the dispersion from the mean position of a random walker varies with the time. This paper, which preceded Einstein's work on Brownian motion (1905), contained many of the ideas which evolved into the modern theory of stochastic processes. In his review of the theory of stochastic processes Chandrasekhar **[2]** briefly touches on 1 D walks in the presence of reflecting and absorbing barriers. Lattice walks are a special case of his discussion of the theory of random flights.

In more recent times problems of solid state physics have stimulated either explicitly or implicitly a number of investigations on lattice walks. The motions of defects in crystals **[3]** are direct examples of such walks while the dynamics of various excitations such as spin waves **[4; 5]** are mathematically equivalent to certain lattice walk problems.

The aim of this paper is to give a self-contained review of the theory of lattice walks. As a preview we list below several of the topics to be considered.

The existence of a qualitative difference between random walks on 3 D lattices and those on 1 D or 2 D lattices was first noticed by Pólya **[6]** who showed that a random walker on a 1 D or 2 D lattice is certain to return to his starting point while one on a 3 D lattice has a nonvanishing escape probability. The probability of escape was estimated by McCrea and Whipple **[7]** with an improved calculation having been made by Domb **[8]**. The author has derived exact values for walks on simple cubic, body centered and face centered cubic lattices **[9; 10]**. Here we will discuss the Pólya problem as well as the closely connected problem of the average number of steps required to reach a given lattice point for the first time.

---

[1] *The random walk or Brownian motion of the stock market* was rediscovered independently some years later by M. F. M. Osborne, Operations Res. **7** (1959), 145, 808. B. Mandelbrot has emphasized the importance of long tails in certain distribution functions.

Dvoretsky and Erdös [11] and Vineyard [12] have discussed the number of distinct lattice points visited by a lattice walker. We rederive their results in a more direct manner by employing a certain Tauberian theorem.

The importance of Green's function in the theory of random walks on lattices was recognized by R. Courant [13] and his collaborators [14]. Our work in this paper is based completely on the Green's function technique. As one might expect there is considerable connection between random walks on lattices and discrete potential theory [15]. The use of Green's functions is especially applicable to random walks on lattices with a small number of defective points [16]. The analysis of such situations is quite similar to that of the effect of defects on lattice vibrations [17; 18; 19; 20],[2] and will be presented in §IV.

A 3 D lattice is defined as follows. Consider a set of three unit vectors, $\boldsymbol{i}_1$, $\boldsymbol{i}_2$, and $\boldsymbol{i}_3$ which are not coplanar. The end points of the vectors

$$\boldsymbol{l} \equiv (l_1, l_2, l_3) \equiv l_1\boldsymbol{i}_1 + l_2\boldsymbol{i}_2 + l_3\boldsymbol{i}_3$$

which are generated by letting the l's range through the integers $0, \pm 1, \pm 2, \cdots$ form a space lattice of three dimensions. Periodic lattices of $1, 2, 4, 5, \cdots$ dimensions can be defined in a similar manner.

We begin our discussion with the basic calculation of

I. The probability of going from a given lattice point to another in t steps. We discuss this first in the context of walks on the one dimensional lattice of Figure 1 such that at each step a walker steps to the right with a probability p and to

$$\dot{-2} \quad \dot{-1} \quad \dot{0} \quad \dot{1} \quad \dot{2}$$

FIGURE 1

the left with a probability $q = 1 - p$. The coefficient p of $e^{i\phi}$ in the expression

$$(p\, e^{i\phi} + q\, e^{-i\phi})$$

represents the probability of the first step being to the right while the coefficient q of $e^{-i\phi}$ represents the probability of the first step being to the left. The coefficient p^2 of $e^{2i\phi}$ in

$$(p\, e^{i\phi} + q\, e^{-i\phi})^2$$

represents the probability of a walker being at $l = 2$ after two steps, the coefficient $2pq$ of $e^{0i\phi}$ the probability that he has returned to the origin, and the coefficient q^2 of $e^{-2i\phi}$ the probability that he ends at $l = -2$ after two steps. Generally

$$\begin{aligned} P_t(l) &= \text{probability that walker is at } l \text{ after } t \text{ steps} \\ &= \text{coefficient of } e^{-il\phi} \text{ in } (p\, e^{i\phi} + q\, e^{-i\phi})^t \qquad (1) \\ &= \frac{1}{2\pi}\int_{-\pi}^{\pi} (p\, e^{i\phi} + q\, e^{-i\phi})^t\, e^{-il\phi}\, d\phi \end{aligned}$$

[2] [18] contains many earlier Russian references.

since the identity

$$\frac{1}{2\pi}\int_{-\pi}^{\pi} e^{-i\phi m}\, d\phi = \delta_{m.0}$$

implies that the integral operator

$$\frac{1}{2\pi}\int_{-\pi}^{\pi} \exp(-i\phi l)\, d\phi\,\cdot$$

filters out the coefficient of exp $il\phi$ in the Fourier series representation of a periodic function of period 2π. In the symmetrical case with $p = q = 1/2$

(2) $$P_t(l) = \frac{1}{2\pi}\int_{-\pi}^{\pi} (\cos\phi)^t\, e^{-i\phi l}\, d\phi = 2^{-t}\frac{t!}{l!(t-l)!}.$$

The appearance of the binomial coefficient $t!/l!(t-l)!$ could of course have been predicted from purely combinational arguments.

The above argument can be generalized immediately to the investigation of walks on a two dimensional square lattice in which

p_1 = prob. of step in positive x direction,
q_1 = prob. of step in negative x direction,
p_2 = prob. of step in positive y direction,
q_2 = prob. of step in negative y direction.

The probability of going from the origin to lattice point $\boldsymbol{l} \equiv (l_1, l_2)$ is

(3a) $$P_t(\boldsymbol{l}) = P_t(l_1, l_2) = \frac{1}{(2\pi)^2}\iint_{-\pi}^{\pi} [p_1 e^{i\phi_1} + q_1 e^{-i\phi_1} + p_2 e^{i\phi_2} + q_2 e^{-i\phi_2}]\, e^{-i\boldsymbol{\phi}\cdot\boldsymbol{l}}\, d\phi_1\, d\phi_2,$$

where

(3b) $$p_1 + q_1 + p_2 + q_2 = 1,$$

(3c) $$\phi_1 l_1 + \phi_2 l_2 = \boldsymbol{\phi}\cdot\boldsymbol{l}.$$

In the symmetrical case $p_1 = q_1 = p_2 = q_2 = 1/4$ and

(4) $$P_t(\boldsymbol{l}) = \frac{1}{(2\pi)^2}\iint_{-\pi}^{\pi} [\tfrac{1}{2}(\cos\phi_1 + \cos\phi_2)]^t\, e^{-i\boldsymbol{\phi}\cdot\boldsymbol{l}}\, d\phi_1\, d\phi_2.$$

Indeed, in general, on a hypercubic lattice of s dimensions with $2s$ possible steps of equal weight from each lattice point to a nearest neighbor lattice point **[6; 10]**

(5) $$P_t(\boldsymbol{l}) = \frac{1}{(2\pi)^s}\int \cdots \int_{-\pi}^{\pi} \left[\frac{1}{s}(c_1 + c_2 + \cdots + c_s)\right]^t e^{-i\boldsymbol{\phi}\cdot\boldsymbol{l}}\, d^s\phi,$$

where

(6) $$c_j = \cos\phi_j \quad\text{and}\quad d^s\phi = d\phi_1 \cdots d\phi_s.$$

If one analyzes more exotic walks than those which involve successive steps to nearest neighboring points on a simple cubic lattice he can easily get dizzy trying to generate walks in the elementary manner described above. A more systematic approach to the problem involves the difference equation [10]

$$P_{t+1}(\boldsymbol{l}) = \sum_{\boldsymbol{l}'} p(\boldsymbol{l} - \boldsymbol{l}')P_t(\boldsymbol{l}'), \tag{7a}$$

where $p(\boldsymbol{l})$ = probability of step from $\boldsymbol{l}'$ to $\boldsymbol{l}'' \equiv \boldsymbol{l}' + \boldsymbol{l}$ (independently of t), i.e., of a displacement $\boldsymbol{l}$ at any given step and

$$\sum p(\boldsymbol{l}) = 1. \tag{7b}$$

We consider first the case of a finite $N \times N \times \cdots \times N$ lattice with periodic boundary conditions. In the 1 D case this would correspond to a ring of regularly spaced points. In the 2 D case it corresponds to square grid of points wrapped into the form of a torus, etc. Then

$$\begin{aligned} P_t(l_1, l_2, \cdots, l_s) &= P_t(l_1 + N, l_2, \cdots, l_s) \\ &= P_t(l_1, l_2 + N, l_3, \cdots, l_s) = \text{etc.} \end{aligned} \tag{8}$$

If we assume that $P_t(\boldsymbol{l})$ can be expressed as a linear combination of the complete set of functions

$$\exp 2\pi i(k_1 l_1 + \cdots + k_s l_s)/N \tag{9a}$$

with

$$k_j = 0, 1, \cdots, N - 1 \tag{9b}$$

and that

$$\begin{aligned} \lambda(2\pi\boldsymbol{k}/N) &\equiv \lambda(2\pi k_1/N, \cdots, 2\pi k_s/N) \\ &= \sum_{\boldsymbol{l}} p(\boldsymbol{l}) \exp (2\pi i \boldsymbol{l} \cdot \boldsymbol{k}/N), \end{aligned} \tag{10}$$

then

$$\begin{aligned} \sum_{\boldsymbol{l}} P_{t+1}(\boldsymbol{l}) e^{2\pi i \boldsymbol{k}\cdot \boldsymbol{l}/N} &= \sum_{\boldsymbol{l},\boldsymbol{l}'} p(\boldsymbol{l} - \boldsymbol{l}')\, e^{2\pi i(\boldsymbol{l}-\boldsymbol{l}')\cdot \boldsymbol{k}/N} P_t(\boldsymbol{l}')\, e^{2\pi i \boldsymbol{l}'\cdot \boldsymbol{k}/N} \\ &= \lambda(2\pi\boldsymbol{k}/N) \sum_{\boldsymbol{l}} P_t(\boldsymbol{l})\, e^{2\pi i \boldsymbol{l}\cdot \boldsymbol{k}/N}. \end{aligned} \tag{11}$$

If we use the initial condition that

$$P_0(\boldsymbol{l}) = \delta_{\boldsymbol{l},0} \tag{12}$$

it is clear by inverting (11) that

$$P_t(\boldsymbol{l}) = N^{-s} \sum_{\boldsymbol{k}} [\lambda(2\pi\boldsymbol{k}/N)]^t \exp (-2\pi i \boldsymbol{k} \cdot \boldsymbol{l}/N). \tag{13}$$

In the limit of an infinite lattice we let $\phi_j = 2\pi k_j/N$ and $d\phi_j = 2\pi/N$. Then as $N \to \infty$

$$(14) \qquad P_t(\boldsymbol{l}) = \frac{1}{(2\pi)^s} \int \cdots \int_{-\pi}^{\pi} [\lambda(\boldsymbol{\phi})]^t e^{-i\boldsymbol{\phi}\cdot\boldsymbol{l}} \, d^s\phi.$$

With this formula we can easily reproduce (5). For example consider the simple cubic lattice with $s = 3$ and

$$p(\boldsymbol{l}) = \begin{cases} \frac{1}{6} & \text{for} \quad \boldsymbol{l} = (0, 0, \pm 1), (0, \pm 1, 0) \quad \text{and} \quad (\pm 1, 0, 0), \\ 0 & \text{otherwise.} \end{cases}$$

Then

$$(15) \qquad \begin{aligned} \lambda(\phi_1, \phi_2, \phi_3) &= \tfrac{1}{6}(e^{i\phi_1} + e^{-i\phi_1} + e^{i\phi_2} + e^{-i\phi_2} + e^{i\phi_3} + e^{-i\phi_3}) \\ &= \tfrac{1}{3}(c_1 + c_2 + c_3). \end{aligned}$$

Expressions for $\lambda(\phi_1, \phi_2, \phi_3)$ for a 3 D face centered and body centered cubic lattices are obtained as follows.

The random walk between nearest neighbor points on a face centered cubic lattice is equivalent to one on a simple cubic lattice of lattice spacing 1 on which a walker can only take steps which correspond to the twelve displacements $(\pm 1, \pm 1, 0), (\pm 1, 0, \pm 1), (0, \pm 1, \pm 1)$.

Then

$$(16) \qquad \lambda(\boldsymbol{\phi}) \equiv \tfrac{1}{3}(c_1 c_2 + c_2 c_3 + c_3 c_1).$$

The random walk between nearest neighbor points on a body centered cubic lattice is equivalent to one on a simple cubic lattice of lattice spacing 1 on which a walker can only take steps which correspond to the eight displacement vectors $(\pm 1, \pm 1, \pm 1)$ which result from all possible selections of plus and minus signs. Then if each possible step can occur with the same probability, 1/8,

$$(17) \qquad \lambda(\boldsymbol{\phi}) = c_1 c_2 c_3.$$

Various moments of the distribution function $P_t(\boldsymbol{l})$ can be obtained by inverting (14). The inverse function $\Lambda_t(\boldsymbol{\phi})$ or characteristic function of $P_t(\boldsymbol{l})$ is

$$(18) \qquad \Lambda_t(\boldsymbol{\phi}) \equiv [\lambda(\boldsymbol{\phi})]^t = \sum_{\boldsymbol{l}} P_t(\boldsymbol{l}) \, e^{i\boldsymbol{\phi}\cdot\boldsymbol{l}}.$$

The mathematical expectation of l_j after t steps is just (we use the physicist's notation $\langle \boldsymbol{l} \rangle$ rather than the mathematician's $E(\boldsymbol{l})$ for the average value of $\boldsymbol{l}$)

$$(19) \qquad \begin{aligned} \langle l_j \rangle &= \sum_{\boldsymbol{l}} l_j P_t(\boldsymbol{l}) = -\lim_{\phi \to 0} it[\lambda(\boldsymbol{\phi})]^{t-1} \partial\lambda/\partial\phi_j \\ &= t \sum_{\boldsymbol{l}} l_j p(\boldsymbol{l}) \equiv t\mu_j \end{aligned}$$

since $\lambda(0) = 1$. As a special example consider the 1 D walk with

$$p(1) = p, \quad p(-1) = q = 1 - p,$$
$$p(l) = 0 \quad \text{if} \quad l \neq 1 \quad \text{or} \quad -1.$$

Then

$$\langle l \rangle = t(p - q). \tag{20}$$

Second moments can be found in a similar manner

$$\begin{aligned} \langle l_j l_k \rangle = \sum_{\boldsymbol{l}} l_j l_k P_t(\boldsymbol{l}) &= - \lim_{\boldsymbol{\phi}\to 0} \partial^2 \Lambda / \partial\phi_j \partial\phi_k \\ &= - t \frac{\partial^2 \lambda}{\partial\phi_j \partial\phi_k}\bigg]_{\boldsymbol{\phi}=0} - t(t-1) \frac{\partial\lambda}{\partial\phi_j}\frac{\partial\lambda}{\partial\phi_k}\bigg]_{\boldsymbol{\phi}=0} \\ &= t\mu_{jk} + t(t-1)\mu_j\mu_k, \end{aligned} \tag{21}$$

where

$$\mu_{jk} = \sum_{\boldsymbol{l}} l_j l_k p(\boldsymbol{l}). \tag{22}$$

Also

$$\langle l_j l_k \rangle - \langle l_j \rangle \langle l_k \rangle = t(\mu_{jk} - \mu_j \mu_k). \tag{23}$$

By an application of the central limit theorems for a sum of vectors, each with the same distribution function, one can show that the joint distribution of $l_1, l_2, \cdots, l_s$ after t steps is an s dimensional Gaussian distribution which is characterized by the mean values (19) and the correlations (21), (22).

II. Random walk generating functions. Most of the questions discussed in the remainder of this paper can be derived from random walk generating functions. The most important of these is the generating function of all walks which end at lattice point $\boldsymbol{l}$ independently of t:

$$U(z, \boldsymbol{l}) = \sum_{t=0}^{\infty} z^t P_t(\boldsymbol{l}). \tag{1}$$

On an infinite lattice one finds from §I, (1), §I, (5), and §I, (14):

(a) for 1 D walk

$$U(z, l) = \frac{1}{2\pi} \int_{-\pi}^{\pi} \frac{\exp(-i\phi l)\, d\phi}{1 - z(p\, e^{i\phi} + q\, e^{-i\phi})}; \tag{2}$$

(b) for s D symmetric walk on a simple cubic lattice (all steps being taken to nearest neighbor points)

$$U(z, \boldsymbol{l}) = \frac{1}{(2\pi)^s} \int_{-\pi}^{\pi} \cdots \int \frac{\exp(-i\boldsymbol{\phi}\cdot\boldsymbol{l})\, d^s\phi}{1 - \dfrac{z}{s}(c_1 + \cdots + c_s)}; \tag{3}$$

(c) for arbitrary s D lattice [**6**; **10**; **21**]

(4) $$U(z, \boldsymbol{l}) = \frac{1}{(2\pi)^s} \int_{-\pi}^{\pi} \cdots \int \frac{\exp(-i\boldsymbol{\phi} \cdot \boldsymbol{l})\, d^s\phi}{1 - z\lambda(\phi)}.$$

In particular the generating function for all walks which start and end at the same point (say the origin) is

(5) $$U(z, 0) = \frac{1}{(2\pi)^s} \int_{-\pi}^{\pi} \cdots \int \frac{d^s\phi}{1 - z\lambda(\boldsymbol{\phi})}.$$

A set of difference equations for $U(z, \boldsymbol{l})$ can be obtained from §I, (7), and §I, (12) by noting that

$$U(z, \boldsymbol{l}) = \delta_{l,0} + \sum_{t=0}^{\infty} z^{t+1} P_{t+1}(\boldsymbol{l})$$
$$= \delta_{l,0} + z \sum_{l'} p(\boldsymbol{l} - \boldsymbol{l}') \sum_{t=0}^{\infty} P_t(\boldsymbol{l}'),$$

which implies

(6) $$U(z, \boldsymbol{l}) - z \sum_{l'} p(\boldsymbol{l} - \boldsymbol{l}') U(z, \boldsymbol{l}') = \delta_{l,0}.$$

This is a Green's function type of equation.

A simple expression for $\sum_l U(z, \boldsymbol{l})$ follows from (6) by summing over all $\boldsymbol{l}$ for (remembering §I, (7b))

$$\sum_l U(z, \boldsymbol{l}) = 1 + z \sum_{l,l'} p(\boldsymbol{l} - \boldsymbol{l}') U(z, \boldsymbol{l}')$$
$$= 1 + z \sum_{l''} p(\boldsymbol{l}'') \sum_l U(z, \boldsymbol{l} - \boldsymbol{l}'')$$
$$= 1 + z \sum_l U(z, \boldsymbol{l})$$

so that

(7) $$\sum_l U(z, \boldsymbol{l}) = 1/(1 - z),$$

a result which is also valid for a finite lattice with periodic boundary conditions.

The analogue of (4) for a finite lattice with periodic boundary conditions is (from §I, (13))

(8) $$U_N(z, \boldsymbol{l}) = \frac{1}{N^s} \sum_{k_1=0}^{N-1} \cdots \sum_{k_s=0}^{N-1} \frac{\exp -2\pi i(l_1k_1 + \cdots + l_sk_s)/N}{1 - z\lambda(2\pi \boldsymbol{k}/N)}.$$

From §I, (7a), and §I, (10) one finds

(9) $$\lambda(0) = 1$$

and no other $\lambda(\boldsymbol{k})$ are unity. Hence $U_N(z, \boldsymbol{l})$ can be expressed as a sum of a singular and a nonsingular part.

$$U_N(z, \boldsymbol{l}) = \frac{1}{N^s(1 - z)} + \phi(z, \boldsymbol{l}), \tag{10a}$$

where the nonsingular part $\phi(z, \boldsymbol{l})$ is the sum

$$\phi(z, \boldsymbol{l}) = \frac{1}{N^s} \sum_{\boldsymbol{k}}{}' \frac{\exp -2\pi i \boldsymbol{k} \cdot \boldsymbol{l}/N}{1 - z\lambda(2\pi \boldsymbol{k}/N)} \tag{10b}$$

with the term corresponding to $\boldsymbol{k} = 0$ omitted.

On the infinite lattice ($N \to \infty$) the singular part inversely proportional to N^s vanishes but $\phi(z, \boldsymbol{l})$, which then becomes identical to $U(z, \boldsymbol{l})$, develops new singularities of a weaker type. Since the detailed character of $U(z, \boldsymbol{l})$ as $z \to 1$ will be of considerable importance, we consider its properties here. Since the remainder of this section is essentially a table of integrals, the reader may prefer to go directly to §III, referring back to formulae here as indicated in the later sections.

The integral (2) in the symmetric case $p = q = 1/2$ can be found in various tables of definite integrals. Its value is

$$\begin{aligned} U(z, l) &= \{1 - (1 - z^2)^{1/2}\}^{|l|}/z^l(1 - z^2)^{1/2} \\ &= x^{|l|}/(1 - z^2)^{1/2} \end{aligned} \tag{11a}$$

with

$$x = [1 - (1 - z^2)^{1/2}]/z. \tag{11b}$$

As is shown in Appendix 1, the generating function for a ring of N points is

$$U_N(z, l) = \left\{\frac{x^l + x^{N-l}}{1 - x^N}\right\} \Big/ (1 - z^2)^{1/2}. \tag{12}$$

Since as $z \to 1$

$$x \sim 1 - [2(1 - z)]^{1/2} + (1 - z) - \frac{3\sqrt{2}}{4}(1 - z)^{3/2} + (1 - z)^2 - \cdots, \tag{13}$$

we find

$$U_N(z, 0) \sim \{N(1 - z)[1 - \tfrac{1}{6}(1 - z)(N^2 - 1) + O(1 - z)^2]\}^{-1} \tag{14}$$

while for $l \geqq 0$

$$\begin{aligned} U_N(z, l)/U_N(z, 0) \sim 1 &- l(N - l)(1 - z) \\ &+ \tfrac{1}{6}l(N - l)\{(N^2 - 5) + l(N - l)\}(1 - z)^2 - \cdots \end{aligned} \tag{15}$$

and

$$U_N(z, l) = U_N(z, -l). \tag{16}$$

In the 2 D infinite square lattice case with

$$p(1, 0) = p(-1, 0) = p_1,$$
$$(17) \qquad p(0, 1) = p(0, -1) = p_2,$$
$$p(0, 0) = r \quad \text{and} \quad p(l_1, l_2) = 0 \text{ for other } (l_1, l_2)$$

and with

$$2p_1 + 2p_2 + r = 1$$

one finds

$$(18) \qquad U(z; l_1, l_2) = \frac{1}{(2\pi)^2} \iint_{-\pi}^{\pi} \frac{\exp(-i\boldsymbol{l} \cdot \boldsymbol{\phi})\, d^3\phi}{(1 - zr) - 2zp_1 \cos \phi_1 - 2zp_2 \cos \phi_2}$$
$$= \frac{1}{(2\pi)^2} \int_0^\infty dx \iint_{-\pi}^{\pi} d^2\phi \exp\{-i\boldsymbol{l} \cdot \boldsymbol{\phi} - x(1 - zr) + 2xz(p_1 \cos \phi_1 + p_2 \cos \phi_2)\}$$

$$(19) \qquad = \int_0^\infty e^{-x(1-zr)} I_{l_1}(2zxp_1) I_{l_2}(2zxp_2)\, dx,$$

where $I_l(x)$ is the lth Bessel function of purely imaginary argument. When $l_1 = l_2 = m \geqq 0$ a closed form expression exists for $U(z; m, m)$ (also note that $U(z; l_1, l_2) = U(z; -l_1, l_2) = U(z; l_1, -l_2) = U(z; -l_1, -l_2)$) **[22]**

$$(20) \qquad U(z; m, m) = \frac{1}{2\pi z(p_1 p_2)^{1/2}} Q_{m-1/2}\left(\frac{(1 - zr)^2 - 4z^2(p_1^2 + p_2^2)}{8z^2 p_1 p_2}\right),$$

where $Q_n(x)$ is the nth Legendre function of the second kind. Also

$$(21) \qquad Q_{-1/2}(\cosh \eta) = 2\, e^{-\eta/2} K(e^{-\eta}),$$

where $K(k)$ is the complete elliptic integral of the second kind. Note that

$$(1 - zr)^2 - 4z^2(p_1^2 + p_2^2) = 8z^2 p_1 p_2 + (1 - z)\{(1 + z) + 2zr\}.$$

Since as $\varepsilon \to 0$

$$Q_{m-1/2}(1 + \varepsilon) \sim -\tfrac{1}{2} \log(\tfrac{1}{2}\varepsilon) - \gamma - \psi(m + \tfrac{1}{2}) + O(\varepsilon),$$

where $\gamma = 0.57721$ is Euler's gamma and $\psi(x) = d \log \Gamma(x)/dx$, we find

$$(22) \qquad U(z; m, m) = \frac{1}{2\pi z(p_1 p_2)^{1/2}} \left\{-\tfrac{1}{2} \log \frac{(1 - z)[(1 + z) + 2rz]}{16z^2 p_1 p_2} - \gamma - \psi(m + \tfrac{1}{2}) + O(1 - z)\right\}$$

which has a logarithmic divergence as $z \to 1$. Note also that since

$$\psi(n+x) - \psi(x) = \frac{1}{x} + \frac{1}{1+x} + \cdots + \frac{1}{x+n+1},$$

(23)

$$-U(z; m, m) + U(z; 0, 0) = \left\{1 + \frac{1}{3} + \frac{1}{5} + \cdots + \frac{1}{2m-1}\right\} \Big/ \pi z(p_1 p_2)^{1/2} + O(1-z).$$

It can also be shown that for large l_1, l_2, l_3, and l_4 one has the limit result

$$U(1; l_1, l_2) - U(1; l_3, l_4) = \frac{1}{2\pi(p_1 p_2)^{1/2}} \log\left(\frac{p_2 l_3^2 + p_1 l_4^2}{p_2 l_1^2 + p_1 l_2^2}\right). \tag{24}$$

In the 3 D case as $N \to \infty$ the integral $U(z; l)$ converges as $z \to 1$. The limit has been evaluated by Watson for $U(1; 0)$ in the case of the three cubic lattices on which a walker can step only to nearest neighbor points with an equal a priori probability of stepping to each such point. He found **[23]**:

(a) simple cubic lattice

$$\begin{aligned} U(1, 0) &= \frac{1}{(2\pi)^3} \iiint_{-\pi}^{\pi} \frac{d^3\phi}{1 - \frac{1}{3}(c_1 + c_2 + c_3)} \\ &= \frac{4}{3\pi^2} [18 + 12\sqrt{2} - 10\sqrt{3} - 7\sqrt{6}] K^2[(2 - \sqrt{3})(\sqrt{3} - \sqrt{2})] \\ &= 1.5163860591; \end{aligned} \tag{25}$$

(b) face centered cubic lattice

$$\begin{aligned} U(1, 0) &= \frac{1}{(2\pi)^3} \iiint_{-\pi}^{\pi} \frac{d^3\phi}{1 - \frac{1}{3}(c_1 c_2 + c_2 c_3 + c_3 c_1)} \\ &= 9\{\Gamma(\tfrac{1}{3})\}^6 / 2^{14/3}\pi^4 = 1.3446610732; \end{aligned} \tag{26}$$

(c) body centered cubic lattice

$$\begin{aligned} U(1, 0) &= \frac{1}{(2\pi)^3} \iiint_{-\pi}^{\pi} \frac{d^3\phi}{1 - c_1 c_2 c_3} \\ &= \frac{1}{4\pi^3} \{\Gamma(\tfrac{1}{4})\}^4 = 1.3932039297. \end{aligned} \tag{27}$$

The correction to $U(1, 0)$ as z decreases from 1 is proportional to $(1-z)^{1/2}$. For example, in the simple cubic case **[24]**,

$$U(z, 0) \sim 1.51638 \cdots - \frac{3}{\pi}\sqrt{\frac{3}{2}}(1-z)^{1/2} + 0.131625\,(1-z) - \cdots. \tag{28}$$

In Table 1 we exhibit some values of $U(1, l)$ as defined by (3) for the 3 D case. More extensive tables of $U(z, l)$ for both the symmetric and several unsymmetric cases $0 \leqq z \leqq 1$ can be found in reference **[22]**. By methods indicated in references **[15]** and **[24]** one finds

$$(29) \qquad U(1, l) \sim \frac{3}{2\pi l}\left[1 + \frac{1}{8l^2}\left\{-3 + \frac{5(l_1^4 + l_2^4 + l_3^4)}{l^4}\right\} + \cdots\right]$$

as $l = (l_1^2 + l_2^2 + l_3^2)^{1/2} \to \infty$.

(l_1, l_2, l_3)	$U(1, l)$	(l_1, l_2, l_3)	$U(1, l)$
001	0.516387	023	0.132451
002	0.257336	111	0.261470
003	0.165271	112	0.191792
011	0.331149	113	0.144196
012	0.215590	122	0.156953
013	0.153139	123	0.126946
022	0.168331	222	0.135908

TABLE 1. VALUES OF $U(1, l)$ FOR A SQUARE LATTICE WHEN $l^2 = l_1^2 + l_2^2 + l_3^2 < 15$. THESE NUMBERS CORRESPOND TO THE SYMMETRICAL CASE WITH $U(1; l_1, l_2, l_3) = U(1; l_2, l_1, l_3) = \cdots$ ETC.

III. **Recurrence and first passage times.** §I was concerned with the probability $P_t(\boldsymbol{l})$ of a walker going from the origin to the point $\boldsymbol{l}$ in t steps without asking whether the walker had already been at $\boldsymbol{l}$ at an earlier time. We now consider the probability $f_t(\boldsymbol{l})$ of a walker arriving at $\boldsymbol{l}$ *for the first time* after t steps. The generating function of all those walks which reach $\boldsymbol{l}$ for the first time independently of t,

$$(1) \qquad F(z, \boldsymbol{l}) = \sum_{t=1}^{\infty} z^t f_t(\boldsymbol{l})$$

is related to $U(z, \boldsymbol{l})$ through

$$(2) \qquad F(z, \boldsymbol{l}) = \frac{1}{U(z, 0)}\{U(z, \boldsymbol{l}) - \delta_{0,\boldsymbol{l}}\}.$$

This equation is derived by noting that

$$(3) \qquad P_0(\boldsymbol{l}) = \delta_{\boldsymbol{l},0},$$

$$(4) \qquad P_t(\boldsymbol{l}) = \sum_{j=1}^{t} F_j(\boldsymbol{l})P_{t-j}(0) \quad \text{if} \quad t > 0$$

since in order for our walker to arrive at $\boldsymbol{l}$ in t steps he must have first arrived at $\boldsymbol{l}$ at some step j and then returned to $\boldsymbol{l}$ after $t - j$ steps. Then

$$(5) \qquad \begin{aligned} U(z, \boldsymbol{l}) &= \sum_{t=0}^{\infty} z^t P_t(\boldsymbol{l}) = \delta_{\boldsymbol{l},0} + \sum_{t=1}^{\infty}\sum_{j=1}^{\infty} z^j F_j(\boldsymbol{l}) z^{t-j} P_{t-j}(0) \\ &= \delta_{\boldsymbol{l},0} + F(z, \boldsymbol{l})U(z, 0) \end{aligned}$$

which is equivalent to (2).

Note that $F(1, \boldsymbol{l})$ is just the probability that the walker ever reaches the point $\boldsymbol{l}$ since $\Sigma f_t(\boldsymbol{l})$ is the sum of probabilities of the independent ways the walker can reach l for the first time. If $U(1, 0) = \infty$ then $F(1, 0) = 1$ and the walker is certain to return to the origin. If $U(1, 0) = u < \infty$ then the probability $F(1, 0) = 1 - u^{-1}$ of return is less than 1 by u^{-1} which represents the probability of escape without return to origin. The discussion of the effect of dimensionality on escape was first given by Pólya **[6]** who showed that when steps are made only to nearest neighbor sites walkers are certain to return to the origin on 1 D and 2 D lattices while a certain escape probability exists on s D lattices with $s \geqq 3$. An exposition of this result and others concerning the theory of recurrent events has also been given by Feller **[25]**. We repeat calculations made by the author **[9; 10]** elsewhere for escape probabilities.

Before proceeding with the exact calculation of probabilities of return to the origin let us examine the qualitative behavior of §II, (5) when $z = 1$:

(6) $$U(1, 0) = \frac{1}{(2\pi)^s} \int_{-\pi}^{\pi} \cdots \int \frac{d^s\phi}{1 - \lambda(\boldsymbol{\phi})}.$$

The convergence of this integral depends on the behavior of the denominator of the integrand. As $(\phi_1, \phi_2, \cdots, \phi_s) \to 0$

$$1 - \lambda(\boldsymbol{\phi}) = \sum_{\boldsymbol{l}} p(\boldsymbol{l})[1 - e^{i\boldsymbol{\phi}\cdot\boldsymbol{l}}] \to 0.$$

In the symmetric case with $p(\boldsymbol{l}) = p(-\boldsymbol{l})$ and $p(l_x) = p(l_y) = p(l_z)$

$$\sum_{\boldsymbol{l}} l_x^{2k+1} p(\boldsymbol{l}) = 0$$

and

$$\sum l_x^2 p(\boldsymbol{l}) = \tfrac{1}{3} \sum l^2 p(\boldsymbol{l}) \equiv \tfrac{1}{3}\mu_2.$$

Hence as $(\phi_1, \cdots, \phi_s) \to 0$

(7) $$1 - \lambda(\boldsymbol{\phi}) \sim \tfrac{1}{6}\phi^2 \mu_2.$$

The integral $U(1, 0)$ can be expressed as the sum of two components, the first being over an s dimensional sphere of a small radius, a, whose center is at the origin and the second the integral over our s D hypercube of volume $(2\pi)^s$ with the central small sphere excluded. In a region not including the origin the integrand is well behaved; no divergence can come from the second component of the integral. We calculate the contribution of the integral over a small spherical shell about the origin of our ϕ space in the neighborhood of $\boldsymbol{\phi} = 0$ but omit the contribution of the sphere of radius ε and then let $\varepsilon \to 0$. As long as the exterior radius of the shell is small, the integrand depends only on r so we can use polar coordinates in our integration and $d^s\phi$ is proportional to $r^{s-1}\,dr$. Our required integral is then proportional to

(8) $$I(\varepsilon) = \int_\varepsilon^a \frac{r^{s-1}}{r^2}\,dr = \int_\varepsilon^a r^{s-3}\,dr = \begin{cases} \varepsilon^{-2} - a^{-2} & s = 1, \\ -\log \varepsilon/a & s = 2, \\ (a^{s-2} - \varepsilon^{s-2})/(s-2) & s \geqq 3. \end{cases}$$

As $\varepsilon \to 0$, so that the neighborhood of the origin is included in the integration, $I(\varepsilon) \to \infty$ when $s = 1$ or 2 while $I(\varepsilon) < \infty$ when $s \geqq 3$. Hence $U_s(1, 0)$ *diverges when* $s = 1, 2$ *and converges when* $s \geqq 3$. This is equivalent to Pólya's result: A random walker who walks in the manner prescribed above is certain to return to his point of origin if he walks on a 1 D or 2 D lattice. A nonvanishing escape probability exists in lattices of more than three dimensions.

We now go beyond Pólya to the exact calculation of $U(1, 0)$ for the three 3 D cubic lattices; simple cubic (S.C.), body centered cubic (B.C.C.) and face centered cubic (F.C.C.). By good fortune G. N. Watson [23] has done all the work for us. He evaluated the three integrals §II, (25), (26), and (27) which are needed here. Since the probability of eventual return to the origin is

$$F(1, 0) = 1 - [U(1, 0)]^{-1} \tag{9}$$

we find that on the various cubic lattices is

$$\text{Probability of return to origin} = \begin{cases} 0.340537330 & \text{S.C.,} \\ 0.282229985 & \text{B.C.C.,} \\ 0.256318237 & \text{F.C.C.} \end{cases}$$

The number of nearest neighbors to a lattice point in a simple cubic lattice is 6, in a B.C.C. 8, and in a F.C.C. 12. It is not surprising that the return probability diminishes as the number of nearest neighbors increases since more ways for escape exists. The escape probability also increases with dimensionality for a fixed number of nearest neighbors to each lattice point. For example, the probability of return in a 4 D simple cubic lattice [9] (8 nearest neighbors to each lattice point) is 0.20 as compared with the 0.28 figure mentioned above. Earlier estimates in return probabilities on simple cubic lattices have been 0.35 (McCrea and Whipple [7]) and 0.34054 (Domb [8]).

Since on an s D lattice for $s \geqq 3$ there is a nonvanishing probability that a walker does not return to his point of origin, the average time required for the return is infinite. However, even in the 1 D and 2 D cases in which a walker eventually returns to his point of origin the mean recurrence time is still infinite. In the 1 D symmetrical walk (see §II, (2), with $p = q = 1/2$)

$$\begin{aligned} U(z, l) &= \frac{1}{2\pi} \int_{-\pi}^{\pi} \frac{\exp(-i\phi l)\, d\phi}{1 - z\cos\phi}, \\ &= x^{|l|}(1 - z^2)^{-1/2} \end{aligned} \tag{10a}$$

where

$$x = [1 - (1 - z^2)^{1/2}]/z. \tag{10b}$$

Hence from (2) the generating functions for all walks which return to the origin is

$$\begin{aligned} F(z, 0) &= \sum_{t=1}^{\infty} z^t f_t(0) \\ &= 1 - (1 - z^2)^{1/2}. \end{aligned} \tag{11}$$

The average number of steps required to return to the origin for the first time is

$$\langle t\rangle = \frac{\partial F}{\partial z}\Big]_{z=1} = \sum_{t=1}^{\infty} t f_t(0) \tag{12}$$
$$= \lim_{z\to 1} z(1-z^2)^{-1/2} = \infty.$$

One obtains the same result for a 2 D lattice. These results have already been obtained by Feller [25].

The generating function $U_N(z, l)$ for walks from the origin to the point l on a ring of N particles is

$$U_N(z, l) = \frac{1}{N}\sum_{j=0}^{N-1} \frac{\exp 2\pi i l j/N}{1 - z\cos 2\pi j/N} \tag{13}$$

while on an s D simple cubic lattice of $N \times N \times \cdots \times N$ points wrapped into an $s + 1$ D torus (periodic boundary conditions) it is given by §II, (8). It is convenient to express $U_N(z, \mathbf{l})$ as §II, (10a)

$$U_N(z, \mathbf{l}) = \phi(z) + 1/N^s(1 - z), \tag{14}$$

where $\phi(z)$ is a finite sum which has no singularity in the neighborhood of $z = 1$ (see §II, (10a) and (10b)). As $z \to 1$, $\phi(z)$ being a sum of a finite number of finite terms remains bounded while $(1 - z)^{-1} \to \infty$ and therefore $U_N(z, \mathbf{l}) \to \infty$. Hence from (9) one finds $F(1, 0) = 1$ for all dimensions s and all N so that, as one would expect, every walker eventually returns to his starting point on a finite lattice (with periodic boundary conditions).

We now show that (with periodic boundary conditions) *on a finite lattice the average number of steps required by the walker to return to his point of origin is finite and exactly equal to the number of lattice points.* From (2) we see that the generating functions for returns to the origin for the first time is given on an s D lattice by

$$F(z, 0) = 1 - [U(z, 0)]^{-1} \tag{15}$$
$$= 1 - \frac{(1 - z)N^s}{1 + N^s(1 - z)\phi(z)}.$$

Hence the average number of steps required to return to the origin for the first time is

$$\langle t\rangle = \frac{\partial}{\partial z} F(z, 0)\Big]_{z=1} \tag{16}$$
$$= \lim_{z\to 1} \frac{N^s + 2(1 - z)N^{2s}\phi(z) - (1 - z)^2 N^{2s}\phi'(z)}{[1 + N^s(1 - z)\phi(z)]^2}$$
$$= N^s.$$

This result is actually a special case of a general theorem on recurrence times in Markoff chains. Consider a system which can achieve any one of n states. If: (a) at each successive trial the probability of a transition from the ith state to the jth state is the constant p_{ji} (i.e., transitions are generated by a Markoff chain); (b) on every trial a transition to a *new* state occurs; and (c) the matrix P whose elements are p_{ji} has a single characteristic value of absolute value unity, then it can be shown that (a) this characteristic value is unity; (b) an equilibrium distribution which is independent of the initial distribution develops for the occupation probability of the various states; and (c) if P_j is the equilibrium occupation probability of state j, and one transition occurs per unit time, then the mean recurrence time for state i is

$$\langle t_i \rangle = 1/P_i. \tag{17}$$

It is also known that if $p_{ji} = p_{ij}$ (which is the case for our lattice walks) is added to the conditions listed above, the equilibrium distribution $\{P_i\}$ is the uniform distribution, $P_i = 1/n$ for all i. In this case $t_i = n =$ total number of states, which is equivalent to (16).

The second moment of the distribution $\{f_n\}$ depends on the detailed form of the probability of a displacement $\mathbf{l}$, $p(\mathbf{l})$, from a given lattice point in one step. We have

$$\begin{aligned}\langle n^2 \rangle &= \langle n(n-1) \rangle + \langle n \rangle \\ &= N^s + \frac{\partial^2}{\partial z^2} F_s(z, 0) \bigg]_{z=1}\end{aligned}$$

From §II, (10a) we find

$$\langle n^2 \rangle = N^s + \lim_{z \to 1} 2N^{2s}[\phi(z) - (1 - z)\phi'(z)]. \tag{18}$$

It can be shown from a careful analysis of $\phi(z)$ which will not be given here that

$$\lim_{z \to 1} (1 - z)\phi'(z) = 0.$$

Hence

$$\langle n^2 \rangle = N^s + 2N^{2s}\phi(1). \tag{19}$$

In the 1 D case we find from §II, (14)

$$\phi(1) = \lim_{z \to 1} \left[U_N(z, 0) - \frac{1}{N(1 - z)} \right] = (N^2 - 1)/6N$$

so that

$$\langle n^2 \rangle = N + \tfrac{1}{3}N(N^2 - 1), \tag{20a}$$

from which we find the dispersion to be

$$\langle (n - \bar{n})^2 \rangle = \tfrac{1}{3}N(N - 1)(N - 2). \tag{20b}$$

In the 3 D case $\phi(1)$ has the limit values (25), (26), and (27) for the various cubic lattices as $N \to \infty$. Hence for example in the S.C. case

$$\lim \langle n^2 \rangle / N^6 = 2.03279 \tag{21a}$$

so that

$$\lim \langle (n - \bar{n})^2 \rangle / \langle n \rangle^2 = 1.03279. \tag{21b}$$

As was pointed out in the beginning of this section, the probability that a walker ever reaches $\boldsymbol{l}$ is just

$$F(1, \boldsymbol{l}) = \frac{U(1, \boldsymbol{l})}{U(1,0)}. \tag{22}$$

In the 1 D case one finds from §II, (11a) that

$$F(z, l) = [1 - (1 - z^2)^{1/2}]^{|l|}/z^{|l|} \tag{23}$$

which, as $z \to 1$ approaches unity. Hence our walker is certain to reach any lattice point $\boldsymbol{l}$ on a 1 D lattice. In the 2 D case we first note from §II, (22) which gives $U(z; m, m)$ as $z \to 1$, that the divergent contribution is proportional to $-\log(1 - z)$ independently of $\boldsymbol{l} \equiv (m, m)$. Hence $F(1; m, m) = 1$ and a walker is certain to reach a point (m, m). It is not difficult to generalize this result to all lattice points on a 2 D lattice provided that $p(\boldsymbol{l}') \to 0$ sufficiently rapidly as $|\boldsymbol{l}'| \to \infty$.

In the 3 D case $U(1, 0)$ is finite while for large l (for simple cubic lattice)

$$U(1, \boldsymbol{l}) \sim \frac{3}{2\pi l} + \frac{3}{16\pi l^3}\left\{-3 + \frac{5(l_1^4 + l_2^4 + l_3^4)}{l^4}\right\} + O(1/l^5).$$

Hence the probability of eventually reaching the point $\boldsymbol{l}$,

$$F(1, \boldsymbol{l}) \sim \frac{3}{2\pi l U(1,0)}\left\{1 + \frac{1}{8l^2}\left[-3 + \frac{5(l_1^4 + l_2^4 + l_3^4)}{l^4}\right] + \cdots\right\} \tag{24}$$

diminishes as $1/l$ for large l. $F(1, \boldsymbol{l})$ for small values of l is given in Table 2.

(l_1, l_2, l_3)	$F(1, l)$	(l_1, l_2, l_3)	$F(1, l)$
001	0.3405	023	0.0873
002	0.1697	111	0.1724
003	0.1090	112	0.1265
011	0.2184	113	0.0951
012	0.1422	122	0.1035
013	0.1010	123	0.0837
022	0.1110	223	0.0896

TABLE 2. PROBABILITY, $F(1, l)$, THAT A WALKER WHO STARTS FROM THE ORIGIN EVER REACHES A POINT $l = (l_1, l_2, l_3)$ ON A SIMPLE CUBIC LATTICE. IN THIS SYMMETRICAL WALK $F(1; l_1, l_2, l_3) = F(1; l_2, l_1, l_3)$, ETC.

As in the case of return to the origin, the mean number of steps required to reach the point $\boldsymbol{l}$ for the first time is infinite for infinite lattices of any number of dimensions. On the other hand, when the number of lattice points is finite this mean first passage time is proportional to the number of lattice points. As in the case of return to the origin we consider our lattice to have periodic boundary conditions.

In the 1 D case we find from §II, (15) that

$$F_N(z, l) = \frac{U_N(z, l)}{U_N(z, 0)} \sim 1 - l(N - l)(1 - z) + \tfrac{1}{6}l(N - l)\{(N^2 - 5) + l(N - l)\}(1 - z)^2 - \cdots \tag{25}$$

so that the mean number of steps to reach l for the first time is

$$\langle n \rangle = \sum n z^n f_n(l) = \frac{\partial}{\partial z} F_N(z, l)\Big]_{z=1} = l(N - l) \tag{26a}$$

so that as $N \to \infty$

$$\langle n \rangle / N \sim l \tag{26b}$$

if $l > 0$. By symmetry $\lim \langle n \rangle / N = |l|$ for all l.

A corresponding expression for $\lim \langle n \rangle / N^s$ for the $s = 2$ and 3 cases can be obtained without using formulae as detailed as (25). We go back to §II, (10):

$$U_N(z, \mathbf{l}) = \frac{1}{N^s(1 - z)} + \phi(z, \mathbf{l}),$$

where the nonsingular term $\phi(z, l)$ is bounded as $z \to 1$. Note that

$$F_N(z, \mathbf{l}) = \frac{1 + N^s(1 - z)\phi(z, \mathbf{l})}{1 + N^s(1 - z)\phi(z, 0)}$$

so that

$$\lim_{N\to\infty} \langle n \rangle / N^s = \lim_{z\to 1,\, N\to\infty} N^{-s}\partial F_N / \partial z = \lim_{N\to\infty} [\phi(1, 0) - \phi(1, \mathbf{l})] = \lim_{z\to 1} [U(z, 0) - U(z, \mathbf{l})]. \tag{27}$$

We first verify our 1 D result from §II, (11),

$$U(z, 0) - U(z, l) \sim (1 - z^2)^{-1/2}\{|l|(1 - z^2)^{1/2} + O(1 - z)\} \to |l|$$

as $z \to 1$ which yields (26b).

In the 2 D case consider the point $\mathbf{l} = (l_1, l_2)$ and its "closest" diagonal (m, m) defined so that $|l_1^2 + l_2^2 - 2m^2| =$ minimum (for example, if $(l_1, l_2) = (17, 45)$, then $m = 33$). Also let

$$2\alpha m^2 = l_1^2 + l_2^2,$$

α being 1.007 in the case (17, 45), and generally of $O(1)$. Then from §II, (23) and (24) we see that for large $|l| = (l_1^2 + l_2^2)^{1/2}$

$$U(1; 0, 0) - U(1; l_1, l_2) = U(1; 0, 0) - U(1; m, m) + U(1; m, m) - U(1; l_1, l_2)$$

$$= \frac{4}{\pi}\left[1 + \frac{1}{3} + \frac{1}{5} + \cdots + \frac{1}{2m - 1}\right] + \frac{2}{\pi}\log\left(\frac{l_1^2 + l_2^2}{2m^2}\right)$$

$$\sim \frac{1}{2\pi}\log|l| + O(1).$$

Hence, in the 2 D case the average number of steps required to go from the origin to (l_1, l_2) is, on an $N \times N$ lattice with periodic boundary conditions,

$$\langle n\rangle/N^2 \sim \frac{1}{2\pi} \log |l|. \tag{28}$$

A remarkable property of the 3 D case is that as $|l| \to \infty$, $\langle n\rangle/N^3 \to$ constant. This follows from the fact that (see §II, (25) and (29))

$$U(1; 0, 0, 0) - U(1; l_1, l_2, l_3) \sim 1.516 \cdots - (3/2\pi l) + O(1/l^2)$$

which implies that

$$\langle n\rangle/N^3 \sim 1.516 - (3/2\pi l) \tag{29}$$

so that on the average, the number of steps required to reach for the first time any point sufficiently far from the origin is independent of the exact location of the point. Values of $\langle n\rangle/N^3$ for small l are given in Table 3. Further discussion on the material in the last half of this section can be found in **[26]**.

(l_1, l_2, l_3)	$\langle n\rangle/N^3$	(l_1, l_2, l_3)	$\langle n\rangle/N^3$
001	1.000	023	1.384
002	1.259	111	1.255
003	1.351	112	1.325
011	1.185	113	1.372
012	1.301	122	1.359
013	1.363	123	1.389
022	1.348	222	1.380

TABLE 3. RATIO OF THE AVERAGE NUMBER OF STEPS REQUIRED TO REACH THE LATTICE POINT l FOR THE FIRST TIME, $\langle n\rangle$, TO N^3, THE TOTAL NUMBER OF LATTICE POINTS ON A SIMPLE CUBIC LATTICE WITH PERIODIC BOUNDARY CONDITIONS. THE LIMIT OF THIS RATIO AS $N \to \infty$ IS TABULATED.

IV. **The number of lattice points visited after n steps.** As a lattice walker continues his walk the number of distinct points visited increases. This number can be determined as shown below from the properties of the generating function $U(z, 0)$. This problem was first considered by Dvoretzky and Erdös **[11]**, who showed that the number of points visited after n steps as $n \to \infty$ is

(1a) for 1 D lattice $(8n/\pi)^{1/2}$,

(1b) for 2 D lattice $\pi n/\log n$,

(1c) for s D lattice with $s \geqq 3$, cn,

where the constant c depends on the topology of the lattice. The value of the constant c has been evaluated by Vineyard **[12]** for the 3 D simple cubic, F.C.C. and B.C.C. lattices.

Let S_n be the average number of distinct lattice points visited after n steps and let $F_n(\boldsymbol{l})$ be the probability that the lattice point $\boldsymbol{l}$ has been visited at least once in the first n steps of the walker. Then

(2) $$F_n(\boldsymbol{l}) = f_1(\boldsymbol{l}) + f_2(\boldsymbol{l}) + \cdots + f_n(\boldsymbol{l}),$$

where, as defined in §I, $f_j(\boldsymbol{l})$ is the probability that our walker occupied the point $\boldsymbol{l}$ for the first time on the jth step. Clearly

(3) $$S_n = \sum_{\boldsymbol{l}} F_n(\boldsymbol{l})$$

so that

(4) $$\Delta_n \equiv S_n - S_{n-1} = \sum_{\boldsymbol{l}} [F_n(\boldsymbol{l}) - F_{n-1}(\boldsymbol{l})] = \sum_{\boldsymbol{l}} f_n(\boldsymbol{l}),$$

where the summation extends over all lattice points $\{\boldsymbol{l}\}$.

We now relate the generating function of Δ_n to $U(z, 0)$:

(5) $$\begin{aligned} \Delta(z) &= \sum_{n=1}^{\infty} z^n \Delta_n = \sum_{\boldsymbol{l}} \sum_{n=1}^{\infty} z^n f_n(\boldsymbol{l}) \\ &= \sum_{\boldsymbol{l}} F(z, \boldsymbol{l}) = \frac{1}{U(z, 0)} \left\{-1 + \sum_{\boldsymbol{l}} U(z, \boldsymbol{l})\right\}, \end{aligned}$$

where we have used (4) and §III, (7). Since it has already been shown in §II, (7) that

$$\sum_{\boldsymbol{l}} U(z, \boldsymbol{l}) = (1 - z)^{-1},$$

we find

(6) $$\Delta(z) = z/\{(1 - z)U(z, 0)\},$$

from which it follows that

$$\Delta_n = \text{coef. of } z^n \text{ in } \Delta(z) = \frac{1}{2\pi i} \int_c \frac{dz}{z^n(1 - z)U(z, 0)},$$

the contour being a counter-clockwise one surrounding the origin but not including $z = 1$.

The average number of distinct points visited after n steps by our walker is just (see (4))

(7) $$\begin{aligned} S_0 &= 1, \quad S_1 = 2, \\ S_n &= 1 + \Delta_1 + \Delta_2 + \cdots + \Delta_n, \qquad n \geqq 1. \end{aligned}$$

When n is large the asymptotic properties of S_n can be derived from the asymptotic properties of $\Delta(z)$ as $z \to 1$ by employing the Tauberian theorem (a special case of Theorem 108 in [27]: Let the sum $S(y) = \sum a_n \exp(-ny)$ be convergent for all $y > 0$ and let $a_n > 0$ for all n. If as $y \to 0$

(8a) $$S(y) \sim \phi(y^{-1}),$$

where

(8b) $$\phi(x) \equiv x^\sigma L(x)$$

is a positive increasing function of x (when x is greater than some fixed x_0) which tends to ∞ as $x \to \infty$, and if $\sigma \geqq 0$ and $L(cx) \sim L(x)$ as $x \to \infty$; then as $n \to \infty$

$$a_1 + a_2 + \cdots + a_n \sim \phi(n)/\Gamma(\sigma + 1). \tag{8c}$$

Inserting the asymptotic properties of $U(z, 0)$ as $z \to 1$ (the constants u and u_1 in the 3 D case depend on the lattice structure and in particular the values of u are given in §II, (25)–(27),

$$U(z, 0) = (1 - z^2)^{-1/2} \qquad 1\text{ D}, \tag{9a}$$

$$U(z,0) \sim \begin{cases} -\dfrac{1}{\pi}\log(1 - z) & 2\text{ D}, \quad (9b) \\ u + u_1(1 - z)^{1/2} + \cdots & 3\text{ D}, \quad (9c) \end{cases}$$

into (6) and letting $z = \exp(-y)$ we find that as $y \to 0$

$$\Delta(z) \sim \begin{cases} (2/y)^{1/2} & 1\text{ D}, \\ (\pi/y)/\log(1/y) & 2\text{ D}, \\ 1/uy & 3\text{ D} \quad (\text{and generally } s\text{ D with } s \geqq 3). \end{cases}$$

The Tauberian theorem given above applies directly to our problem if we choose

$$\begin{aligned} &1\text{ D } \sigma = \tfrac{1}{2}, && L(x) = 2^{1/2} = \text{constant}, \\ &2\text{ D } \sigma = 1, && L(x) = \pi/\log x, \\ &3\text{ D } \sigma = 1, && L(x) = 1/u = \text{constant}. \end{aligned}$$

With this choice we obtain the results of Erdös and Dvoretsky for the number of distinct lattice points visited by our walker after n steps as $n \to \infty$

$$S_n \sim \begin{cases} (8n/\pi)^{1/2} & 1\text{ D}, \\ \pi n/\log n & 2\text{ D}, \\ n/u & 3\text{ D}. \end{cases} \tag{1}$$

The values of $1/u$ for various cubic lattices are

$$1/u = \begin{cases} 0.629\,462\,670 & \text{S.C.}, \\ 0.717\,770\,010 & \text{B.C.C.}, \\ 0.743\,681\,763 & \text{F.C.C.} \end{cases} \tag{10}$$

They yield values of S_n in the 3 D case in agreement with those of Vineyard.

Asymptotic expansions for S_n (of which (1) is the leading term) are given in Appendix 2 for the 1 D and 3 D cases. These expansions are valid for small as well as large n.

V. **Random walks on slightly defective lattices.** So far we have been concerned with random walks on perfectly periodic lattices. Sometimes one wishes to investigate the influence of a small number of defective lattice points on random walks. For example one might analyze the effect of a trapping point on the probability of a walker eventually going from his origin to a given lattice point. Defects have been studied in the theory of semiconductors, lattice vibrations, and various other aspects of solid state physics. The methods discussed below are based on those developed for these fields [17–20].

Let us consider the effect of a few defect points on random walks. Using the notation of §I the probability that a random walker is at a point $\boldsymbol{l}$ after t steps, $P_t(\boldsymbol{l})$, is determined from a set of equations

$$P_{t+1}(\boldsymbol{l}) = \sum_{\boldsymbol{l}} p(\boldsymbol{l}, \boldsymbol{l}')P_t(\boldsymbol{l}'), \tag{1}$$

where $p(\boldsymbol{l}, \boldsymbol{l}')$ is the probability of a step from $\boldsymbol{l}'$ to $\boldsymbol{l}$ by a walker known to be at $\boldsymbol{l}'$. In a perfect lattice $p(\boldsymbol{l}, \boldsymbol{l}')$ was postulated to be a function only of $(\boldsymbol{l} - \boldsymbol{l}')$. In an imperfect lattice some points differ from others so this is no longer the case. However, we can express $p(\boldsymbol{l}, \boldsymbol{l}')$ as

$$p(\boldsymbol{l}, \boldsymbol{l}') = p(\boldsymbol{l} - \boldsymbol{l}') + q(\boldsymbol{l}, \boldsymbol{l}'), \tag{2}$$

the component $p(\boldsymbol{l} - \boldsymbol{l}')$ being that of the perfect lattice and $q(\boldsymbol{l}, \boldsymbol{l}')$ the perturbation. After any step a walker is certain to be somewhere. Hence

$$\sum_{\boldsymbol{l}} p(\boldsymbol{l}, \boldsymbol{l}') = 1 \text{ for all } \boldsymbol{l}'. \tag{3a}$$

This corresponds to the conservation of walkers. In the perfect lattice it was expressed as

$$\sum_{\boldsymbol{l}} p(\boldsymbol{l} - \boldsymbol{l}') = 1. \tag{3b}$$

Hence

$$\sum_{\boldsymbol{l}} q(\boldsymbol{l}, \boldsymbol{l}') = 0 \text{ for all } \boldsymbol{l}'. \tag{3c}$$

Let $G(z, \boldsymbol{l})$ be the generating function for $\{P_t(\boldsymbol{l})\}$:

$$G(z, \boldsymbol{l}) = \sum_{t=0}^{\infty} z^t P_t(\boldsymbol{l}). \tag{4}$$

On the supposition that at $t = 0$, before the first step, the walker is at the origin

$$P_0(\boldsymbol{l}) = \delta_{\boldsymbol{l},0}. \tag{5}$$

Multiplication of (1) by z^{t+1}, summation from $t = 0$ to ∞, and incorporation of (2) and (5) yields

$$G(z, \boldsymbol{l}) - \delta_{\boldsymbol{l},0} = z\sum_{\boldsymbol{l}'} p(\boldsymbol{l}, \boldsymbol{l}')G(z, \boldsymbol{l}')$$

or

$$G(z, \boldsymbol{l}) - z\sum_{\boldsymbol{l}'} p(\boldsymbol{l} - \boldsymbol{l}')G(z, \boldsymbol{l}') = \delta_{\boldsymbol{l},0} + z\sum_{\boldsymbol{l}'} q(\boldsymbol{l}, \boldsymbol{l}')G(z, \boldsymbol{l}'). \tag{6}$$

This set of linear equations can be solved in terms of the Green's function $U(z, \boldsymbol{l})$, which is the solution of

$$U(z, \boldsymbol{l}) - z\sum_{\boldsymbol{l}'} p(\boldsymbol{l} - \boldsymbol{l}')U(z, \boldsymbol{l}') = \delta_{l,0}. \tag{7}$$

The exact formula for $U(z, \boldsymbol{l})$, has been given for nearest neighbor walks on various lattices in §I. The inhomogeneous equation

$$G(z, \boldsymbol{l}) - z\sum_{\boldsymbol{l}'} p(\boldsymbol{l} - \boldsymbol{l}')G(z, \boldsymbol{l}') = F(\boldsymbol{l}) \tag{8}$$

has the solution

$$G(z, \boldsymbol{l}) = \sum_{\boldsymbol{l}'} U(z, \boldsymbol{l} - \boldsymbol{l}')F(\boldsymbol{l}'), \tag{9}$$

as can be verified by substituting this expression into the left side of (8) and employing (7) to obtain the right hand side of (8). Now if we let

$$F(\boldsymbol{l}) = \delta_{l,0} + z\sum_{\boldsymbol{l}'} q(\boldsymbol{l}, \boldsymbol{l}')G(z, \boldsymbol{l}')$$

in (8), then (9) becomes [**16**]

$$G(z, \boldsymbol{l}) = U(z, \boldsymbol{l}) + z\sum_{\boldsymbol{l}',\boldsymbol{l}''} U(z, \boldsymbol{l} - \boldsymbol{l}')q(\boldsymbol{l}', \boldsymbol{l}'')G(\boldsymbol{l}'', z). \tag{10}$$

Generally this equation can be solved by iteration. However, under the special conditions that $q(\boldsymbol{l}, \boldsymbol{l}')$ vanishes except at a few points, a closed form solution can be derived [**16**].

First consider the effect of a single defective point on a random walk which on each step the walker would normally go to one of his nearest neighbors (all nearest neighbor steps being given the same weight). Suppose one point, $\boldsymbol{l}_1$, differs from the rest so that there is a probability ε that a walker pauses at $\boldsymbol{l}_1$ each time he normally would have stepped away. If Z is the number of nearest neighbors to any point

$$\begin{aligned} &q(\boldsymbol{l}_1, \boldsymbol{l}_1) = \varepsilon, \\ &q(\boldsymbol{l}, \boldsymbol{l}_1) = -\frac{\varepsilon}{Z} \quad \text{if } l \text{ is an n.n. to } l_1, \\ &q(\boldsymbol{l}, \boldsymbol{l}') = 0 \quad \text{if } \boldsymbol{l}' \neq \boldsymbol{l}_1 \quad \text{or if } \boldsymbol{l}' = \boldsymbol{l}_1 \quad \text{and } \boldsymbol{l} \text{ is not an n.n. to } \boldsymbol{l}_1. \end{aligned} \tag{11}$$

Then

$$G(z, \boldsymbol{l}) = U(z, \boldsymbol{l}) + z\varepsilon U(z, \boldsymbol{l} - \boldsymbol{l}_1) - \frac{z\varepsilon}{Z}\sum_{\{\boldsymbol{l}_k\}} U(z, \boldsymbol{l} - \boldsymbol{l}_k)G(z, \boldsymbol{l}_1), \tag{12}$$

where $\{\boldsymbol{l}_k\}$ is the set of points which are nearest neighbors to $\boldsymbol{l}_1$. One finds from (7) that with our choice of unperturbed transition probabilities

$$(z/Z)\sum_{\{l_k\}} U(z, \boldsymbol{l} - \boldsymbol{l}_k) = U(z, \boldsymbol{l} - \boldsymbol{l}_1) - \delta_{l,l_1} \tag{13}$$

so that

$$G(z, \boldsymbol{l}) = U(z, \boldsymbol{l}) + \varepsilon\{(z - 1)U(z, \boldsymbol{l} - \boldsymbol{l}_1) + \delta_{l,l_1}\}G(z, \boldsymbol{l}_1). \tag{14}$$

An expression can be found for $G(z, \boldsymbol{l}_1)$ by setting $\boldsymbol{l} = \boldsymbol{l}_1$ in (14). Then

$$G(z, \boldsymbol{l}_1) = U(z, \boldsymbol{l}_1) + \varepsilon\{(z-1)U(z, 0) + 1\}G(z, \boldsymbol{l}_1) \tag{15}$$

so that

$$G(z, \boldsymbol{l}_1) = U(z, \boldsymbol{l}_1)/[(1-\varepsilon) + \varepsilon(1-z)U(z, 0)] \tag{16}$$

and generally if $\boldsymbol{l} \neq \boldsymbol{l}_1$

$$G(z, \boldsymbol{l}) = U(z, \boldsymbol{l}) - \frac{\varepsilon(1-z)U(z, \boldsymbol{l}-\boldsymbol{l}_1)U(z, \boldsymbol{l}_1)}{1-\varepsilon+\varepsilon(1-z)U(z, 0)}. \tag{17}$$

In particular if $\boldsymbol{l}_1$ is a trap, $\varepsilon = 1$, so that

$$G(z, \boldsymbol{l}) = U(z, \boldsymbol{l}) - U(z, \boldsymbol{l}-\boldsymbol{l}_1)U(z, \boldsymbol{l}_1)/U(z, 0). \tag{18}$$

Actually this formula could have been derived more directly if one notices that (see §III, (2))

$$U(z, \boldsymbol{l}_1)/U(z, 0) = F(z, \boldsymbol{l}_1)$$

is the generating function for all walks which go through $\boldsymbol{l}_1$ for the first time at various times. Then $U(z, \boldsymbol{l}-\boldsymbol{l}_1)F(z, \boldsymbol{l}_1)$ is the generating function for all walks which start at the origin, proceed through $\boldsymbol{l}_1$ and end at $\boldsymbol{l}$. If $\boldsymbol{l}_1$ is a trap the generating function $G(z, \boldsymbol{l})$, of all those walks which take the walker to $\boldsymbol{l}$ without being trapped is exactly the difference between the generating function for all walks and that for trapping walks.

As an application of (18) let us calculate the effect of a trap at l_1 on the probability of a walker eventually returning to the origin. From §III, (2) the probability of eventual return to the origin is

$$F(1, 0) = 1 - \frac{1}{G(1, 0)}. \tag{19}$$

But from (18) and §II, (11)

$$G(z, 0) = (1 - x^{|2l_1|})/(1-z^2)^{1/2}, \tag{20}$$

where x is $[1-(1-z^2)^{1/2}]/z$. Then as $z \to 1$, $x^{|2l_1|} \sim 1 - 2|l_1|\sqrt{(1-z^2)}$ so that

$$G(1, 0) = |2l_1| \tag{21}$$

and the probability of eventual return to the origin is

$$F(1, 0) = 1 - 1/|2l_1|. \tag{22}$$

The largest probability of a walker being trapped before return to the origin is of course with a trap at $l_1 = \pm 1$ in which case $F(1, 0) = \frac{1}{2}$.

Although the analogue of (18) can also be derived without resorting to our formalism in the case of two or more defect points, the bookkeeping gets quite tedious. We apply the formalism to the 2-defect problem with one pausing or trapping point at $\boldsymbol{l}_1$ and the other at $\boldsymbol{l}_2$. Then (12) becomes

$$\begin{aligned} G(z, \boldsymbol{l}) = U(z, \boldsymbol{l}) &+ \varepsilon\{(z-1)U(z, \boldsymbol{l}-\boldsymbol{l}_1) + \delta_{\boldsymbol{l},\boldsymbol{l}_1}\}G(z, \boldsymbol{l}_1) \\ &+ \varepsilon\{(z-1)U(z, \boldsymbol{l}-\boldsymbol{l}_2) + \delta_{\boldsymbol{l},\boldsymbol{l}_2}\}G(z, \boldsymbol{l}_2). \end{aligned} \tag{23}$$

If one successively sets l equal to l_1 and l_2 he obtains a pair of simultaneous equations for $G(z, l_1)$ and $G(z, l_2)$. Upon solution in the trapping case $\varepsilon = 1$ this yields

$$G(z, l_1) = \frac{U(z, l_1)U(z, 0) - U(z, l_2)U(z, l_1 - l_2)}{(1 - z)[\{U(z, 0)\}^2 - |U(z, l_1 - l_2)|^2]} \tag{24}$$

and the same expression with l_1 and l_2 interchanged for $G(z, l_2)$. Then from (23)

$$G(z, 0) = U(z, 0) - \frac{\{U(z, -l_1)[U(z, 0)U(z, l_1) - U(z, l_1 - l_2)U(z, l_2)] + U(z, -l_2)[U(z, 0)U(z, l_2) - U(z, l_2 - l_1)U(z, l_1)]\}}{[U^2(z, 0) - U^2(z, l_1 - l_2)]}. \tag{25}$$

From this formula we can find the effect of two traps on the probability of a walker eventually returning to his starting point. We let $l_2 < 0 < l_1$ on a 1 D lattice. Then from the expressions §II, (11) derived for $U(z, l)$ in the 1 D case we obtain

$$G(z, 0) = \frac{1}{\sqrt{(1 - z^2)}} \frac{(1 - x^{2l_1})(1 - x^{-2l_2})}{[1 - x^{2(l_1 - l_2)}]}$$

so that

$$G(1, 0) = \frac{2l_1(-l_2)}{l_1 - l_2}. \tag{26}$$

The probability of a walker returning to the origin before he is trapped is

$$F(1, 0) = 1 - \frac{1}{G(1, 0)} = 1 - \frac{(l_1 - l_2)}{2l_1(-l_2)}. \tag{27}$$

As the new trap at $-l_2$ recedes to $-\infty$ this reduces to the one trap formula (22).

(l_1, l_2, l_3)	$F(1, 0)$	(l_1, l_2, l_3)	$F(1, 0)$
001	0.254	023	0.335
002	0.321	111	0.320
003	0.333	112	0.330
011	0.305	113	0.334
012	0.327	122	0.333
013	0.334	123	0.336
022	0.332	222	0.335

TABLE 4. PROBABILITY OF A WALKER EVENTUALLY RETURNING TO THE ORIGIN, $F(1, 0)$, IN THE PRESENCE OF A TRAP AT POINT (l_1, l_2, l_3). THESE NUMBERS ARE TO BE COMPARED WITH THE VALUE 0.341 FOR A TRAPLESS WALK.

In the 3 D case the probability of eventual return to the origin when a trap is located at l is

$$F(1, 0) = 1 - \frac{U(1, 0)}{[U(1, 0)]^2 - [U(1, l)]^2}. \tag{28}$$

This quantity is tabulated in Table 4 (using $U(1, l)$ values of Table 1) for various l values with $(l_1^2 + l_2^2 + l_3^2) < 15$. When l is large one finds that $U(1, l)$ is much smaller than $U(1, 0)$ so that (28) becomes (with $u \equiv U(1, 0)$)

$$F(1, 0) = 1 - \frac{1}{u}\left[1 + \left(\frac{U(1, l)}{u}\right)^2 + \cdots\right]. \tag{29}$$

Then the asymptotic formula §III, (29) implies

$$F(1, 0) = 1 - \frac{1}{u}\left[1 + \left(\frac{3}{2\pi u l}\right)^2 + \cdots\right]. \tag{30}$$

It can be shown from (25) and (19) that when l_1, l_2 and $|l_1 - l_2|$ are all large in the 2-defect case, the probability of return to the origin is diminished in an additive way by the influence of the traps at l_1 and l_2. Then

$$F(1, 0) \sim 1 - \frac{1}{u}\left[1 + \left(\frac{3}{2\pi u}\right)^2 \Sigma l_j^{-2} + \cdots\right], \tag{31}$$

this formula being also valid for any number of widely separated distant traps. Of course interference terms appear when some of the l_j's are close to each other or when they might be near the origin. These terms can be obtained from (25) in the 2-trap case and from the generalization of (25) in the n-trap case.

Appendix 1. Generating Function $U_N(z, l)$ for a Ring of N Equally Spaced Points

This is a derivation of §II, (12) for the generating function $U_N(z, l)$ which satisfies the boundary condition $U_N(z, l) = U_N(z, l + N)$ appropriate for a ring of N points. From §II, (11a), the formula for $U(z, l)$ for an infinite lattice is

$$U_\infty(z, l) = x^{|l|}(1 - z^2)^{-1/2},$$

where x is defined by §II, (11b). This is the generating function for walks from 0 to l on an infinite lattice. The generating function for walks from 0 to l on a ring of N points is equivalent to the sum of the generating function for all those walks on an infinite line which represent walks from 0 to l, from 0 to $l + N$, from 0 to $l + 2N$, etc., as well as from 0 to $l - N$, $l - 2N$, etc. Hence

$$\begin{aligned} U_N(z, l) &= U_\infty(z, l) + U_\infty(z, l + N) + U_\infty(z, l + 2N) + \cdots \\ &\quad + U_\infty(z, l - N) + U_\infty(z, l - 2N) + \cdots \\ &= (1 - z^2)^{-1/2}[x^l + x^{l+N} + x^{l+2N} + \cdots + x^{N-l} + x^{2N-l} + \cdots] \\ &= \left(\frac{x^l + x^{N-l}}{1 - x^N}\right)\Big/(1 - z^2)^{1/2} \end{aligned}$$

which is exactly §II, (12).

Appendix 2

The Tauberian theorem used in §IV to determine the number of distinct points visited gives asymptotic results easily for long walks. In this appendix we develop a more systematic procedure that yields results applicable to short as well as long walks. Using the notation of §IV, S_n is the average number of distinct points visited in a walk of n steps. The generating function for $\Delta_n = S_n - S_{n-1}$ was (§IV, (6))

$$\Delta(z) = \sum_1^\infty \Delta_n z^n = z/(1-z)U(z,0). \tag{1}$$

If we let $S_0 = 1$ (the starting point being occupied before the walk starts), then the generating function for $s_n = S_n - 1$ is (see §IV, (7))

$$\begin{aligned} s &= \sum_1^\infty s_n z^n = \sum_{n=1}^\infty (\Delta_1 + \Delta_2 + \cdots + \Delta_n) z^n = (1-z)^{-1}\Delta(z) \\ &= z/\{(1-z)^2 U(z,0)\}. \end{aligned} \tag{2}$$

In the 1 D case

$$s = z(1-z^2)^{1/2}/(1-z)^2 \tag{3}$$

$$= 2^{1/2} \frac{[1-(1-z)]}{(1-z)^{3/2}} (1 - \tfrac{1}{2}[1-z])^{1/2}$$

$$= 2^{1/2}\{(1-z)^{-3/2} - \tfrac{5}{4}(1-z)^{-1/2} + \tfrac{7}{32}(1-z)^{1/2} + \cdots\}. \tag{4}$$

Our required coefficient s_n of z^n in the power series expansion of this quantity can be obtained by adding together the coefficients of z^n in the expansion of each term in the bracket. One finds

$$S_n - 1 = s_n = \frac{(2n+1)!}{2^{2n-1/2} n! n!} \left\{1 - \frac{5}{4(2n+1)} + \frac{7}{32(4n^2-1)} + \cdots\right\}. \tag{5}$$

Exact values of S_n are obtained for $n \leqq 10$ by considering the coefficient of z^n in (3) for $n = 1, 2, \cdots, 10$. These are given below.

n	S_n	n	S_n
1	2	6	19/4
2	3	7	81/16
3	7/2	8	43/8
4	4	9	723/128
5	35/8	10	379/64

When $n = 8$, $S_8 = 5.375$ while from (5), using the three terms explicitly exhibited one finds $S_8 \cong 5.376$. Even for n as small as 2 we find that $S_2 \cong 3.02$ from (5) as compared with the exact value 3. When n is large the various factorials can be approximated by employing Stirling's formula so that

$$(6) \qquad S_n \sim 1 + \left(\frac{8n}{\pi}\right)^{1/2} \left[1 - \frac{1}{4n} + \frac{5}{64n^2} - \cdots\right].$$

We proceed in essentially the same way to improve on the asymptotic 3 D formula given by §IV, (1). It has been shown in reference [24] that in the 3 D case as $z \to 1$

$$(7) \qquad U(z, 0) = u[1 + c_1(1 - z)^{1/2} + c_2(1 - z) + c_3(1 - z)^{3/2} + \cdots].$$

Then from (2) the 3 D analogue of (4) is

$$s = u^{-1}\{(1 - z)^{-2} - c_1(1 - z)^{-3/2} + (c_1^2 - c_2 - 1)(1 - z)^{-1} + (2c_1c_2 + c_1 - c_1^3 - c_3)(1 - z)^{-1/2} + \cdots\}.$$

By adding together the coefficient of z^n from each term we find

$$S_n = (n/u) - (c_1/u)\frac{(2n + 1)!}{2^{2n}n!n!} + [1 + (c_1^2 - c_2 - 1)u^{-1}] + u^{-1}(2c_1c_2 + c_1 - c_1^3 - c_3)\frac{(2n)!}{2^{2n}n!n!} + \cdots.$$

When n is sufficiently large we employ Stirling's formula for the various factorials and find

$$(8) \qquad S_n \sim (n/u)\left\{1 - \frac{2c_1}{(\pi n)^{1/2}} + \frac{1}{n}[u + c_1^2 - c_2 - 1] + \frac{\pi}{(n\pi)^{3/2}}[2c_1c_2 + \tfrac{1}{4}c_1 - c_1^3 - c_3] + \cdots\right\}.$$

In the case of a simple cubic lattice $1/u$ is given by §IV, (10) while from reference [24]

$$c_1 = -(3/\pi u)(3/2)^{1/2}.$$

Hence

$$(9) \qquad S_n \sim 0.629462n\left\{1 + \frac{4}{u}\left(\frac{3}{2\pi}\right)^{3/2} n^{-1/2} + \cdots\right\}.$$

References

1. L. Bachelier, *Théorie de la spéculation*, Ann. Sci. École Norm. Sup. (3) **17** (1900), 21.

2. S. Chandrasekhar, *Stochastic problems in physics and astronomy*, Rev. Modern Phys. **15** (1943), 1–89.

3. A. C. Damask and C. J. Dienes, *Point defects in metals* (to appear).

4. F. J. Dyson, *General theory of spin-wave interactions*, Phys. Rev. **102** (1956), 1217–1230; *Thermodynamic behavior of an ideal ferromagnet*, ibid., 1230–1244.

5. W. Opachowski, *On the calculation of the partition function of a ferromagnetic crystal*, Physica **25** (1959), 476–486.

6. G. Pólya, *Über Eine Aufgabe der Wahrscheinlichkeitrechnung Betreffena die Irrfahrt in Stratzennetz*, Math. Ann. **84** (1921), 149.

7. W. H. McCrea and F. J. W. Whipple, *Random paths in two and three dimensions*, Proc. Roy. Soc. Edinburgh **60** (1939), 281.

8. C. Domb, *On multiple returns in the random-walk problem*, Proc. Cambridge Philos, Soc. **50** (1954), 586–591.

9. E. W. Montroll, *Random walks in multidimensional spaces, especially on periodic lattices*, J. Soc. Indust. Appl. Math. **4** (1956), 241–260.

10. ———, *Topics in statistical mechanics of interacting particles*, La théorie des gaz neutres et ionisés (Grenoble, 1959), pp. 15–148, p. 17, Hermann, Paris, 1960.

11. A. Dvoretzky and P. Erdös, *Some problems on random walk in space*, Proc. 2nd Berkeley Sympos. Math. Statist. and Prob. (1950), pp. 353–367, Univ. of California Press, Berkeley, Calif., 1951.

12. G. H. Vineyard, *The number of distinct sites visited in a random walk on a lattice*, J. Mathematical Phys. **4** (1963), 1191–1193.

13. R. Courant, Vol. **3**. p. 83, Atti Congresso Internazionale Dei Matematica Bologna, Bologna, 1928.

14. R. Courant, K. Friedrichs, and H. Lewy, Math. Ann. **100** (1928), 32.

15. R. J. Duffin, *Discrete potential theory*, Duke Math. J. **20** (1953), 223–251.

16. E. W. Montroll, *Applied combinatorial mathematics*, E. F. Beckenbach, ed. (to appear).

17. E. W. Montroll and R. Potts, *Effect of defects on lattice vibrations*, Phys. Rev. **100** (1955), 525–543; **102** (1956), 72.

18. I. M. Lifshitz, Nuovo Cimento Supp. (X) **3** (1956), 716.

19. A. Maradudin, E. Montroll, and G. Weiss, *Lattice vibrations in the harmonic approximation*, Academic Press, New York, 1963.

20. M. Toda, ed., *Proceedings of symposium on the theory of lattice vibrations of imperfect crystals held at Kyoto University*, Supplement of the Progress of Theoretical Physics **23** (1962).

21. F. G. Foster and I. G. Good, *On a generalization of Pólya's random-walk theorem*, Quart, J. Math. Oxford Ser. (2) **4** (1953), 120–126.

22. A. Erdélyi, W. Magnus, F. Oberhettinger, and F. Tricomi, *Tables of integral transforms*, Vol. 1, p. 183, McGraw-Hill, New York, 1954.

23. G. N. Watson, Quart. J. Math. Oxford Ser. **10** (1939), 266.

24. A. Maradudin, E. Montroll, G. Weiss, R. Herman, and H. Milnes, *Green's functions for monatomic simple cubic lattices*, Acad. Roy. Belg. Cl. Sci. Mém. Coll. in-4° (2) **14** (1960), no. 7, 176 pp.

25. W. Feller, *An introduction to probability theory and its applications*, Wiley, New York, 1951.

26. E. Montroll and G. Weiss, J. Mathematical Phys. (to appear).

27. G. H. Hardy, *Divergent series*, Oxford, at the Clarendon Press, 1949.

UNIVERSITY OF MARYLAND,
COLLEGE PARK, MARYLAND

ON STATISTICAL SPECTRAL ANALYSIS[1]

BY

EMANUEL PARZEN

DEDICATED TO PROFESSOR CHARLES LOEWNER ON HIS 70TH BIRTHDAY

1. **Introduction.** Statistical spectral analysis may be defined as a theory which seeks to provide a method whereby from observed records, of finite length, of an empirical phenomenon one can interpret the time function representing the phenomenon as a superposition (finite or infinite linear combination) of harmonics cos ωt and sin ωt. In other words, statistical spectral analysis attempts to provide a modern solution to what classically has been called "the search for hidden periodicities" in a phenomenon. In modern terms, statistical spectral analysis is concerned with the estimation of the "spectrum" of observed time series.

Spectral analysis seems to be one of the most useful tools available for time series analysis. The theory of time series analysis is concerned with the analysis and the synthesis of stochastic models which may be used to describe (and perhaps also to control) the mechanisms generating a time series and relating various time series. Because the concepts of time series analysis possess meanings of their own which do not depend on particular applications, the theory of time series analysis provides mathematical procedures which can be used to solve problems arising in diverse fields. In my view, time series analysis is an interdisciplinary field since it provides a medium for the exchange of ideas between research workers concerned with quite different subject matters.

Much of the impetus for the recent development of statistical spectral analysis has come from noise theory. This might lead one to believe that the problem of statistical spectral analysis is best discussed in the language of communication engineering, using such notions as "black box" and "filter." This is clearly the right point of view as far as interpreting the spectrum is concerned. But I believe that in developing a theory of *estimation* of the spectrum it is necessary to bring to bear in addition other points of view, derived from approximation theory and from statistical theory. In particular, it seems to me that the problem involved in estimating the spectrum is to some extent a special case of the problem of how to best approximate a function given only its first N Fourier coefficients.

It is not my aim to review the extensive development of the theory of statistical spectral analysis in the last decade. Fortunately there are available a number of review papers which do this (see [**5**; **8**; **11–13**; **18–20**; **22**]). Rather, my aim is to

[1] Prepared under Contract Nonr 225(21) for the Office of Naval Research.

sketch (without proofs) the theory of statistical spectral analysis adopting what may be called a *covariance approach* rather than a *spectral approach.* There are four sections: definition of the spectrum, estimation of the spectrum, estimation of spectral density, estimation of spectral jumps. Applications of spectral analysis are not discussed. But it should be noted that spectral analysis can be applied to one of the central problems of noise theory, namely signal detection and estimation in the presence of stationary noise of unspecified structure. Similarly, spectral analysis seems to be applicable to one of the central problems of economic time series analysis, namely how to seasonally adjust time series and how to determine the effect of the seasonal adjustment procedures that are employed.

2. **Definition of the spectrum.** Early researchers envisaged a time series $\{X(t), t = 1, 2, \cdots\}$ as satisfying the model

$$X(t) = \sum_{j=1}^{q} C_j \cos(\omega_j t + \phi_j) + \eta(t), \qquad t = 1, 2, \cdots, \tag{2.1}$$

in which the following assumptions are made. The number of terms q, the amplitudes C_j, the angular frequencies ω_j, and the phases ϕ_j are constants, some of which are given while the others are to be estimated. The sequence $\{\eta(t), t = 1, 2, \cdots\}$ is a white noise process; that is, it consists of independent identically distributed random variables with means 0 and common variance σ_η^2. A technique, known as the *periodogram*, was introduced by Schuster [**21**] as a method for discovering the hidden frequencies ω_j (or, equivalently, the hidden periods $2\pi/\omega_j$).

Let $\{X(t), t = 1, 2, \cdots, T\}$ be a finite sample of a time series. In order to detect the presence in the time series $\{X(t), t = 1, 2, \cdots\}$ of a harmonic component,

$$C \cos(\omega t + \phi) = A \cos \omega t + B \sin \omega t, \tag{2.2}$$

of frequency ω one would form the (discrete) *Fourier coefficients*

$$\begin{aligned} A_T(\omega) &= \frac{2}{T} \sum_{t=1}^{T} X(t) \cos \omega t, \\ B_T(\omega) &= \frac{2}{T} \sum_{t=1}^{T} X(t) \sin \omega t \end{aligned} \tag{2.3}$$

and then form the *intensity*

$$S_T(\omega) = A_T^2(\omega) + B_T^2(\omega) = \left| \frac{2}{T} \sum_{t=1}^{T} X(t)\, e^{-i\omega t} \right|^2 \tag{2.4}$$

or equivalently the periodogram

$$I_T(\omega) = \frac{T}{2} S_T(\omega) = \frac{2}{T} \left| \sum_{t=1}^{T} X(t)\, e^{-i\omega t} \right|^2. \tag{2.5}$$

If there were no noise fluctuations present in the time series, then the intensity $S_T(\omega)$ would, for large values of T be approximately equal to $A^2 + B^2$, no matter what other harmonics were present. Therefore to test the hypothesis that there is no component of frequency ω present in the time series one would test whether the observed value of $S_T(\omega)$ is small enough as to be compatible with $A^2 + B^2 = 0$. Under the assumption that the noise process $\eta(t)$ is white, the distribution of $S_T(\omega)$ is *exponential* (or chi-square with two degrees of freedom) with mean

$$E[S_T(\omega)] = \frac{4\sigma^2}{T}. \tag{2.6}$$

Using this fact, significance tests for the presence of hidden periodicities in a time series were developed by Schuster [**21**], Walker [**23**], and Fisher [**4**]. By the decades of the 1940's, however, these methods were discredited for practical use since when applied to empirical time series they seemed to provide evidence for the existence of "spurious cycles" (for an example of this phenomenon on a constructed time series, see Brooks and Carruthers [**3**, Chapters 19–22]).

The development of a theory of spectral analysis of empirically observed time series which would provide consistent and interpretable results is made possible by introducing the notion of the *sample covariance function* of a time series $\{X(t), t = 1, 2, \cdots, T\}$:

$$R_T(v) = \begin{cases} \dfrac{1}{T}\displaystyle\sum_{t=1}^{T-v} X(t)X(t+v), & v = 0, 1, \cdots, T-1; \\ 0, & v \geqq T; \\ R_T(-v), & v < 0. \end{cases} \tag{2.7}$$

I hope to indicate in this paper the central role of the sample covariance function in the theory of statistical spectral analysis. There are those who reject this "covariance" approach in favor of what may be called the "spectral" approach to spectral analysis. In any event I believe it fair to claim that the "covariance" approach corresponds to the attitude adopted by Wiener [**25**] in his monumental paper on generalized harmonic analysis and represents the "radical recasting" which Wiener says (p. 118) is necessary in order "to make the Schuster theory assume a form suitable for extension and generalization."

It is worth noting that one can even adopt a "correlation" approach. A theory of statistical spectral analysis of somewhat wider applicability can be developed using the sample *correlation* function, defined by

$$\rho_T(v) = \frac{R_T(v)}{R_T(0)}. \tag{2.7'}$$

Rearranging the double sum involved in (2.5), one sees that the periodogram is essentially the Fourier transform of $R_T(v)$:

$$I_T(\omega) = 2 \sum_{|v|<T} e^{-i\omega v} R_T(v) \tag{2.8}$$

so that

$$R_T(v) = (4\pi)^{-1}\int_{-\pi}^{\pi} e^{iv\omega} I_T(\omega)\, d\omega. \tag{2.9}$$

In order to obtain Fourier transformation formulas which are somewhat more familiar than (2.8) and (2.9) we introduce the *sample spectral density function* $f_T(\omega)$, defined by

$$f_T(\omega) = \frac{1}{4\pi} I_T(\omega) = \frac{1}{2\pi T}\left|\sum_{t=1}^{T} e^{-i\omega t} X(t)\right|^2. \tag{2.10}$$

Then

$$\begin{aligned} f_T(\omega) &= \frac{1}{2\pi}\sum_{|v|<T} e^{-iv\omega} R_T(v) \\ &= \frac{1}{2\pi} R_T(v) + \frac{1}{\pi}\sum_{v=1}^{T-1} \cos v\omega R_T(v); \end{aligned} \tag{2.11}$$

$$R_T(v) = \int_{-\pi}^{\pi} e^{iv\omega} f_T(\omega)\, d\omega. \tag{2.12}$$

The tools are now at hand to give a general definition of the spectrum of a time series $\{X(t),\ t = 1, 2, \cdots\}$. One assumes that there exists a function $R(v)$, called the covariance function, such that

$$\lim_{T\to\infty} E[R_T(v)] = R(v), \qquad v = 0, \pm 1, \pm 2, \cdots. \tag{2.13}$$

From (2.12) and (2.13) it follows (by the continuity theorem of probability theory) that there exists a bounded nondecreasing function of a real variable ω, denoted $F(\omega)$ and called the spectral distribution function, such that

$$R(v) = \int_{-\pi}^{\pi} e^{iv\omega}\, dF(\omega), \qquad v = 0, \pm 1, \pm 2, \cdots, \tag{2.14}$$

and such that for every continuous function $g(\omega)$

$$\lim_{T\to\infty} \int_{-\pi}^{\pi} g(\omega) E[f_T(\omega)]\, d\omega = \int_{-\pi}^{\pi} g(\omega)\, dF(\omega). \tag{2.15}$$

If further the sample covariance function $R_T(v)$ is a consistent estimate of $R(v)$, in the sense that for each $v = 0, \pm 1, \cdots$

$$\lim_{T\to\infty} R_T(v) = R(v) \tag{2.16}$$

as a limit in mean square then for every continuous function $g(\omega)$

$$\lim_{T\to\infty} \int_{-\pi}^{\pi} g(\omega) f_T(\omega)\, d\omega = \int_{-\pi}^{\pi} g(\omega)\, dF(\omega) \tag{2.17}$$

as a limit in mean square.

One important case in which (2.13) holds is when $\{X(t), t = 0, 1, \cdots\}$ has zero means and its covariance kernel $E[X(s)X(t)]$ is stationary in the sense that

$$E[X(s)X(t)] = R(|s - t|) \tag{2.18}$$

for some even function $R(v)$; this property is called *covariance stationarity* in Parzen [**14**, p. 70]. Then

$$E[R_T(v)] = \left(1 - \frac{|v|}{T}\right) R(v) \to R(v). \tag{2.19}$$

Consequently the spectral representation, equation (2.14), holds. From the spectral representation for the covariance function of a stationary time series one obtains a spectral representation for the time series itself:

$$X(t) = \int_{-\pi}^{\pi} e^{it\omega}\, dZ(\omega), \qquad t = 0\ \pm 1, \pm 2, \cdots, \tag{2.20}$$

where $\{Z(\omega), -\pi \leqq \omega \leqq \pi\}$ is a process with orthogonal increments and

$$E[|dZ(\omega)|^2] = dF(\omega). \tag{2.21}$$

From (2.21) one obtains an intuitive interpretation of the spectral distribution function $F(\omega)$; its increment across a frequency band is a measure of the mean square average of the Fourier components of the time series in this frequency band.

The problem of statistical spectral analysis can now be defined as the problem of estimating the spectral distribution function of a time series which satisfies (2.13). It is to be emphasized that this problem is well defined not only for stationary time series but also for asymptotically stationary ones (see Parzen [**12**]).

Like a probability distribution function, $F(\omega)$ can be uniquely written as the sum,

$$F(\omega) = F_{\mathrm{d}}(\omega) + F_{\mathrm{sc}}(\omega) + F_{\mathrm{ac}}(\omega) \tag{2.22}$$

of three distribution functions which are respectively discrete (or purely discontinuous), singular continuous, and absolutely continuous. $F_{\mathrm{ac}}(\omega)$ is the integral of a non-negative function called the *spectral density function* of the time series,

$$F_{\mathrm{ac}}(\omega) = \int_{-\pi}^{\omega} f(\lambda)\, d\lambda, \qquad -\pi \leqq \omega \leqq \pi. \tag{2.23}$$

$F_{\mathrm{d}}(\omega)$ may be written as a sum over the discontinuity points $\{\omega_j\}$ of $F(\omega)$ of its jumps

$$J(\omega) = F(\omega + 0) - F(\omega - 0) \tag{2.24}$$

by the formula

$$F(\omega) = \sum_{\substack{\omega_j \text{ such that} \\ J(\omega_j) > 0 \text{ and } \omega_j \leqq \omega}} J(\omega_j). \tag{2.25}$$

Observed time series are usually assumed to have a *mixed spectrum*, in the sense that the singular continuous part of the spectral distribution function vanishes. The spectrum of the time series is said to be *continuous* if the spectral jump function $J(\omega)$ vanishes for all ω, and to be *discrete* if the spectral density function $f(\omega)$ vanishes for all ω.

An important example of a time series with a mixed spectrum is one satisfying the model (2.1), but with a more general assumption on the *residuals* or *fluctuations* $\eta(t)$. It is assumed that $\{\eta(t), t = 1, 2, \cdots\}$ is a *normal stationary* stochastic process with zero means,

$$E[\eta(t)] = 0, \tag{2.26}$$

and covariance kernel satisfying

$$E[\eta(s)\eta(t)] = R_\eta(s - t) = \int_{-\pi}^{\pi} \cos \omega(s - t) f(\omega)\, d\omega. \tag{2.27}$$

The observed time series $\{X(t), t = 0, 1, \cdots\}$ then satisfies (2.13) with

$$\begin{aligned} R(v) &= \frac{1}{2}\sum_{j=1}^{q} |A_j|^2 \cos \omega_j v + R_\eta(v) \\ &= \sum_{j=1}^{q} J(\omega_j) \cos \omega_j v + \int_{-\pi}^{\pi} \cos v\omega\, f(\omega)\, d\omega \end{aligned} \tag{2.28}$$

defining

$$J(\omega) = \begin{cases} \frac{1}{2}|A_j|^2 & \text{if } \omega = \omega_j, \\ 0 & \text{if } \omega \text{ is not equal to } \omega_1, \cdots, \omega_q. \end{cases} \tag{2.29}$$

The spectral distribution function is thus of *mixed type*; its absolutely continuous part is given by the spectral density function $f(\omega)$ of the fluctuation process $\{\eta_t\}$ and its discrete part has jumps at the frequencies $\omega_1, \cdots, \omega_q$, the respective jumps being of size $J(\omega_1), \cdots, J(\omega_q)$.

It should be noted that since we are using (for mathematical convenience) both negative and positive frequencies, in defining in (2.29) the jump function $J(\omega)$ we perhaps should define it as an even function as follows:

$$J(\omega) = \begin{cases} \frac{1}{4}|A_j|^2 & \text{if } \omega = \omega_j \text{ or } \omega = -\omega_j \text{ and } \omega_j \neq 0; \\ \frac{1}{2}|A_j|^2 & \text{if } \omega = \omega_j = 0; \\ 0 & \text{otherwise.} \end{cases} \tag{2.30}$$

However, we will not employ this definition in this paper.

3. **Estimation of the spectrum.** If one knew the covariance function $R(v)$, one could recover from it (by well-known inversion formulas) the spectral jump function $J(\omega)$ and the spectral density function $f(\omega)$. For ease of exposition,

we assume in this section that the spectrum is continuous. Then if one forms a linear combination of covariances,

$$\sum_{v=-\infty}^{\infty} a(v)R(v) = \int_{-\pi}^{\pi} \left\{ \sum_{v=-\infty}^{\infty} a(v) \cos v\omega \right\} f(\omega)\, d\omega, \tag{3.1}$$

with coefficients $a(v)$ one obtains a *spectral average*

$$J(A) = \int_{-\pi}^{\pi} A(\omega) f(\omega)\, d\omega \tag{3.2}$$

corresponding to a *spectral window*,

$$A(\omega) = \sum_{v=-\infty}^{\infty} a(v) \cos v\omega, \tag{3.3}$$

which is the Fourier transform of the coefficients. Note that conversely

$$a(v) = \frac{1}{\pi} \int_{-\pi}^{\pi} A(\omega) \cos v\omega\, d\omega. \tag{3.4}$$

Alas we do not know $R(v)$ but only its sample estimates $R_T(v)$. Therefore let us introduce

$$D_T(v) = R_T(v) - R(v), \qquad v = 0, \pm 1, \pm 2, \cdots,$$

the *deviations* of the sample covariance function about the true covariance function. We may then write

$$R_T(v) = R(v) + D_T(v). \tag{3.5}$$

For a stationary normal time series with zero means and continuous spectrum, the deviation time series $\{D_T(v), v = 0, \pm 1, \cdots, \pm T\}$ may be shown (for references, see Parzen [**13**, p. 982]) to be approximately normal for large values of T with means

$$E[D_T(v)] = E[R_T(v)] - R(v) \to 0 \tag{3.6}$$

as $T \to \infty$ and covariance kernel satisfying (for non-negative v_1 and v_2)

$$\begin{aligned} T \operatorname{Cov}[D_T(v_1), D_T(v_2)] &\to \sum_{u=-\infty}^{\infty} R_\eta(u)\{R_\eta(u + v_1 - v_2) + R_\eta(u + v_1 + v_2)\} \\ &= 4\pi \int_{-\pi}^{\pi} \cos \lambda v_1 \cos \lambda v_2 f^2(\lambda)\, d\lambda \end{aligned} \tag{3.7}$$

as $T \to \infty$, where $f(\omega)$ is the spectral density function of $\{\eta_t\}$.

From (3.7) we obtain heuristically a conclusion (which can be shown rigorously; see Parzen [**10**]) of some interest, namely while at each v the sample covariance $R_T(v)$ is a consistent estimate of $R(v)$, the entire function $\{R_T(v), v = 0, \pm 1, \cdots\}$

is not a satisfactory estimate of the entire covariance function $\{R(v), v = 0, \pm 1, \cdots\}$ since in particular

$$(3.8)\quad \begin{aligned} E\left[\sum_{v=-(T-1)}^{T-1} \{R_T(v) - R(v)\}^2\right] &= \sum_{|v|<T} E[D_T^2(v)] \\ &= \frac{4\pi}{T} \sum_{|v|<T} \int_{-\pi}^{\pi} \cos^2 \lambda v f^2(\lambda)\, d\lambda \\ &\to \left\{2\pi \int_{-\pi}^{\pi} f^2(\lambda)\, d\lambda\right\} > 0 \quad \text{as} \quad T \to \infty. \end{aligned}$$

By introducing suitable weights $\{k_T(v),\ v = 0, 1, \cdots, T\}$ one can obtain estimates

$$(3.9)\qquad R_T^*(v) = k_T(v) R_T(v)$$

of the covariance functions which do have the property that

$$(3.10)\qquad E\left[\sum_{v=0}^{T} |R_T^*(v) - R(v)|^2\right] \to 0 \quad \text{as} \quad T \to \infty.$$

In a sense (3.10) indicates the statistical role of weights in spectral analysis; they help damp out fluctuations in the sample covariance function. *We next indicate the role that weights play in estimating spectral averages from the point of view of approximation theory.*

A linear combination of sample covariances may be written

$$(3.11)\quad \begin{aligned} \sum_{|v|<T} a(v) R_T(v) &= \sum_{|v|<T} a(v) R(v) + \sum_{|v|<T} a(v) D_T(v) \\ &= \int_{-\pi}^{\pi} \left\{\sum_{|v|<T} a(v) \cos \omega v\right\} dF(\omega) + \sum_{|v|<T} a(v) D_T(v). \end{aligned}$$

We hereafter assume that the deviation time series may be considered to be normal with zero means and covariance given by (3.7). Then the statistic $\sum_{|v|<T} a(v) R_T(v)$ is normal with *mean*

$$(3.12)\qquad \int_{-\pi}^{\pi} \left\{\sum_{|v|<T} a(v) R(v)\right\} dF(\omega)$$

and *variance*

$$(3.12)\quad \sum_{|v_1|<T} \sum_{|v_2|<T} a(v_1) a(v_2) \operatorname{Cov}[D_T(v_1), D_T(v_2)] = \int_{-\pi}^{\pi} \left|\sum_{|v|<T} a(v) \cos v\lambda\right|^2 f^2(\lambda)\, d\lambda$$

assuming, as we do hereafter, that

$$(3.13)\qquad a(-v) = a(v).$$

One thus sees that if one desires to consider

$$(3.14)\qquad \sum_{|v|<T} a(v) R_T(v)$$

as an estimate of the spectral average

$$J(A) = \sum_{v=-\infty}^{\infty} a(v)R(v) = \int_{-\infty}^{\infty} A(\omega)\, dF(\omega) \tag{3.15}$$

that there are two kinds of error to be considered. One type of error, called *bias*, arises because the mean of (3.14) is not equal to (3.15) but rather is equal to the spectral average

$$J\left(\sum_{|v|<T} a(v) \cos \omega v\right) \tag{3.16}$$

whose spectral window is the truncated Fourier series of the desired spectral window $A(\omega)$. The other type of error, the *variance*, is given by (3.12).

To make these considerations more meaningful, let us consider the case of an important spectral average, namely (for fixed ω and $\Delta > 0$) the *spectral mass in the interval* $(\omega - \Delta, \omega + \Delta)$ represented by

$$\frac{1}{2}\left\{\int_{-\omega-\Delta}^{-\omega+\Delta} dF(\omega') + \int_{\omega-\Delta}^{\omega+\Delta} dF(\omega')\right\}, \tag{3.17}$$

which corresponds to the spectral window

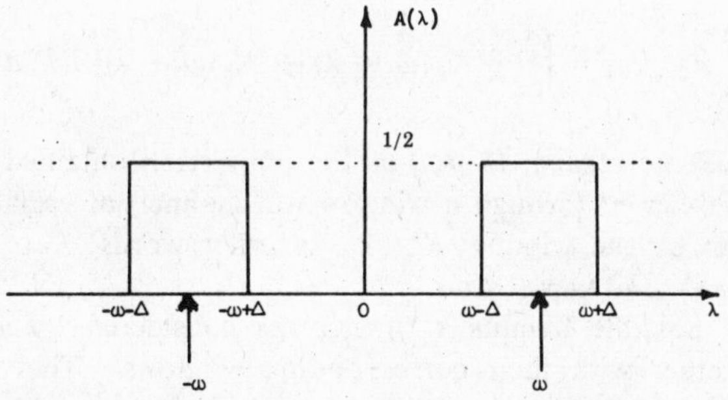

The Fourier coefficients of the even function $A(\lambda)$ are given by

$$\begin{aligned} a(v) &= \frac{1}{\pi}\int_{-\pi}^{\pi} A(\lambda) \cos \lambda v\, d\lambda = \frac{1}{\pi}\int_{\omega-\Delta}^{\omega+\Delta} \cos \lambda v\, d\lambda \\ &= \frac{\sin(\omega+\Delta)v - \sin(\omega-\Delta)v}{\pi v} \qquad (3.18) \\ &= \cos \omega v \frac{\sin \Delta v}{\pi v}. \end{aligned}$$

It would seem that to estimate the spectral average $J(A)$ one would adopt the estimate

$$\sum_{|v|<T} \cos \omega v \frac{\sin \Delta v}{\pi v} R_T(v). \tag{3.19}$$

However, it is a well-known fact that because of the Gibbs phenomenon (see Hamming [**6**, p. 295], Lanczos [**9**, p. 225]) the truncated Fourier series

$$\sum_{|v|<T} \cos \omega v \frac{\sin \Delta v}{\pi v} \cos \lambda v \tag{3.20}$$

can be improved as a pointwise (rather than least squares) approximation to $A(\lambda)$ by introducing *weights* $k_T(v)$ and using the function

$$A^*_{T;k}(\lambda) = \sum_{|v|<T} \cos \omega v \frac{\sin \Delta v}{\pi v} \cos \lambda v \, k_T(v) \tag{3.21}$$

as an approximation to $A(\lambda)$.

The Fourier transform

$$K_T(z) = \frac{1}{2\pi} \sum_{|v|<T} \cos \omega v \, k_T(v) \tag{3.22}$$

is defined to be a *window*, since one may write

$$A^*_{T;k}(\omega) = \int_{-\pi}^{\pi} \tfrac{1}{2}\{K_T(\omega - \lambda) + K_T(\omega + \lambda)\} A(\lambda) \, d\lambda. \tag{3.23}$$

In view of (3.23) we regard $A^*_{T;k}(\omega)$ as the impression obtained of the function $A(\omega)$ when it is viewed through a window (or channel) of variable transmission properties given by the window $K_T(z)$. In other words, $K_T(z)$ is the window through which $A^*_{T;k}(\omega)$ views $A(\omega)$.

A variety of possible weights $k_T(v)$ may be considered. These are listed in Table 3A, together with their corresponding windows. They are graphed in Figure 3A for $N = 6$. Since we are not considering any precise criterion by which to judge these windows, it may be a matter of debate which is most desirable. It is my opinion that *different windows are best compared by comparing window generating functions* (this notion is defined at the end of this section).

Windows are used in spectral analysis in three important ways.

(i) When forming estimates of the spectral mass in a band of frequencies, instead of (3.19) one would use the windowed estimate

$$\sum_{|v|<T} \cos \omega v \frac{\sin \Delta v}{\pi v} k_T(v) R_T(v). \tag{3.24}$$

This use of windows helps guard against the leakage into the mean of our estimate of spectral mass from outside the band under study.

TABLE 3A. WEIGHTS $k_N(n)$ AND WINDOWS $K_N(z)$

$$k_N(0) = 1, \quad k_N(-n) = k_N(n), \quad k_N(n) = \int_0^{2\pi} \cos nz K_N(z)\,dz; \; K_N(z) = \frac{1}{2\pi}\sum_{j=-N}^{N} k_N(j)\cos jz$$

$k_N(n)$	$2\pi K_N(z)$
I. Truncated Fourier Series $1, n = 0, 1, \cdots, N.$	$2\pi D_N(z) = \dfrac{\sin(N+\frac{1}{2})}{\sin\frac{1}{2}z}$
II. Modified Truncated Fourier Series $1, n = 0, 1, \cdots, N-1;$ $\frac{1}{2}, n = N.$	$2\pi D_N^*(z) = \dfrac{\sin Nz}{\tan\frac{1}{2}z}$
III. Fejer weights $1 - \dfrac{\lvert n\rvert}{N+1}, n = 0, 1, \cdots, N.$	$2\pi F_N(z) = \dfrac{1}{N+1}\left\{\dfrac{\sin(N+1)\frac{1}{2}z}{\sin\frac{1}{2}z}\right\}^2$
IV. Tukey–Hamming weights $\dfrac{1}{2}\left(1 + \cos\dfrac{\pi n}{N}\right), n = 0, 1, \cdots, N-1.$	$2\pi T_N(z) = 2\pi\left\{\dfrac{1}{2}D_N^*(z) + \dfrac{1}{4}D_N^*\left(z + \dfrac{\pi}{N}\right) + \dfrac{1}{4}D_N^*\left(z - \dfrac{\pi}{N}\right)\right\}$ $= \sin Nz\left\{\dfrac{1}{2}\operatorname{cotan}\dfrac{1}{2}z - \dfrac{1}{4}\operatorname{cotan}\dfrac{1}{2}\left(z + \dfrac{\pi}{N}\right) - \dfrac{1}{4}\operatorname{cotan}\dfrac{1}{2}\left(z - \dfrac{\pi}{N}\right)\right\}$
V. Lanczos weights $\dfrac{\sin\left(\dfrac{\pi n}{N}\right)}{\dfrac{\pi n}{N}}, n = 0, 1, \cdots, N.$	$2\pi L_N(z) = N\displaystyle\int_{-\pi/N}^{\pi/N} D_N(z+u)\,du$
VI. Parzen weights $1 - 6\left(\dfrac{n}{N}\right)^2 + 6\left(\dfrac{n}{N}\right)^3, n = 0, 1, \cdots, \dfrac{N}{2}.$ $2\left(1 - \dfrac{n}{N}\right)^3, \quad n = \dfrac{N}{2} + 1, \cdots, N.$	$2\pi P_N(z) = \dfrac{3}{4N^3}\left\{\dfrac{\sin\frac{1}{4}Nz}{\frac{1}{2}\sin\frac{z}{2}}\right\}^4\left\{1 - \dfrac{2}{3}\left(\sin\dfrac{z}{2}\right)^2\right\}$ for N even

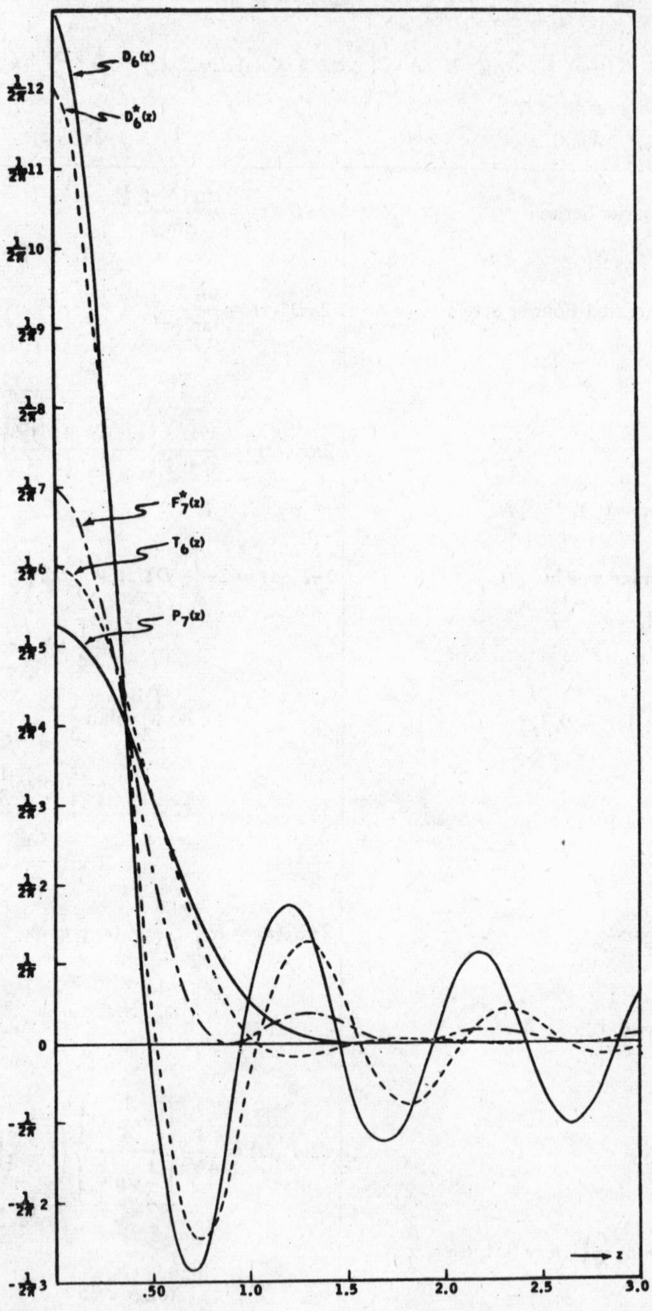

FIGURE 3A. Windows.

(ii) If the weights $k_T(v)$ in (3.24) are chosen so that for some $M < T$

$$k_T(v) = 0 \tag{3.25}$$

for $|v| > M$, then a computational saving is made in forming the estimate since the sample covariances $R_T(v)$ need not be computed for $|v| > M$. If (3.25) holds, we say that the estimate is truncated at M, and call M the *truncation point* of the estimate.

(iii) Weights are used to form estimates of the spectral density function (see §4).

A general way of generating weights which lead to truncated estimates is to consider a function $k(u)$ of a real variable with the following properties:

$$\begin{aligned} &\text{(i)} \quad k(0) = 1, \\ &\text{(ii)} \; k(-u) = k(u), \\ &\text{(iii)} \quad k(u) = 0 \qquad \text{for } |u| > 1. \end{aligned} \tag{3.26}$$

Next, choose a real number M (in theory, M will be a member of a sequence M_T of numbers which tend to ∞ as T tends to ∞). One may define weights by

$$k_T(v) = k\left(\frac{v}{M}\right). \tag{3.27}$$

Many of the weights listed in Table 3A may be generated in this way, as is shown in Table 3B. Therefore we call a function $k(u)$, satisfying (3.26), a *weight* or *lag window generator*.

Its Fourier transform

$$\begin{aligned} K(z) &= \frac{1}{2\pi}\int_{-\infty}^{\infty} e^{-iuz}\, k(u)\, du \\ &= \frac{1}{2\pi}\int_{-1}^{1} e^{-iuz} k(u)\, du, \qquad -\infty < z < \infty, \end{aligned} \tag{3.28}$$

is called a *window generator*. It may be shown that the Fourier transform

$$K_M(z) = \frac{1}{2\pi}\sum_{|v|<T} \cos vz\, k\left(\frac{v}{M}\right) \tag{3.29}$$

approximately satisfies, for large values of M,

$$K_M(z) = MK(Mz). \tag{3.30}$$

From (3.30) it follows that *the essential features of the graph of $K_M(z)$ can be obtained from a graph of $K(z)$*. An exposition of these facts is given in Parzen [**16**].

TABLE 3B. WINDOW GENERATORS $K(z)$

Weight generating function $k(u)$	$k_T(v) = k\left(\frac{v}{M}\right)$	$K(z) = \frac{1}{2\pi}\int_{-\infty}^{\infty} e^{-iuz}k(u)\,du$	Approximation $2\pi K_M(z) = 2\pi M K(Mz)$
I. Dirichlet			
$k_D(u) = \begin{cases} 1, & \lvert u\rvert \leqq 1; \\ 0, & \lvert u\rvert > 0. \end{cases}$	$k_T(v) = \begin{cases} 1, & v = 0, \pm 1, \cdots, \pm M; \\ 0, & \text{otherwise.} \end{cases}$	$K_D(z) = \frac{1}{\pi}\frac{\sin z}{z}$	$\frac{\sin Mz}{\frac{z}{2}}$
II. Modified Dirichlet			
$k_D^*(u) = \begin{cases} 1, & \lvert u\rvert < 1; \\ \frac{1}{2}, & \lvert u\rvert = 1; \\ 0, & \lvert u\rvert > 1. \end{cases}$	$k_T(v) = \begin{cases} 1, & v = 0, \pm 1, \cdots, \pm(M-1); \\ \frac{1}{2}, & v = M; \\ 0, & \text{otherwise.} \end{cases}$	$\frac{1}{\pi}\frac{\sin z}{z}$	$\frac{\sin Mz}{\frac{z}{2}}$
III. Fejer			
$k_F(u) = \begin{cases} 1 - \lvert u\rvert, & \lvert u\rvert \leqq 1; \\ 0, & \lvert u\rvert > 0. \end{cases}$	$k_T(v) = \begin{cases} 1 - \frac{\lvert v\rvert}{M}, & n = 0, \cdots, \pm M; \\ 0, & \text{otherwise.} \end{cases}$	$K_F(z) = \frac{1}{2\pi}\left\{\frac{\sin \frac{z}{2}}{\frac{z}{2}}\right\}^2$	$\frac{1}{M}\left\{\frac{\sin \frac{Mz}{2}}{\frac{z}{2}}\right\}^2$
IV. Tukey–Hamming			
$k_T(u) = \frac{1}{2}(1 + \cos \pi u), \quad \lvert u\rvert \leqq 1$	$k_T(v) = \begin{cases} \frac{1}{2}\left(1 + \cos \frac{\pi v}{M}\right), & v = 0, \pm 1, \cdots, \pm M; \\ 0, & \text{otherwise.} \end{cases}$	$K_T(z) = \frac{1}{2\pi}\frac{\sin z}{z}\frac{\pi^2}{\pi^2 - z^2}$	$\frac{\sin Mz}{z}\frac{\pi^2}{\pi^2 - (Mz)^2}$

V. Lanczos			
$k_L(u) = \begin{cases} \dfrac{\sin \pi u}{\pi u}, & \lvert u\rvert \leqq 1 \\ 0, & \lvert u\rvert > 1 \end{cases}$	$k_T(v) = \begin{cases} \dfrac{\sin \frac{\pi v}{M}}{\frac{\pi v}{M}}, & v = 0, \pm 1, \cdots, \pm M; \\ 0, & \text{otherwise.} \end{cases}$	$K_L(z) = \dfrac{1}{2\pi^2}\{Si(z+\pi) - Si(z-\pi)\}$, where $Si(x) = \begin{cases} \int_0^x \frac{\sin u}{u}\, du, \\ \int_0^1 \frac{\sin xu}{u}\, du, \end{cases}$ $Si(-x) = -Si(x)$,	$\dfrac{M}{\pi}\{Si(Mz+\pi) - Si(Mz-\pi)\}$
VI. Parzen			
$k_P(u) = \begin{cases} 1 - 6u^2 + 6\lvert u\rvert^3, & \lvert u\rvert \leqq \frac{1}{2} \\ 2(1-\lvert u\rvert)^3, & \frac{1}{2} \leqq \lvert u\rvert \leqq 1 \end{cases}$	$k_T(v) = 1 - 6\left(\dfrac{v}{M}\right)^2 + 6\left\lvert\dfrac{v}{M}\right\rvert^3$, $v = 0, \pm 1, \cdots, \pm \dfrac{M}{2}$; $= 2\left(1 - \left\lvert\dfrac{v}{M}\right\rvert\right)^3$, $v = \pm\left(\dfrac{M}{2}+1\right), \cdots, \pm M$.	$K_P(z) = \dfrac{3}{8\pi}\left\{\dfrac{\sin \frac{z}{4}}{\frac{z}{4}}\right\}^4$	$\dfrac{3}{4M^3}\left\{\dfrac{\sin \frac{Mz}{4}}{\frac{z}{4}}\right\}^4$

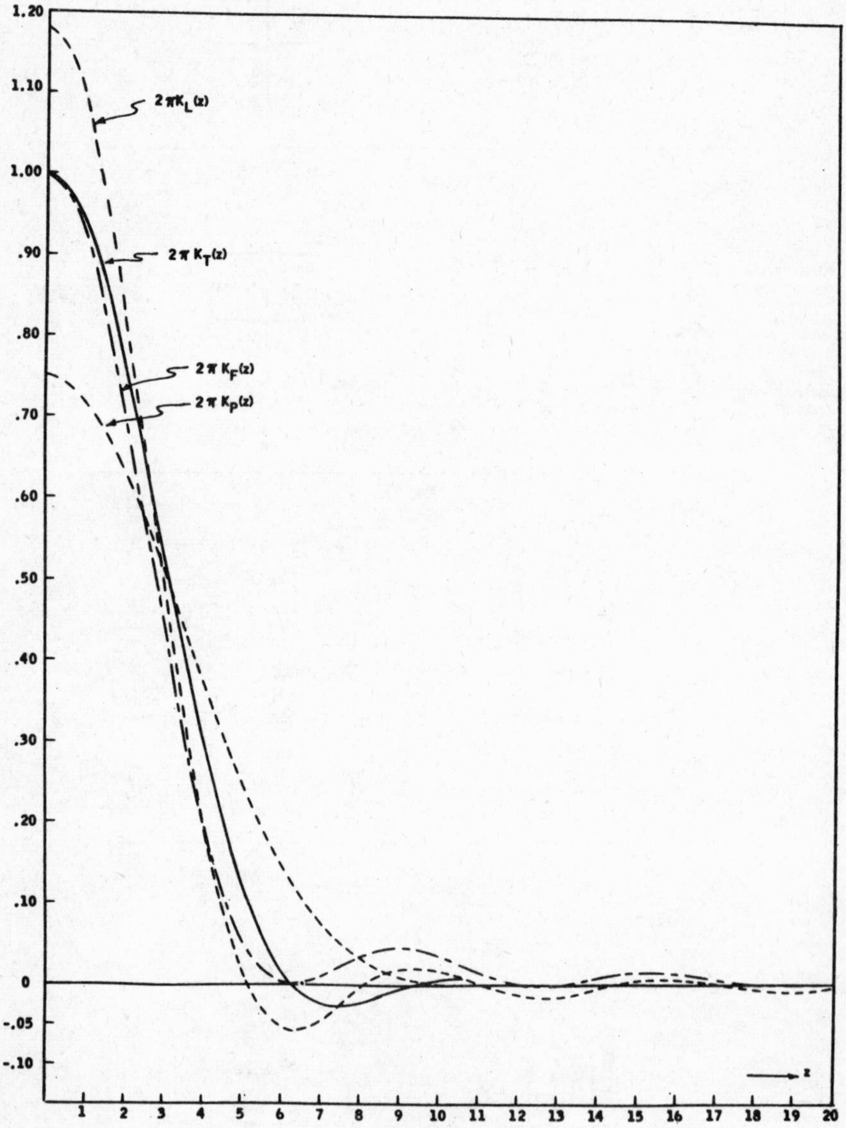

FIGURE 3B. Amplitude window generators.

4. **Estimation of spectral density.** The problem which up to recently seems to have received most attention in the literature of statistical spectral analysis has been that of estimating the spectral density function $f(\omega)$ under the assumption that the observed time series possesses a continuous spectrum. For sufficiently small values of Δ, the problem of estimating $f(\omega)$ at a frequency ω is equivalent to the problem of estimating the average spectral mass

$$\frac{1}{2\Delta}\int_{\omega-\Delta}^{\omega+\Delta} dF(\omega') = \frac{1}{2\Delta}\int_{\omega-\Delta}^{\omega+\Delta} f(\omega')\,d\omega' = f(\omega) \tag{4.1}$$

in a very narrow band of width 2Δ, centered at ω. To estimate the expression in (4.1), one might use the estimate (3.24) divided by 2Δ, and weights of the form of (3.27). We would then have the estimate

$$\frac{1}{2\pi}\sum_{|v|<T} \cos v\omega\, \frac{\sin \Delta v}{\Delta v}\, k\left(\frac{v}{M}\right) R_T(v). \tag{4.2}$$

Estimates of this form have not been explicitly examined in the statistical literature although I wonder if they are not worth consideration. What has been considered is the version of (4.2) obtained by setting $\Delta = 0$.

We are thus led to estimates of the spectral density which we denote

$$f_{T;k,M}(\omega) = \frac{1}{2\pi} R(0) + \frac{1}{\pi}\sum_{v=1}^{T-1} \cos v\omega R_T(v)\, k\left(\frac{v}{M}\right), \tag{4.3}$$

where M is a positive constant (called the truncation point of the estimate) and $k(u)$ is a kernel satisfying (3.26). If $k(u)$ is identically one, and $M = T$, then $f_{T;k,M}(\omega)$ is the sample spectral density function which is well known *not* to be a consistent estimate of $f(\omega)$.

The mean of the estimate (4.3), given by

$$\begin{aligned} E[f_{T;k,M}(\omega)] &= \int_{-\pi}^{\pi} d\lambda\, f(\lambda)\left\{\frac{1}{2\pi}\sum_{|v|<T} \cos v\omega\, k\left(\frac{v}{M}\right) \cos v\lambda\right\} \\ &= \int_{-\pi}^{\pi} d\lambda\, f(\lambda) \tfrac{1}{2}\{K_M(\omega-\lambda) + K_M(\omega+\lambda)\}, \end{aligned} \tag{4.4}$$

essentially views the true spectral density $f(\omega)$ through the window $K_M(\omega)$. In interpreting computed values of this estimate, this fact should always be borne in mind. Nevertheless for theoretical purposes it is useful to note the following asymptotic evaluation of the mean [which holds for a twice differentiable spectral density and twice differentiable kernel $k(u)$]:

$$\lim_{M\to\infty} M^2\{E[f_{T;k,M}(\omega)] - f(\omega)\} = -k_2 f''(\omega) \tag{4.5}$$

where

$$k_2 = -\frac{1}{2}k''(0) = \frac{1}{2}\int_{-\infty}^{\infty} \omega^2 K(\omega)\,d\omega, \tag{4.6}$$

assuming absolute convergence of the integral in (4.6).

The variance of $f_{T;k,M}(\omega)$, denoted by

$$D(\omega) = \text{Var}\,[f_{T;k,M}(\omega)]$$

and approximately given by

$$D(\omega) = \frac{\pi}{T}\int_{-\pi}^{\pi} d\lambda\, f^2(\lambda)\{K_M(\omega+\lambda) + K_M(\omega-\lambda)\}^2, \tag{4.7}$$

may be shown to satisfy, as $T \to \infty$,

$$D(\omega) \sim \begin{cases} \dfrac{M}{T}\displaystyle\int_{-\infty}^{\infty} k^2(u)\,du & \text{if } 0 < \omega < \pi, \\ 2\dfrac{M}{T}\displaystyle\int_{-\infty}^{\infty} k^2(u)\,du & \text{if } \omega = 0 \text{ or } \omega = \pi. \end{cases} \tag{4.8}$$

Heuristically (4.8) may be obtained as follows:

$$\begin{aligned} TD(\omega) &\doteq 2\pi f^2(\omega)\int_{-\pi}^{\pi} K_M^2(z)\,dz \\ &= 2\pi f^2(\omega)\int_{-\infty}^{\infty} M^2K^2(Mz)\,dz \\ &= Mf^2(\omega)2\pi\int_{-\infty}^{\infty} K^2(z)\,dz \\ &= Mf^2(\omega)\int_{-\infty}^{\infty} k^2(u)\,du. \end{aligned} \tag{4.9}$$

From the point of view of the practical use of the theory of spectral estimation the fundamental questions to be settled concerns the actual computing program to be used to estimate spectra. Briefly some of the issues involved in this question are as follows (see also Parzen [**12**, p. 233]):

(i) How to choose the number M of lag values at which the sample covariance function $R_T(v)$ is to be computed (one may want to use several values of M).

(ii) At what values of ω in the interval $0 \leqq \omega \leqq \pi$ should one compute the estimate $f_{T;k,M}(\omega)$? Even though the estimate is determined by its values at the frequencies $\omega_j = \pi j/M$, for $j = 0, 1, \cdots, M$, does it suffice to plot it only at these frequencies in order to fairly represent it as a function defined at all frequencies ω?

(iii) What lag window, or kernel, $k(u)$ should one employ? Two kernels frequently considered seem to be the kernel suggested by the author (and related to a kernel known in the theory of approximation as the Jackson-de la Vallée Poussin kernel; see Achieser [**1**, p. 119]):

$$k_P(u) = \begin{cases} 1 - 6u^2 + 6|u|^3, & |u| \leqq \frac{1}{2}, \\ 2(1-|u|)^3, & \frac{1}{2} \leqq |u| \leqq 1, \\ 0, & \text{otherwise}; \end{cases} \tag{4.10}$$

and a kernel suggested by Tukey, called "hanning" or (slightly modified) "Hamming" (see Blackman and Tukey [2, p. 14]):

$$k_H(u) = \begin{cases} \frac{1}{2}(1 + \cos \pi u), & |u| \leq 1, \\ 0, & \text{otherwise.} \end{cases} \tag{4.11}$$

We refer to $k_P(u)$ as the Parzen kernel and to $k_H(u)$ as the Tukey–Hamming kernel.

One difference between these kernels is that, when used with a positive definite sample covariance function, (4.10) leads to non-negative estimates while (4.11) may yield negative estimates. Is this a consideration to be borne in mind when deciding between kernels?

Another criterion to be used in comparing two kernels is the variability of the estimates to which they lead. It may be shown that

$$\int_{-\infty}^{\infty} k_P^2(u)\, du = 0.54, \tag{4.12}$$

$$\int_{-\infty}^{\infty} k_H^2(u)\, du = 0.75. \tag{4.13}$$

Using (4.8) one sees that, if used with the same truncation point M the Parzen kernel leads to an estimate whose variance is 54/75 = 72% that of the Hamming–Tukey kernel. However, this comparison is not quite fair, as one discovers by looking at the corresponding windows. At 0 the windows have values satisfying

$$2\pi M K_P(0) = \tfrac{3}{4}M, \tag{4.14}$$

$$2\pi M K_H(0) = M. \tag{4.15}$$

If one uses the Parzen kernel with a truncation point $\frac{4}{3}M$, where M is the truncation point used with the Hamming–Tukey kernel, it turns out (see Figure 4A) that the resulting estimates correspond to rather similar windows. The variance of the Parzen kernel with the increased truncation point is

$$\frac{4}{3}\frac{M}{T}(0.54) = \frac{M}{T}(0.72) \tag{4.16}$$

which is 96% of the variance 0.75 (M/T) of the Hamming–Tukey kernel.

In general, to evaluate a kernel $k(u)$ from the point of view of its variability, one evaluates the ratio

$$\frac{\int_{-\infty}^{\infty} k^2(u)\, du}{2\pi K(0)} = \frac{\int_{-\infty}^{\infty} k^2(u)\, du}{\int_{-\infty}^{\infty} k(u)\, du} \tag{4.17}$$

which (when multiplied by M/T) is a measure of its asymptotic variance when the window $K(z)$ is normalized to have height $(2\pi)^{-1}$ at $z = 0$ (as well as unit area). The

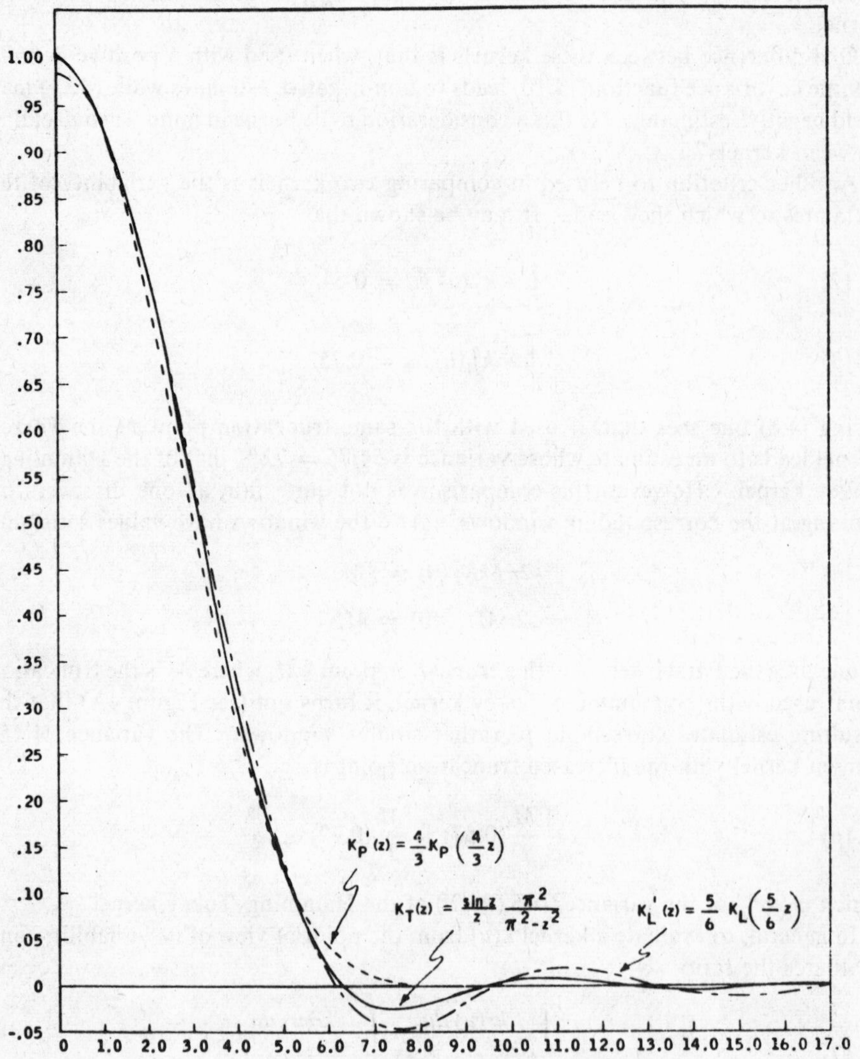

FIGURE 4A. Window generators normalized to have approximately same height at center frequency.

value of the ratio in (4.17) is 0.72 for the Parzen kernel, and 0.75 for the Tukey–Hamming kernel. For comparison we list its value for a kernel suggested by Lanczos (and known as Lanczos' σ factors; see Lanczos [**9**, p. 221] and Hamming [**6**, p. 298]):

(4.18)
$$k_L(u) = \begin{cases} \dfrac{\sin \pi u}{\pi u}, & |u| \leqq 1, \\ 0, & \text{otherwise}; \end{cases}$$

(4.19)
$$\int_{-\infty}^{\infty} k_L^2(u)\, du = \frac{2}{\pi} \int_0^{2\pi} \frac{\sin x}{x}\, dx;$$

(4.20)
$$2\pi K_L(0) = \frac{2}{\pi} \int_0^{\pi} \frac{\sin x}{x}\, dx,$$

(4.21)
$$\frac{\int_{-\infty}^{\infty} k^2(u)\, du}{\int_{-\infty}^{\infty} k(u)\, du} = \frac{1.42}{1.85} = 0.77.$$

5. **Estimation of spectral jumps.** The problem of estimating the discrete as well as the continuous spectrum of a time series possessing a mixed spectrum has only recently been attacked. A basic contribution to the solution of this problem has recently been made by Priestley [**17–19**] who also summarizes previous results (Whittle [**24**], Hannan [7]). Further work on this problem is now being done at Stanford by my student George Hext who has advanced the idea of computing the weighted sample spectral density for several values (say, $M_1 < M_2 < M_3 < M_4$) of the truncation point M, and then to perform at each frequency ω a regression analysis on the resulting estimates $f_{T;k,M_i}(\omega)$ by means of which one can hope in theory to simultaneously obtain a measure of (i) the jump in the spectrum at ω, (ii) the spectral density at ω, and even (iii) the second derivative of the spectral density at ω. A brief outline of this approach is given below.

In any event, it is my belief that *computing programs for spectral analysis should at each frequency print out the estimate corresponding to several truncation points.* I hope that in the near future we will have quantitative, as well as qualitative, procedures for interpreting the spectra obtained from several choices of M. We may then finally have an answer to one of the central questions which arises in any computing program for statistical spectral analysis, namely how to choose the truncation point.

It appears to me that ultimately the answer will turn out to be of the following form. Given an observed time series $\{X(t), t = 1, 2, \cdots, T\}$ of length T, choose a maximum truncation point M which will be an integer between 20% and 40% of the sample size T. Then choose several (say four) integers

$$M_1 < M_2 < M_3 < M_4 = M$$

and write

$$\alpha_1 = \frac{M_1}{M}, \quad \alpha_2 = \frac{M_2}{M}, \quad \alpha_3 = \frac{M_3}{M}, \quad \alpha_4 = \frac{M_4}{M}. \tag{5.1}$$

Compute the weighted sample spectral density function $f_{T;k,M}(\omega)$ for the four values of M (that is, for $M = M_1, M_2, M_3, M_4$) and for $Q + 1$ equidistant values of ω;

$$\omega = 0, \frac{\pi}{Q}, 2\frac{\pi}{Q}, \cdots, \pi. \tag{5.2}$$

The integer Q can be chosen at will. Often one lets $Q = M$, the maximum truncation point. Usually, Q will be an integer, approximately equal to M, such that the frequencies which are multiples of π/Q are of physical interest. Thus if one had 240 observations of an economic time series observed at monthly intervals one might choose $M = 64$ and $Q = 60$. With $Q = 60$, and monthly data, the following multiples of π/Q correspond to interesting periods:

k	Period
10	one year
20	six months
30	four months
40	three months
60	two months.

For a given value of ω, we then have four estimates to be denoted $f_i(\omega)$:

$$f_i(\omega) = f_{T;k,M_i}(\omega), \qquad i = 1, 2, 3, 4. \tag{5.3}$$

We next obtain approximate expressions for the mean and variance of the weighted sample spectral density function for a time series satisfying the model (2.1) with normal stationary residuals.

For the mean we obtain, approximately for large values of T,

$$\begin{aligned} E[f_{T;k,M}(\omega)] &= \frac{1}{2\pi} \sum_{|v|<T} \cos v\omega \, k\left(\frac{v}{M}\right) E[R_T(\omega)] \\ &= \sum_{j=1}^{k} J(\omega_j) \left\{\frac{1}{2\pi} \sum_{|v|<T} \cos v\omega \, k\left(\frac{v}{M}\right) \cos v\omega_j\right\} \\ &\quad + \int_{-\pi}^{\pi} d\lambda f(\lambda) \left\{\frac{1}{2\pi} \sum_{|v|<T} \cos v\omega \, k\left(\frac{v}{M}\right) \cos v\lambda\right\} \\ &= \sum_{j=1}^{k} J(\omega_j) \tfrac{1}{2}\{K_M(\omega + \omega_j) + K_M(\omega - \omega_j)\} \\ &\quad + \int_{-\pi}^{\pi} d\lambda f(\lambda) \tfrac{1}{2}\{K_M(\omega + \lambda) + K_M(\omega - \lambda)\}. \end{aligned} \tag{5.4}$$

In words, the mean of the weighted sample spectral density functions is composed of two parts, one an average over the continuous spectrum, represented by the spectral density function $f(\omega)$, and the other an average over the discrete spectrum, represented by the spectral jump function $J(\omega)$. The terms on the right-hand side of (5.4) will be called respectively the *discrete mean* E_d and the *continuous mean* E_c.

George Hext has obtained an approximate expression for variance:

$$\tag{5.5} \begin{aligned} T \operatorname{Var}[f_{T;k,M}(\omega)] &= 4\pi \int_{-\pi}^{\pi} d\lambda f^2(\lambda) \tfrac{1}{4}\{K_M(\omega+\lambda) + K_M(\omega-\lambda)\}^2 \\ &\quad + 8\pi \sum_{j=1}^{q} J(\omega_j) f(\omega_j) \tfrac{1}{4}\{K_M(\omega+\lambda) + K_M(\omega-\lambda)\}^2. \end{aligned}$$

The continuous mean and the variance are evaluated as in §4. Assuming that for all truncation points M_i under consideration, the spectral density function $f(\omega)$ is varying slowly compared to the window $K_{M_i}(\omega)$, it follows that to a first approximation the continuous mean is independent of M,

$$\tag{5.6} E_c[f_{T;k,M}(\omega)] = f(\omega),$$

while to a second approximation

$$\tag{5.7} E_c[f_{T;k,M}(\omega)] = f(\omega) + \frac{1}{M^2} k_2 f''(\omega).$$

We next obtain an approximate expression for the discrete mean, and find that *its contribution, if nonzero, increases linearly with truncation point* M:

$$\tag{5.8} \begin{aligned} E_d(\omega) &= \sum_{j=1}^{k} J(\omega_j) \tfrac{1}{2}\{K_M(\omega+\omega_j) + K_M(\omega-\omega_j)\} \\ &= \begin{cases} M\tfrac{1}{2}J(\omega_j)K(0) & \text{if } \omega = \omega_j \text{ and } \omega_j \neq 0; \\ MJ(\omega_j)K(0) & \text{if } \omega = \omega_j \text{ and } \omega_j = 0 \text{ or } \pi; \\ 0 & \text{otherwise.} \end{cases} \end{aligned}$$

We now sum up these results from the point of view of their dependence on M for fixed T, ω, and $k(\cdot)$:

$$\tag{5.9} f_{T;k,M}(\omega) = E_M(\omega) + \varepsilon_M(\omega),$$

where $E_M(\omega)$ and $\varepsilon_M(\omega)$ are to begin with defined by

$$E_M(\omega) = E[f_{T;k,M}(\omega)], \qquad \varepsilon_M(\omega) = f_{T;k,M}(\omega) - E_M(\omega).$$

For each M, $\varepsilon_M(\omega)$ is a random variable. The covariance between $\varepsilon_{M_1}(\omega)$ and $\varepsilon_{M_2}(\omega)$ for two distinct values M_1 and M_2 of M is approximately given by (for $0 < \omega < \pi$)

(5.10)
$$\begin{aligned} T \operatorname{Cov}\left[\varepsilon_{M_1}(\omega), \varepsilon_{M_2}(\omega)\right] &= 2\pi f^2(\omega) M_1 M_2 \int_{-\infty}^{\infty} K(M_1 z) K(M_2 z)\, dz \\ &\quad + 2\pi J(\omega) f(\omega) M_1 M_2 K^2(0). \end{aligned}$$

The tools are now at hand to examine the properties of the estimates $f_i(\omega)$ defined by (5.3).

If we adopt the first approximation (5.6) to the mean of the weighted sample spectral density function, we may write

(5.11)
$$\begin{aligned} f_i(\omega) &= f(\omega) + M_{i}^{\frac{1}{2}} J(\omega) K(0) + \varepsilon_i(\omega) \\ &= f(\omega) + \alpha_i M^{\frac{1}{2}} J(\omega) K(0) + \varepsilon_i(\omega), \end{aligned}$$

where $\varepsilon_i(\omega)$ denotes the fluctuation of $f_i(\omega)$ about its mean. The random variables $\varepsilon_1(\omega), \cdots, \varepsilon_4(\omega)$ may be assumed to be jointly normal with covariance matrix (for $0 < \omega < \pi$)

(5.12)
$$\{\operatorname{Cov}\left[\varepsilon_i(\omega), \varepsilon_j(\omega)\right]\} = \frac{1}{T} C,$$

where the entries of the matrix

(5.13)
$$C = \begin{bmatrix} C_{11} & C_{12} & C_{13} & C_{14} \\ C_{21} & C_{22} & C_{23} & C_{24} \\ C_{31} & C_{32} & C_{33} & C_{34} \\ C_{41} & C_{42} & C_{43} & C_{44} \end{bmatrix}$$

may be shown to be approximately given by

(5.14)
$$\begin{aligned} C_{ij} &= M_i M_j \{J(\omega) K^2(0)\}\{2\pi f(\omega)\} \\ &\quad + \sqrt{(M_i M_j)}\, f^2(\omega) \int_{-\infty}^{\infty} k\left(u\sqrt{\frac{M_i}{M_j}}\right) k\left(u\sqrt{\frac{M_j}{M_i}}\right) du. \end{aligned}$$

To facilitate computation of the C matrix, define

(5.15)
$$I(\beta) = \int_{-\infty}^{\infty} k(v) k(\beta v)\, dv.$$

This function is given in Table 5A for the Parzen and Tukey kernels.

Estimates of $f(\omega)$ and $J(\omega)$ can now be obtained by regression analysis, using the theory of minimum variance unbiased estimation of a straight line in the presence of correlated residuals. Because the parameters being estimated also appear in the covariance matrix C, an iterative procedure is necessary.

The foregoing remarks are necessarily incomplete. Further work along these lines will be reported by George Hext in his thesis.

TABLE 5A. FUNCTION $I(\beta) = \int_{-\infty}^{\infty} k(u)k(\beta u)\, du$

Parzen's kernel

$$I_P(\beta) = \begin{cases} \frac{3}{4} - \beta^2 \frac{3}{8} + \beta^3 \frac{93}{560} & \text{for } 0 \leqq \beta \leqq \frac{1}{2}; \\ \frac{3}{4} - \beta^2 \frac{3}{8} + \beta^3 \frac{93}{560} - \frac{(2\beta - 1)^7}{\beta^4} \frac{1}{560} & \text{for } \frac{1}{2} \leqq \beta \leqq 1. \end{cases}$$

Tukey's kernel

$$I_T(\beta) = \begin{cases} \frac{1}{2}\left\{1 + \frac{\sin \pi\beta}{\pi\beta} \frac{1}{1 - \beta^2}\right\} & \text{for } 0 \leqq \beta < 1; \\ \frac{3}{4} & \text{for } \beta = 1. \end{cases}$$

REFERENCES

1. N. I. Achieser, *Theory of approximation*, Ungar, New York, 1956.

2. R. B. Blackman and J. W. Tukey, *The measurement of power spectra from the point of view of communications engineering*, Dover, New York, 1950.

3. C. E. P. Brooks and N. Carruthers, *Handbook of statistical methods in meteorology*, H.M. Stationery Office, London, 1953.

4. R. A. Fisher, *Tests of significance in harmonic analysis*, Proc. Roy. Soc. Ser. A **125** (1929), 54.

5. N. R. Goodman, *Spectral analysis of multiple stationary time series*, Proc. Sympos. Time Series Analysis (Brown Univ., 1962), pp. 260–266, Wiley, New York, 1963.

6. R. W. Hamming, *Numerical methods for scientists and engineers*, McGraw-Hill, New York, 1962.

7. E. J. Hannan, *Testing for a jump in the spectral function*, J. Roy. Statist. Soc. Ser. B **23** (1961), 394–404.

8. G. M. Jenkins, *General considerations in estimation of spectra*, Technometrics **3** (1961), 133–166.

9. C. Lanczos, *Applied analysis*, Prentice Hall, Englewood Cliffs, N. J., 1956.

10. E. Parzen, *On asymptotically efficient consistent estimates of the spectral density function of a stationary time series*, J. Roy. Statist. Soc. Ser. B **20** (1958), 303–322.

11. ———, *Mathematical considerations in estimation of spectra*, Technometrics **3** (1961), 167–190.

12. ———, *Spectral analysis of asymptotically stationary time series*, Bull. Inst. Internat. Statist. 33rd Session, Vol. 39, Book 2, pp. 87–104, Paris, 1962.

13. ———, *An approach to time series analysis*, Ann. Math. Statist. **32** (1961), 951–989.

14. ———, *Stochastic processes*, Holden Day, San Francisco, 1962.

15. ———, *On spectral analysis with missing observations and amplitude modulation*, Sankhyā, December 1963.

16. ———, *Notes on Fourier analysis and spectral windows*, Tech. Rep. No. 48, Statistics Dept., Stanford Univ., Stanford, Calif., 1963.

17. M. B. Priestley, *The analysis of stationary processes with mixed spectra.* I, J. Roy. Statist. Soc. Ser. B **24** (1962), 215–233.

18. ———, *The analysis of stationary processes with mixed spectra.* II, J. Roy. Statist. Soc. Ser. B **24** (1962), 511–529.

19. ———, *Basic considerations in the estimation of spectra*, Technometrics **4** (1962), 551–564.
20. M. Rosenblatt, *Statistical analysis of stochastic processes with stationary residuals*, Probability and statistics: The Harold Cramér volume, pp. 246–273, Wiley, New York, 1959.
21. A. Schuster, *On the investigation of hidden periodicities with application to a supposed 26-day period of meteorological phenomena*, Terrestrial Magnetism **3** (1897), 13.
22. J. W. Tukey, *An introduction to the measurement of spectra*, Probability and statistics: The Harold Cramér volume, pp. 300–330, Wiley, New York, 1959.
23. G. Walker, *On the criteria for the reality of relationships or periodicities*, Calcutta Ind. Met. Memo. **21** (1914), Part 9.
24. P. Whittle, *The simultaneous estimation of a time-series harmonic components and covariance structure*, Trabajos Estadíst. **3** (1952), 43–57.
25. N. Wiener, *Generalized harmonic analysis*, Acta Math. **55** (1930), 117–258.

Stanford University,
Stanford, California

STABILITY IN SIGNAL DETECTION PROBLEMS[1]

BY

WILLIAM L. ROOT

A device for detecting the presence of a signal in noise may be represented, obviously, as a two-valued function on an appropriate function space. Usually the operation performed by such a detector amounts first to calculating the value of a real-valued functional, which we shall call the test functional, and then comparing this value with a prescribed threshold. It is now common engineering practice to determine as well as possible the statistics of the noise, and from this knowledge and that of the structure of the signal to try to design the detector to be optimum or nearly optimum according to some statistical criterion. How well the detector operates (how accurate the decisions are) depends on the distributions of the test functional and on the threshold. In the special case that the signal is a known function and the probability measure of the noise process is known, the induced distributions of the test functional as determined on either hypothesis, signal present or signal absent, are known, at least in principle. The probabilities of the two kinds of decision error can be calculated. If, however, the actual probability measure of the noise process is different from what was assumed, so are the induced distributions of the test functional and so are the error probabilities. There is the possibility that a slight difference in the actual statistics of the noise from the assumed will result in a large change in the error probabilities. Such a situation will be termed *unstable*. Instability of this kind is obviously undesirable to the system designer, who almost certainly cannot know the noise statistics precisely, but who would like some guarantee of the performance of his system.

This concept of instability, or more precisely a notion of degree of stability, is appropriate in a more general class of problems than the one indicated. It applies to a study of any system in which a statistical inference is made from the value or values of a functional on a sample space, where the functional is carefully chosen from an assumed a priori knowledge of the statistics and is critically dependent on them.

In this paper are developed some preliminary results concerning stability in signal detection and signal measurement. The discussion is limited to hypotheses-test and parameter-estimation problems;[2] filtering and prediction are more or less

[1] This work was supported by the National Aeronautics and Space Administration under research grant NsG–2–59.

[2] Comprehensive treatments of the kinds of problems referred to are given, e.g., by Parzen **[10]**, Hajek **[6]**, Balakrishnan **[2]**.

arbitrarily excluded. Both sure-signal-in-noise and noise-in-noise cases are discussed. All of what might be considered general theory is a direct application of a few well-known results about the weak convergence of probability measures on function spaces.

Models for detection problems. We shall say a signal-detection or signal-measurement problem is of the *sure-signal-in-noise* type if the observed waveform can be represented as the sum of a function known to within finitely many parameters and a sample function from a stochastic process. We write

$$y(t) = s(t; \alpha) + x(t) \tag{1}$$

where $y(t)$ is a real- (or complex-, or vector-) valued function of a real variable t, representing the observed waveform; where for each α $s(t; \alpha)$ is a function of t representing a possible signal, and where $x(t)$ is a sample function from a stochastic process representing the noise. The time variable t belongs to a linear set, which here will always be taken to be a finite interval, the observation interval. The parameter α may have finitely many components, $\alpha = (\alpha_1, \cdots, \alpha_k)$, each of which is either an index taking on finitely or countably many values, or is real- or complex-valued. For example, in the simplest detection problem, $\alpha = 0$ or 1, and $s(t; 0) \equiv 0$, $s(t; 1) = f(t)$, a known function. More generally, in radar and radio communication problems the α_i may determine amplitude, phase, etc., of different portions of the received signal. The process of signal detection or signal measurement consists of making required inferences about the α_i, whose true values are unknown.

Usually the noise process $x(t)$ is assumed to be Gaussian with mean zero and continuous autocorrelation, often stationary. This seems justifiable in many instances because of the nature of the physical origin of the noise.

We shall say a signal-detection or signal-measurement problem is of the *noise-in-noise* type if the observed waveform can be represented as the sum of sample functions from two stochastic processes, one carrying the desired information, the other being unwanted noise. Again we write

$$y(t) = s(t; \alpha) + x(t)$$

but $s(t; \alpha)$ is now a sample function from a process indexed by α. For example, in radiometry, α might be the power level of noise-like radiation from a certain solid-angle of the sky in a certain frequency band.

Again, usually the noise process $x(t)$ is assumed to be Gaussian, and often the signal process $s(t; \alpha)$ is also. However, $s(t; \alpha)$ may have a much simpler structure; it may be a family of functions of t parameterized in some simple way by α, but with α taken to be a random variable. Sometimes in such a case it is more natural to treat the problem as a modified sure-signal-in-noise problem than as noise-in-noise.

In part of what follows we shall impose intuitively reasonable restrictions on the class of processes which are admissible to characterize noise and signals. The most important of these is the requirement that the sample functions be continuous. If a process is stationary and Gaussian (and separable, with continuous autocorrelation function) then it is known from results of Dobrushin **[4]** and Belyaev **[3]**, respectively, that the alternative to the sample functions being continuous with probability one is that with probability one they have discontinuities of the second kind everywhere, and in fact are unbounded in every finite interval. As long, then, as one is discussing stationary Gaussian noise processes the assumption of continuity of sample functions is strongly justified; if a noise process is only nearly stationary and Gaussian it is perhaps still plausible. Kolmogorov's well-known sufficient condition for continuous sample functions is available as a verifiable hypothesis.

A second condition sometimes required concerning the signal and noise taken together is that any two measures on the sample space corresponding to different statistical hypotheses about the signal be equivalent, that is, the statistical inference problems be nonsingular. Arguments have been given that for a Gaussian-noise model of a realizable communication system this must be true.[3]

For stationary second-order processes continuity of sample functions requires of course, that, roughly speaking, the distribution of power at high frequencies falls off sufficiently fast. Non-singularity of the measures implies, roughly, that the distribution of noise power falls off more slowly at high frequencies than that of the signal. For example, Parzen's sufficient condition[4] that noise and noise-plus-signal processes be relatively nonsingular on any finite interval when noise and signal processes are real, stationary, independent, Gaussian, and with spectral densities $S_n(f)$ and $S_s(f)$, respectively, is that

$$\int_{-\infty}^{\infty} \frac{S_s(f)}{S_n(f)}\, df < \infty.$$

An analogous sufficient condition[5] for sure-signal in noise replaces $S_s(f)$ with the square of the modulus of the Fourier transform of the signal, which is supposed to be of integrable square and vanish outside a finite interval.

Most solutions to problems involving signals in Gaussian noise are based on a knowledge of the autocorrelation function or spectrum (if the noise is stationary). In fact, of course, as mentioned before, they are rarely if ever known precisely. The noise spectrum may be determined from a knowledge of the structure of the generating process, as, for example, when thermal noise is passed through a filter of known characteristics, or it may be estimated from measurements. In the first instance errors result because of imprecise characterization of the generating process, in the second because of errors inherent in statistical measurements.

Let us digress slightly to consider one point that applies particularly to the

---

[3] See Parzen **[9]** and Root **[13]**. For a general survey of the theory of equivalence of Gaussian measures, see also Yaglom **[15]**.

[4] See Parzen **[9**, Example 4**]**.

[5] See Kelly, Reed and Root **[8]**.

situation where the spectrum or autocorrelation is determined empirically. At best the autocorrelation can be determined only for a finite interval. Even if it be known exactly for this interval, the spectrum cannot be known in principle unless the autocorrelation has a unique extrapolation as a positive definite function. There are necessary and sufficient conditions that a finite section of a positive definite function have a unique positive definite extrapolation,[6] but none that I know are in an easily applicable form. However, one sufficient condition for a nonunique extrapolation is a condition which one might normally expect to be satisfied by electrical noise. *If a second-order stationary process with absolutely continuous spectrum is nondeterministic, then a restriction of its autocorrelation function to any finite interval has a nonunique positive definite extrapolation.*[7]

In fact, let $S(f)$ be the spectral density of such a process and $R(t)$ its autocorrelation function. Then $S(f)$ is absolutely integrable and satisfies the condition

$$\int_{-\infty}^{\infty} \frac{|\log S(f)|}{1+f^2}\, df < \infty. \tag{2}$$

Let

$$S_1(f) = \begin{cases} S(f), & S(f) \leqq 1 \\ S^{1/2}(f), & S(f) > 1. \end{cases}$$

Then $S_1(f)$ is of integrable square on the interval $(-\infty, \infty)$ and also satisfies the condition (2). By a well-known theorem of Paley and Wiener $(1/3)S_1(f)$ is the modulus of a function $G(f)$ belonging to L_2 (and here, also to L_1) with a Fourier transform $g(t)$ which vanishes for $t < -a$, a arbitrarily chosen greater than zero. Let

$$h(t) = g(t) + \overline{g(-t)}.$$

Then $h(t)$ vanishes for $-a < t < a$. Let $H(f)$ be the Fourier transform of $h(t)$. We have that $H(f)$ is real and

$$|H(f)| \leqq 2|G(f)| \leqq \tfrac{2}{3}S_1(f) < S(f).$$

Hence $S(f) + H(f)$ is non-negative and integrable and is itself the spectral density of a process with autocorrelation function $R(t) + h(t)$, which agrees with $R(t)$ on $(-a, a)$.

If $R(t)$ is real, the construction described will yield real nonunique extensions, since $g(t)$ may be chosen to be real.

To a certain extent the fact just noted is irrelevant to the consideration of a signal-in-Gaussian-noise problem, because knowledge of the autocorrelation function over just the observation interval completely determines the statistics of the problem; that is, there is in principle no reason to introduce the spectrum of the noise at all. However, since such a great amount of the technique of design in engineering is

[6] See Akutowicz [1].

[7] J. Chover has an independent proof of this result. He has pointed out to me further that it is in Krein's fundamental work.

based on the idea of frequency spectra, it is practically important whenever possible to state conditions in terms of frequency spectra.

Detection stability for sure signals in Gaussian noise. In this section we discuss two examples, the simple detection of a known signal in Gaussian noise, and the estimation of linear regression coefficients of a signal in Gaussian noise. In each example (and obviously in other similar ones) there is a natural notion of stability that can be treated quite simply and directly. We start without a formal definition of stability and introduce a definition in context. Both examples are phrased in terms of the Karhunen–Loève expansion as a matter of personal choice and convenience.

Let G be a set of real-valued Gaussian random processes, each with parameter set the interval $[a, b]$, mean-value zero, and continuous autocorrelation function. That is, G is a set of measure spaces $(X, \mathscr{B}, \mu_g)$, where X is a fixed set of real-valued functions $x(\cdot)$ on $[a, b]$, $\mathscr{B}$ is a Borel field of subsets of X and $\{\mu_g\}$ is a family of Gaussian probability measures on $\mathscr{B}$ such that the mean-value and autocorrelation functions are as prescribed. One of the measures, μ_0, is called the *nominal* one; expectations with respect to this measure are denoted by E_0, and the autocorrelation function of the corresponding process is

$$R_0(t, s) = E_0 x(t)x(s).$$

G is to be thought of as a set of possible noise processes for the signal detection problem. The actual noise process is unknown, but the one which has been assumed in the design of the detector is the nominal process; or in other words, the autocorrelation function of the noise has been assumed to be $R_0(t, s)$.

We take $\{\lambda_n, \phi_n\}$ to be the eigenvalues and corresponding eigenfunctions (real and orthonormal) of the integral operator R_0 given by

$$R_0 f(t) = \int_a^b R_0(t, s) f(s)\, ds, \qquad a \leqq t \leqq b.$$

Then for the nominal process,

$$x(t) = \sum_n x_n \phi_n(t),$$

where

$$x_n = \int_a^b x(t)\phi_n(t)\, dt, \qquad E_0 x_n \bar{x}_k = \lambda_n \delta_{nk},$$

and the convergence is in the sense of mean-square with respect to μ_0 for each t.

Consider now the first example. The received waveform is

$$y(t) = s_i(t) + x(t), \qquad a \leqq t \leqq b,\ i = 0, 1,$$

where $s_0(t) \equiv 0$ and $s_1(t) = a(t)$ is a known real-valued function of integrable square on $[a, b]$. The detector is to indicate signal present when $i = 1$, no signal when $i = 0$. The maximum-likelihood test[8] for this decision problem on the

[8] See Grenander [5].

assumption $x(t)$ is a sample from the nominal noise process can be written in terms of the test functional

(3) $$f(y) = \sum_k \frac{y_k a_k}{\lambda_k},$$

where

$$a_k = \int_a^b s_1(t)\phi_k(t)\,dt,$$

$$y_k = \int_a^b y(t)\phi_k(t)\,dt.$$

The test is:

accept hypothesis "signal present" if $f(y) > \eta$

reject hypothesis "signal present" if $f(y) \leqq \eta$,

where η is a prescribed constant. We shall assume the hypothesis-test problem with the nominal noise sample is nonsingular, which is equivalent to the condition[8]

(4) $$\sum \frac{a_k^2}{\lambda_k} < \infty.$$

This condition guarantees that the series for $f(y)$ converges with probability one with respect to μ_0.

Suppose now that the actual signal $s_1(t)$ is exactly as specified, but the noise, although Gaussian with mean zero, has autocorrelation

$$R_1(t, s) = R_0(t, s) + A(t, s),$$

so that $A(t, s)$ represents the difference between the true autocorrelation function and the nominal one. Because of the boundedness of R_0 and R_1 on $[a, b] \times [a, b]$, the double norm of A, denoted by $\|A\|$, and defined by

$$\|A\|^2 = \int_0^1\int_0^1 |A(t, u)|^2\,dt\,du,$$

is necessarily finite. We denote the measure on $\mathscr{B}$ corresponding to R_1 by μ_1, and expectations with respect to μ_1 by $E_1(\cdot)$. We shall determine the effect on the error probabilities of the change from μ_0 to μ_1. The test functional, $f(y)$ is to remain unchanged, of course, since the object here is to find the effect on detection of the use of incorrect noise statistics in the design of the detector.

Then,

$$E_1 f(y) = E_0 f(y) = \sum_k \frac{a_k^2}{\lambda_k} = \beta,$$

where β is defined by this equation. Also,

$$E_1 x_k x_j = \lambda_k \delta_{kj} + (A\phi_k, \phi_j),$$

where A is the integral operator on $L_2[a, b]$ with kernel $A(t, u)$, and the inner product is that of $L_2[a, b]$. Consider a truncated test functional,

$$f_N(y) = \sum_{k=1}^{N} \frac{y_k a_k}{\lambda_k}.$$

The variance of f_N is

$$\sigma^2(f_N) = E_1 \sum_{k=1}^{N} \frac{y_k a_k}{\lambda_k} \sum_{j=1}^{N} \frac{y_j a_j}{\lambda_j} - \left(\sum_{k=1}^{N} \frac{a_k^2}{\lambda_k}\right)^2$$

$$= \sum_{k=1}^{N} \frac{a_k^2}{\lambda_k} + \sum_{\substack{k=1 \\ j=1}}^{N} \frac{a_k a_j}{\lambda_k \lambda_j} (A\phi_k, \phi_j).$$

If now it is required that

$$\sum_k \frac{a_k^2}{\lambda_k^2} < \infty \tag{5}$$

then

$$\Delta = \sum_{\substack{k=1 \\ j=1}}^{\infty} \frac{a_k a_j}{\lambda_k \lambda_j} (A\phi_k, \phi_j)$$

exists, and it is easily justified that $\sigma^2(f) = \beta + \Delta$. Under this assumption the error probabilities are:

$$P\{\text{signal detected} | \text{no signal sent}\} = \frac{1}{\sqrt{(2\pi)}} \int_{\eta/\sqrt{(\beta+\Delta)}}^{\infty} e^{-u^2/2}\, du,$$

$$P\{\text{no signal detected} | \text{signal sent}\} = \frac{1}{\sqrt{(2\pi)}} \int_{-\infty}^{(\eta-\beta)/\sqrt{(\beta+\Delta)}} e^{-u^2/2}\, du.$$

The change in noise statistics influences the error probabilities only through the number Δ. As $\Delta \to 0$, the changes in error probabilities approach zero. One has,

$$|\Delta| \leq \sum^{\infty} \frac{a_k^2}{\lambda_k^2} \|A\| \leq \sum^{\infty} \frac{a_k^2}{\lambda_k^2} |A|$$

so that in the presence of the condition (5) the "stability parameter," Δ, is dominated by a constant times the root-mean-square error in the determination of the autocorrelation function.

If, on the other hand,

$$\sum_k \frac{a_k^2}{\lambda_k^2} = +\infty$$

then, given an arbitrary $\varepsilon > 0$, one can choose, by the Banach–Steinhaus theorem, a sequence of real numbers b_k such that $\sum b_k^2 \leq \varepsilon$ and

$$\sum_k \frac{a_k b_k}{\lambda_k} = +\infty.$$

Let $A(t, u) = \sum_{k,j} b_k b_j \phi_k(t)\phi_j(u)$. Then $|A| \leq \varepsilon$, and

$$\Delta = \sum_{k,j} \frac{a_k}{\lambda_k} \frac{a_j}{\lambda_j} (A\phi_k, \phi_j) = +\infty.$$

Furthermore A, and hence R_1, are positive definite.

Thus, if the condition (5) is satisfied, the error probabilities approach their nominal values as $|A|$ approaches zero; if (5) is not satisfied, they do not necessarily. We shall say that in the first case the detector is stable, that in the second case it is not. Obviously the smaller the value of the sum $\sum(a_k^2/\lambda_k^2)$, the more stable the detector.

There is a trivial generalization of the above to allow for imperfect knowledge of the signal. If the true signal function $a(t)$ differs from the nominal one by $\delta(t)$, where

$$\|\delta\|^2 = \int_0^1 |\delta(t)|^2 \, dt < \infty$$

then the mean of the test functional is changed by an amount less than or equal to $\|\delta\|(\sum(a_k^2/\lambda_k^2))^{1/2}$, where the a_k are the Fourier coefficients of the nominal signal. The variance of f is as above. Again condition (5) is necessary and sufficient for stability.

It is of interest to re-formulate the stability condition for this simple but basic example. First, of course, the condition

$$\sum \frac{a_k^2}{\lambda_k^2} < \infty$$

is equivalent to the condition that the function $s_1(t)$ belong to the domain of the (unbounded) inverse of R_0, $s_1 \in \mathscr{D}(R_0^{-1})$, or in other words that

$$\int_a^b R_0(t, u) g(u) \, du = s_1(t), \qquad a \leq t \leq b$$

have a solution $g \in L_2[a, b]$. If it does then the test functional can be written

$$f(y) = \int_a^b y(t) g(t) \, dt,$$

and the quantity Δ which determines the degree of stability is given by

$$\Delta = (Ag, g).$$

If $R_0(t, u) = \rho(t - u)$ is a stationary autocorrelation function which is absolutely integrable on E^1, then it necessarily has a bounded spectral density $S(f)$, and it also belongs to $L_2(-\infty, \infty)$ (henceforth written L_2). In this case the stability condition may be written as follows (for convenience $[a, b]$ is taken to be $[-T, T]$):

Let $a(t)$, $t \in [-T, T]$, belong to $L_2[-T, T]$. Then $a \in \mathscr{D}(R_0^{-1})$ if and only if $a(t)$ has an extension $\tilde{a}(t)$ to the real number line such that

(1) $\tilde{a}(t) \in L_2$;

(2) *the Fourier transform* $\tilde{A}(f)$ *of* $\tilde{a}(t)$ *satisfies the conditions that* $\tilde{A}(f)/S(f) \in L_2$ *and is an integral function of exponential type with index* $\leqq 2\pi T$.

In fact, suppose there is a function $\phi(t) \in L_2[-T, T]$ which satisfies

$$\int_{-T}^{T} \rho(t-s)\phi(s)\,ds = a(t), \qquad -T \leqq t \leqq T. \tag{6}$$

Consider $a(t)$ and $\phi(t)$ to be defined for all real numbers t, by putting them equal to zero for $|t| > T$. Then (6) can be rewritten,

$$c_T(t)\int_{-\infty}^{\infty} \rho(t-s)\phi(s)\,ds = a(t), \tag{7}$$

where $c_T(t)$ is the indicator function of the interval $[-T, T]$. We denote the Fourier transform of c_T by $D_T(f)$, and the Fourier transforms of $\phi(t)$, $a(t)$ by $\Phi(f)$, $A(f)$ respectively. Then

$$\int_{-\infty}^{\infty} D_T(f-g)S(g)\Phi(g)\,dg = A(f), \tag{8}$$

where $\Phi(g)$ is necessarily an element of L_2 and is of exponential type with index $\leqq 2\pi T$. Let $\Psi(g) = S(g)\Phi(g)$. Then $\Psi(g) \in L_1 \cap L_2$, and the fact that it satisfies the equation

$$\int_{-\infty}^{\infty} D_T(f-g)\Psi(g)\,dg = A(f) \tag{9}$$

implies that its inverse Fourier transform $\psi(t)$ satisfies $c_T(t)\psi(t) = a(t)$. Thus $\psi(t)$ is an extension of $a(t)$ which meets the conditions for $\tilde{a}(t)$.

Conversely, suppose $\psi(t)$ is an extension of $a(t)$ with the required properties. Then (9) is satisfied by its transform $\Psi(f)$. Define $\Phi(g) = \Psi(g)/S(g)$. Then (8) is satisfied, and since $A(f) \in L_2$, (7) is also satisfied. Since $\Phi(g)$ is of exponential type with index $\leqq T$, (7) is equivalent to (6).

In particular it is sufficient that $a(t)$ satisfy the conditions on $\tilde{a}(t)$; this happens, for example, if $S(f)$ is the reciprocal of a polynomial and $A(f)/S(f) \in L_2$. The original condition applies, of course, to the $S(f)$ determined by any integrable positive definite extension of $\rho(t)$, $-T \leqq t \leqq T$.

For a second example we consider the estimation of the unknown real parameters β_k which appear in

$$y(t) = \sum^{K} \beta_k s_k(t) + x(t), \qquad a \leqq t \leqq b. \tag{10}$$

Again $y(t)$ represents the observed waveform; the $s_k(t)$, $k = 1, \cdots, K$ represent known signals, and $x(t)$ is Gaussian noise. Let $a_{ki} = (s_k, \phi_i)$, assume $\sum_i (a_{ki}^2/\lambda_i) < \infty$ for $k = 1, \cdots, K$, and define the matrix

$$B = [B_{jk}], \qquad B_{jk} = \sum_i \frac{a_{ji}a_{ki}}{\lambda_i}, \qquad j, k = 1, \cdots, K$$

and the column vector

$$Z = [Z_j], \qquad Z_j = \sum_i \frac{a_{ji}y_i}{\lambda_i}, \qquad j = 1, \cdots, K.$$

The series for B_{jk} converges, and the series for Z_j converges with probability one with respect to the nominal measure μ_0. We assume B is nonsingular. The maximum-likelihood estimator $\hat{\beta}$ for the column vector $\beta = [\beta_k]$, $k = 1, \cdots, K$, with respect to μ_0, is

$$\hat{\beta} = B^{-1}Z.$$

The estimator $\hat{\beta}$ is Gaussian, unbiased and has covariance matrix with respect to μ_0,

$$E\hat{\beta}\hat{\beta}' = B^{-1}.$$

If now, as in the first example, the autocorrelation function of $x(t)$ is changed to $R_1(t, s) = R_0(t, s) + A(t, s)$ while the mean remains zero, the estimator $\hat{\beta}$ with respect to the new Gaussian measure μ_1 is unbiased but has covariance matrix

$$E_1(\hat{\beta}\hat{\beta}') = B^{-1} + B^{-1}\Delta B^{-1}$$

where the matrix Δ is given by

$$\Delta = [\Delta_j k], \qquad \Delta_j k = \sum_{i,n} \frac{a_{ji}a_{kn}}{\lambda_i\lambda_n}(A\phi_i, \phi_n).$$

If stability is to mean that the distribution of $\hat{\beta}$ with respect to μ_1 measure necessarily approaches the distribution of $\hat{\beta}$ with respect to μ_0 measure as $\|A\| \to 0$, then the condition for it is

$$\sum_i \frac{|a_{ji}|^2}{\lambda_i^2} < \infty.$$

The discussion of the stability criterion for the first example re-applies with trivial modification.

A general stability criterion. Since in the examples of the previous section the functionals are linear and the family of measures is restricted to include only Gaussian ones, the functionals have Gaussian distributions which are determined by a routine calculation of moments. In general the estimators or test functionals are not linear, as, e.g., in the problem of estimating the range of a radar target, and their distributions, even with Gaussian noise and perhaps Gaussian signals, are either unknown or known only in a form ill-adapted to further calculation. In any case, the restriction to Gaussian measures were better removed, even though the noise is nearly Gaussian, if the stability criteria are to be believable in practice. One would like, therefore, to treat detection stability in greater generality, with the expectation, of course, of less specific results.

The following informal definition is suggested as being both obvious and natural. Suppose the decision or inference made by a signal detecting or measuring device (henceforth, simply *detector*) depends on the value taken on by a functional f on a sample space of functions. The detector is *stable* if the induced probability distribution of f converges in the usual sense to its nominal distribution as the actual probability measure on the sample space converges in some reasonable sense to the nominal measure. In terms of this definition the study of detector stability becomes a direct application of results from the theory of weak convergence of probability measures on function spaces. There is available a choice of function spaces and topologies for which a well-developed theory of weak convergence of measures exists.[9] For reasons previously indicated, it seems appropriate to take the space of continuous real-valued functions, say on [0, 1], in the uniform topology. Also, $C[0, 1]$ has the attraction that it provides a relatively simple theory. We shall use certain results of Prokhorov,[10] which are stated below for convenience (the base space is specialized to be $C[0, 1]$).

We take $\mathscr{B}$ to be the Borel field of subsets of $C[0, 1]$ generated by the closed sets, and $\mathscr{M}$ to be the set of regular probability measures μ on $\mathscr{B}$. A sequence of measures $\{\mu_n\}$ from $\mathscr{M}$ converges weakly to μ, $\mu_n \Rightarrow \mu$, if for any continuous bounded functional g on $C[0, 1]$, $\int g d\mu_n \to \int g d\mu$. If ξ is a μ-almost-everywhere continuous mapping of $C[0, 1]$ into a metric space $\mathscr{R}$, it induces a regular probability measure μ^ξ in $\mathscr{R}$. For the convergence $\mu_n \Rightarrow \mu$ it is necessary and sufficient that for any real-valued μ-almost-everywhere continuous function ξ, $\mu_n^\xi \Rightarrow \mu^\xi$. The Lévy distance $L(\mu_1, \mu_2)$ between two measures μ_1 and μ_2 in $\mathscr{M}$ is defined as follows: let F be a closed subset of $C[0, 1]$ and let F^ε be the open ε-neighborhood of F,

$$F^\varepsilon = \left\{x: \inf_{x_0 \in F} |x - x_0| < \varepsilon\right\}$$

where $|x|$ is the $C[0, 1]$ norm of x. Let ε_{12} and ε_{21} be the lower bounds, respectively, of those ε for which for all closed sets $F \subset C[0, 1]$,

$$\mu_2(F) < \mu_1(F^\varepsilon) + \varepsilon \quad \text{and} \quad \mu_1(F) < \mu_2(F^\varepsilon) + \varepsilon.$$

Then $L(\mu_1, \mu_2)$ is defined to be max $(\varepsilon_{12}, \varepsilon_{21})$. Convergence of probability measures on $\mathscr{B}$ with respect to the Lévy distance is equivalent to weak convergence. Finally, a sufficient condition that a sequence $\{\mu_n\}$, $\mu_n \in \mathscr{M}$, converge weakly to a measure $\mu \in \mathscr{M}$ is that:

(1) the finite-dimensional distributions induced by μ_n converge to limit distributions, and

(2) for all n, all $t_1, t_2 \in [0, 1]$,

$$E|x(t_2) - x(t_1)|^a \leqq k|t_2 - t_1|^\alpha$$

for some fixed $a > 0$, $k > 0$, $\alpha > 1$ (Kolmogorov's condition for continuity).

Thus, if we accept the Lévy distance as a suitable indication of the closeness of two measures, a sufficient condition that a detector be stable in the sense described is that the functional f be continuous on $C[0, 1]$. This formulation does not allow much hope for actually calculating useful bounds on errors, but it does allow

[9] See, e.g., Prokhorov [12], Skorokhod [14], and Kallianpur [7].
[10] See Prokhorov [12].

comparison between what might be called the degrees of stability of two detectors. In particular, Prokhorov gives the following estimate: if for arbitrary $h > 0$ a compact subset K of $C[0, 1]$ is such that both the μ_0- and μ_1-measure of its complement is less than $h/2$, and if $\delta < h/2$ is sufficiently small that $|f(x_1) - f(x_2)| < h/2$ for all $x_1, x_2 \in K$ satisfying $|x_1 - x_2| < \delta$, then $L(\mu_0, \mu_1) \lesssim \delta$ implies that the Lévy distance between μ_0^f and μ_1^f is less than h. Thus, a rough comparison of the stability of two test functionals can be obtained from a comparison of their moduli of continuity on compact sets.

Application of the stability criterion. First, let us look again at the simple detection example already discussed. We suppose the nominal probability measure μ_0 of the noise process to be Gaussian, but no longer restrict all the family of possible measures to be Gaussian. According to the criterion proposed, the detector is stable if $f(y) = \sum(a_k y_k/\lambda_k)$ is continuous on $C[0, 1]$. The condition used previously amounted to $f(y)$ being continuous on $L_2[0, 1]$, which of course implies its continuity on $C[0, 1]$. If one for the moment thinks of the case where all the possible noise measures are Gaussian, the weakening of the condition for stability simply reflects the fact that a tighter notion of closeness of autocorrelation function is now in effect. Probably neither notion is exactly appropriate if the actual nature of estimational errors of autocorrelation is taken into account. The topology used for the space of sample functions is arbitrary; so the stability criteria developed, although they may be precise mathematically, cannot be regarded as being sharp from a practical point of view. This precautionary comment applies to all our examples.

It is likely in practice that the actual implementation of a test functional can be represented directly as an integral,

$$f(y) = \int_0^1 y(t)\, dg(t)$$

where the weighting function $g(t)$ is of bounded variation. In this case the detector is necessarily stable, and the smaller the total variation of $g(t)$, the more stable the detector. Essentially the same remarks as these apply to the linear parameter estimation problem.

The estimation of time delay of a known signal, as in the measurement of range with a radar, is a common example in which the maximum-likelihood estimator is not a linear functional. We now describe a class of problems which is a slight generalization of it and make some preliminary remarks about stability. Let

$$y(t) = bs(t, \alpha) + x(t), \qquad 0 \leq t \leq 1,$$

where $y(t)$ is the observed waveform, $s(t, \alpha)$ is for each α a known real-valued continuous function (signal), $x(t)$ is a noise process with mean zero, and b, α are unknown real parameters with α required to be in some closed finite interval. It is desired to estimate α. Assume that with the nominal measure, μ_0, $x(t)$ is

Gaussian with autocorrelation function $R_0(t, s)$. Signal and noise are expanded in terms of the eigenfunctions $\phi_n(t)$ as before, and we write

$$s_n(\alpha) = \int_0^1 s(t, \alpha)\phi_n(t)\, dt.$$

Since it is required that the estimation problem be nonsingular for the nominal noise process, the sum

$$\sum \frac{s_n^2(\alpha)}{\lambda_n}$$

must converge for all α, and without loss of generality the signal may be normalized so that this sum is equal to one for all α. Then a maximum-likelihood estimator for α is that value $\hat{\alpha}$ which maximizes

(11) $$z(\alpha) = \sum \frac{s_n(\alpha) y_n}{\lambda_n}$$

if such exists. Let b^0 and α^0 denote the true values of b and α. Then, with the measure induced from μ_0, $z(\alpha)$ is a Gaussian process with some closed finite interval as parameter set, and with mean-value and covariance functions

(12) $$Ez(\alpha) = b^0 \sum \frac{s_n(\alpha) s_n(\alpha^0)}{\lambda_n} = b^0 q(\alpha, \alpha^0)$$

and

(13) $$E[z(\alpha) - Ez(\alpha)][z(\alpha') - Ez(\alpha')] = \sum \frac{s_n(\alpha) s_n(\alpha')}{\lambda_n} = q(\alpha, \alpha')$$

respectively, where $q(\alpha, \alpha')$[11] is defined by the last equation. Since it is convenient to treat $\hat{\alpha}$ as a functional on the space of functions z, a natural first step in analyzing stability is to establish conditions so that a sequence of probability measure μ_n converging weakly to the nominal measure μ_0 on the space of sample functions induces a weakly convergent sequence of measures μ_n^z on the space of functions z. The Kolmogorov continuity condition is satisfied for the nominal induced measure on z if

$$|q(\alpha', \alpha^0) - 2q(\alpha, \alpha') + q(\alpha, \alpha^0) + (b^0)^2[q^2(\alpha', \alpha^0) - 2q(\alpha, \alpha^0)q(\alpha', \alpha^0) + q^2(\alpha, \alpha^0)]| \leqq k|\alpha' - \alpha|^p$$

for some $k > 0$, $p > 1$. Then it is sufficient, by a theorem of Prokhorov quoted in the preceding section, for $\mu_n^z \Rightarrow \mu_0^z$ that the Kolmogorov condition be met by all the μ_n with $a = 2$ (second moment form of the condition) and the same k and p as above, and that, say,

$$\sum \frac{s_n^2(\alpha)}{\lambda_n^2} < C = \text{constant for all } \alpha.$$

[11] See Kelly, Reed and Root **[8]**.

Under these conditions $z(\alpha)$ may be taken to be a process with continuous sample functions, and the measures μ_0^z and μ_n^z are regular. In a sense the stage is set for analyzing the behavior of $\hat{\alpha}(z)$ as $\mu_n \Rightarrow \mu_0$, but this is not attempted here. One simple observation, however, is the following. The function $q(\alpha, \alpha^0)$ has a local maximum at $\alpha = \alpha^0$. If for given $\delta > 0$, $M > 0$, $q(\alpha, \alpha^0) + M < q(\alpha^0, \alpha^0) - M$ whenever $|\alpha - \alpha^0| > \delta$, then

$$\text{Prob}\,\{|\hat{\alpha} - \alpha^0| < \delta\} \geqq \text{Prob}\,\{|z(\alpha)| \leqq M\}, \tag{14}$$

an estimate for the error of $\hat{\alpha}$ appropriate to the case of high signal-to-noise ratio (large b^0). Now if μ_n^z converges weakly to μ_0^z, $\mu_n^z\{|z(\alpha)| \leqq M\}$ converges to $\mu_0^z\{|z(\alpha)| \leqq M\}$ for any M for which $\mu_0^z\{\max_\alpha |z(\alpha)| = M\} = 0$, making the right side of the error estimate (14) continuous except for at most a countable set of values of M.

As a final example consider the detection of a noise-like signal in noise. The observed waveform $y(t)$ is a sample from one of two random processes, the first representing, say, noise alone, the second, signal plus noise. The nominal probability measure for the first process is μ_0, for the second, ν_0. We assume both μ_0 and ν_0 are Gaussian and have mean zero, and that they are strongly equivalent. We want to find a condition for the stability of the maximum-likelihood test between the two hypotheses. A formula for the likelihood ratio given by Pitcher[12] is taken as the starting point.

Let R_0 be the integral operator on $L_2[0, 1]$ previously defined, associated with μ_0, and Q_0 the corresponding integral operator associated with ν_0. Since the processes are equivalent, $Q_0^{1/2}R_0^{-1/2}$ has a bounded extension X. Again, since the processes are equivalent, $I - X^*X$ is Hilbert–Schmidt; and we let λ_n and $\psi_n(t)$ be the eigenvalues and associated (orthonormal) eigenfunctions of X^*X. $R_0^{-1/2}$ is densely-defined, so there is a sequence $\{\psi_{nj}\}_j$, for each n, such that $\psi_{nj} \in \mathscr{D}(R_0^{-1/2})$ and $\psi_{nj} \to \psi_n$ (strongly, in $L_2[0, 1]$) as $j \to \infty$. Define

$$\phi_{nj}(x) = \int_0^1 y(t)[R_0^{-1/2}\psi_{nj}](t)\,dt. \tag{15}$$

Then, for each n, the ϕ_{nj} converge in mean square with respect both to μ_0 and ν_0 to limit $\theta_n(x)$. The likelihood ratio (derivative of μ_0 with respect to ν_0) is

$$\frac{d\mu_0}{d\nu_0}(y) = \exp\left[\frac{1}{2}\sum\theta_n^2(y)\left(\frac{1}{\lambda_n} - 1\right) + \log\lambda_n\right]$$

or, if $\sum|1/\lambda_n - 1| < \infty$, the case of strong equivalence,

$$\log\frac{d\mu_0}{d\nu_0}(y) = \sum\log\lambda_n + \frac{1}{2}\sum\theta_n^2(y)\left(\frac{1}{\lambda_n} - 1\right). \tag{16}$$

---

[12] See Pitcher [11], also Root [13].

It is therefore sufficient to consider the functional

(17) $$f(y) = \sum \theta_n^2(y)\left(\frac{1}{\lambda_n} - 1\right).$$

We show now that if the sum

(18) $$\sum_n \left(\int_0^1 |[R_0^{-1/2}\psi_{nj}](t)|\, dt\right)^2 \left|\frac{1}{\lambda_n} - 1\right|$$

converges uniformly for $j = 1, 2, \cdots$ to a limit $B_j < B$, then $f(y)$ as given by (17) is a stable test functional.

Since the ϕ_{nj} converge in mean square to θ_n with respect to μ_0 and ν_0, one can find a subsequence of the j's (which will not be relabeled) and a subset C_0' of $C[0, 1]$ of μ_0- and ν_0-measure one such that $\phi_{nj}(y)$ converges to $\theta_n(y)$, for every $y \in C_0'$ and for all n. Since $\sum|1/\lambda_n - 1|$ converges, and since the θ_k are independent Gaussian random variables with respect to μ_0 with $E_0\theta_k = 0$, $E_0\theta_k^2 = 1$, the sum $\sum\theta_n^2(1/\lambda_n - 1)$ converges with probability one with respect to μ_0, and hence with respect to ν_0. Hence there is a set $C_0 \subset C_0'$, $\mu_0 C_0 = \nu_0 C_0 = 1$, such that $\sum\theta_n^2(y)(1/\lambda_n - 1)$ converges for all $y \in C_0$.

The sums

(19) $$f_j(y) = \sum_n \phi_{nj}^2(y)\left(\frac{1}{\lambda_n} - 1\right), \qquad j = 1, 2, \cdots,$$

converge uniformly in j for all $y \in C[0, 1]$ by the condition (18) since

$$|\phi_{nj}(y)| \leqq |y| \int_0^1 |[R^{-1/2}\psi_{nj}](t)|\, dt.$$

Furthermore, for $y, \eta \in C[0, 1]$,

$$|\phi_{nj}^2(y + \eta) - \phi_{nj}^2(y)| \leqq 2|\eta||y| \left(\int_0^1 |[R^{-1/2}\psi_{jn}](t)|\, dt\right)^2 + |\eta|^2 \left(\int_0^1 |[R^{-1/2}\psi_{jn}](t)|\, dt\right)^2$$

so that

(20) $$\left|\sum_n \phi_{nj}^2(y)\left(\frac{1}{\lambda_n} - 1\right) - \sum_n \phi_{nj}^2(y + \eta)\left(\frac{1}{\lambda_n} - 1\right)\right| \leqq 2|\eta|\, |y| B + |\eta|^2 B.$$

The functionals $f_j(y)$ converge a.e. with respect to μ_0 to $f(y)$. In fact, for $y \in C_0$ and arbitrary $\varepsilon > 0$, one can choose N_0 sufficiently large that

$$\left|\sum_{N_0}^{\infty} \theta_n^2(y)\left(\frac{1}{\lambda_n} - 1\right)\right| < \frac{\varepsilon}{3},$$

$$\left|\sum_{N_0}^{\infty} \phi_{nj}^2(y)\left(\frac{1}{\lambda_n} - 1\right)\right| < \frac{\varepsilon}{3}, \qquad j = 1, 2, \cdots,$$

and then choose j_0 sufficiently large that

$$|\theta_n^2(y) - \phi_{nj}^2(y)| < \frac{\varepsilon}{3N_0\left(\dfrac{1}{\lambda_n} - 1\right)}, \; n = 1, \cdots, N_0, \; j > j_0.$$

Then $|f(y) - f_j(y)| < \varepsilon, j > j_0$.

Now suppose there is a sequence of probability measures $\{\mu_n\}$ on $C[0, 1]$ which converge weakly to μ_0 and all of which are equivalent to μ_0. Then, given $h > 0$, one can choose a compact set $K_h \subset C[0, 1]$ such that $\mu_n(C[0, 1] - K_h) < h/2$ for all n. Let $|y| < M$ for $y \in K_h$. Then choose $\varepsilon > 0$ small enough so that $2\varepsilon MB + \varepsilon^2 B < h/2$. It follows that if the Lévy distance between μ_n and μ_0 is less than min $(\varepsilon, h/2)$, then the Lévy distance between the corresponding induced distributions of $f_j(y)$, $\mu_n^{f_j}$ and $\mu_0^{f_j}$ respectively, is less than h for all $j = 1, 2, \cdots$. Since the μ_n are all equivalent to μ_0, the functionals f_j converge a.e. $[\mu_n]$ to f, and hence the distributions $\mu_n^{f_j}$ converge in Lévy metric to μ_n^f. Finally then, if $L(\mu_n, \mu_0)$ is less than min $(\varepsilon, h/2)$, $L(\mu_n^f, \mu_0^f) \leqq h$. The same argument shows that if $\{\nu_n\}$ is a sequence of probability measures on $C[0, 1]$ which converge weakly to ν_0, and are equivalent to ν_0, then $\nu_n^f \Rightarrow \nu_0^f$.

The condition (18) is unfortunately impractical, largely because the formula for the likelihood ratio has already considerable implicit complexity. In special cases where the derivative of the two nominal Gaussian measures can be written more explicitly (as, e.g., when the θ_n's are given directly) it can obviously be simplified.

For example, in the relatively trivial case that R_0 and Q_0 have the same eigenfunctions with eigenvalues $\{\mu_n\}$, $\{\eta_n\}$, respectively, the condition (18) reduces to the condition that

$$\sum_n \left|\frac{\mu_n - \eta_n}{\mu_n \eta_n}\right| < \infty.$$

Concluding remark. The phenomenon that a statistical inference procedure delicately adjusted to certain underlying statistics may be very sensitive to changes in those statistics is well recognized. It suggests the question, of interest to statisticians, of when to forego parametric methods altogether. We have not, of course, touched on this question here, but have concerned ourselves only with the damage incurred by parametric inferences as the underlying statistics are changed. In many detection-theory problems it is desirable to introduce some degree of parametrization.

The actual appearance of instability as defined here seems nearly impossible. The examples indicate that the infinite-dimensionality of the observations must be fully exploited in ways which can hardly be implemented for the detector to be completely unstable.

Bibliography

1. E. J. Akutowicz, *On extrapolating a positive definite function from a finite interval*, Math. Scand. 7 (1959), 157–169.

2. A. V. Balakrishnan, *Estimation and detection theory for multiple stochastic processes*, J. Math. Anal. Appl. **1** (1960), 386–410.

3. Yu. K. Belyaev, *Continuity and Hölder's conditions for sample functions of stationary Gaussian processes*, Proc. 4th Berkeley Sympos. Math. Statist. and Prob., Vol. II, pp. 23–25, Univ. of California Press, Berkeley, Calif., 1960.

4. R. D. Dobrushin, *Properties of sample functions of a stationary Gaussian process*, Theor. Probability Appl. **5** (1960), 120–122.

5. U. Grenander, *Stochastic processes and statistical inference*, Ark. Mat. **1** (1960), 195–277.

6. J. Hajek, *On linear statistical problems in stochastic processes*, Czechoslovak Math. J. **12** (**87**) (1962), 404–444.

7. G. Kallianpur, *The topology of weak convergence of probability measures*, J. Math. Mech. **10** (1961), 947–969.

8. E. J. Kelly, I. S. Reed and W. L. Root, *The detection of radar echoes in noise*. I, II, J. Soc. Indust. Appl. Math. **8** (1960), 309–341, 481–507.

9. E. Parzen, *Probability density functionals and reproducing kernel Hilbert spaces*, Proc. Sympos. Time Series Analysis (Brown Univ., 1962), pp. 155–169, Wiley, New York, 1963.

10. ———, *An approach to time series analysis*, Ann. Math. Statist. **32** (1961), 951–989.

11. T. Pitcher, Unpublished memorandum, 1960.

12. Yu. V. Prokhorov, *Convergence of random processes and limit theorems in probability theory*, Theor. Probability Appl. **1** (1956), 157–214.

13. W. L. Root, *Singular Gaussian measures in detection theory*, Proc. Sympos. Time Series Analysis (Brown Univ., 1962), pp. 292–316, Wiley, New York, 1963.

14. A. V. Skorokhod, *On the differentiability of measures which correspond to stochastic processes*. I, Theor. Probability Appl. **2** (1957), 407–432.

15. A. M. Yaglom, *On the equivalence or perpendicularity of two gaussian probability measures in function space*, Proc. Sympos. Time Series Analysis (Brown Univ., 1962), pp. 327–349, Wiley, New York, 1963.

UNIVERSITY OF MICHIGAN,
ANN ARBOR, MICHIGAN

THE CONSTRUCTION OF A CLASS OF STATIONARY MARKOFF PROCESSES

BY

EUGENE WONG

Introduction. We take a forward, or Fokker–Planck, equation of diffusion theory

$$\frac{\partial^2}{\partial x^2}[B(x)p] - \frac{\partial}{\partial x}[A(x)p] = \frac{\partial p}{\partial t}, \qquad p = p(x|x_0, t), \qquad 0 < t < \infty, \tag{1}$$

on an interval I with end points x_1 and x_2, and consider the solution $p(x|x_0, t)$ corresponding to an initial value $\delta(x - x_0)$, i.e., the principal solution. The function $B(x)$ can be interpreted as a variance [**15**], and is therefore non-negative on (x_1, x_2). In general, we take, as boundary conditions, those corresponding to reflecting barriers [**9**],

$$\frac{\partial}{\partial x}[B(x)p] - A(x)p = 0, \qquad x = x_1, x_2. \tag{2}$$

The unique solution $p(x|x_0, t)$ is the density function for the transitional probability of a stationary Markoff process $X(t)$ in one dimension,

$$\Pr\{X(t+\tau) \in E | X(\tau) = x_0\} = \int_E p(x|x_0, t)\, dx, \qquad x_0 \in I, \qquad E \subseteq I. \tag{3}$$

Next, we consider the class of first-order probability density functions $W(x)$ which satisfy the Pearson equation [**4**]

$$\frac{dW(x)}{dx} = \frac{ax + b}{cx^2 + dx + e} W(x). \tag{4}$$

In §1 we shall show that by suitably identifying the functions $A(x)$ and $B(x)$ in (1) with the polynomials $ax + b$ and $cx^2 + dx + e$ in (4), a class of stationary Markoff processes is constructed for which

$$\lim_{t \to \infty} p(x|x_0, t) = \int_{x_1}^{x_2} W(x_0) p(x|x_0, t)\, dx_0 = W(x), \tag{5}$$

where $W(x)$ satisfies (4). The identification scheme is such that the Pearson equation (4) uniquely specifies the Fokker–Planck equation (1). In a sense, the Pearson equation serves a rather natural role in bridging the gap between the first-order statistical description characterized by $W(x)$ and the transitional properties represented by $p(x|x_0, t)$.

In §2 we shall exhibit some specific processes of this class. These examples include several well-known ones, as well as some that appear not to have been investigated previously.

In §3 we shall examine some properties of processes of this class and give some physical interpretation to processes in §2. Finally, the distribution of some functionals involving processes of this class are discussed in §4.

1. **Construction.** We note that a straightforward application of separations of variables to (1) yields an equation of the Sturm–Liouville type

$$\frac{d}{dx}\left[B(x)\rho(x)\frac{d\varphi(x)}{dx}\right] + \lambda\rho(x)\varphi(x) = 0. \tag{6}$$

The boundary conditions (2) imply that

$$B(x)\rho(x)\frac{d\varphi(x)}{dx} = 0, \qquad x = x_1, x_2. \tag{7}$$

The function $\rho(x)$ is taken to be non-negative on (x_1, x_2) and satisfies

$$\frac{d}{dx}[B(x)\rho(x)] - A(x)\rho(x) = 0. \tag{8}$$

A comparison of (8) and (4) shows that they become identical if we make the following identifications:

$$\rho(x) = W(x), \tag{9}$$

$$B(x) = \beta(cx^2 + dx + e) \tag{10}$$

and

$$A(x) = \frac{dB(x)}{dx} + \beta(ax + b), \tag{11}$$

subject to the condition that $B(x)$ be non-negative on (x_1, x_2). It is clear that through (10) and (11), $A(x)$ and $B(x)$ are uniquely specified by the Pearson equation (4) up to a common positive multiplicative constant β, which represents a scaling factor in the variable t.

With the substitution of $W(x)$ for $\rho(x)$, (6) and (7) become

$$\frac{d}{dx}\left[B(x)W(x)\frac{d\varphi(x)}{dx}\right] + \lambda W(x)\varphi(x) = 0, \tag{12}$$

and

$$B(x)W(x)\frac{d\varphi(x)}{dx} = 0, \qquad x = x_1, x_2. \tag{13}$$

From the classical Sturm–Liouville theory it is known that the spectrum of (12) is discrete if x_1 and x_2 are finite. If one or both of the boundaries are infinite, then a continuous range of eigenvalues may be present. In terms of the solutions of (12) the principal solution $p(x|x_0, t)$ of (1) can be written as

$$p(x|x_0, t) = W(x)\left\{\sum_n e^{-\lambda_n t}\varphi_n(x_0)\varphi_n(x) + \int e^{-\lambda t}\varphi(\lambda, x_0)\varphi(\lambda, x)\,d\lambda\right\}, \tag{14}$$

where the summation is taken over all discrete eigenvalues and the integral is taken over the continuous range of eigenvalues. The eigenfunctions $\varphi(x)$ in (14) are assumed to be normalized so that corresponding to discrete eigenvalues we have

$$\int_{x_1}^{x_2} W(x)\varphi_m(x)\varphi_n(x) = \delta_{mn}, \tag{15}$$

and corresponding to continuous eigenvalues

$$\int_{x_1}^{x_2} W(x)\varphi(\lambda, x)\varphi(\lambda', x)\,dx = \delta(\lambda - \lambda'). \tag{16}$$

It can be verified directly that corresponding to boundary conditions (13), the Sturm–Liouville equation (12) has at least one discrete eigenvalue, namely, $\lambda = 0$ with corresponding eigenfunction $\varphi(x) = 1$. In addition, if we assume that the spectrum is discrete, then

$$\begin{aligned}\lambda_n &= -\int_{x_1}^{x_2} \varphi_n(x)\frac{d}{dx}\left[B(x)W(x)\frac{d\varphi_n(x)}{dx}\right]dx \\ &= \int_{x_1}^{x_2} B(x)W(x)\left[\frac{d\varphi_n(x)}{dx}\right]^2 dx,\end{aligned} \tag{17}$$

where we have made use of the boundary conditions (13). Since $B(x)W(x)[d\varphi(x)/dx]^2$ is non-negative on (x_1, x_2), it follows from (17) that

$$\lambda_n \geqq 0. \tag{18}$$

Furthermore, the case where a continuous range of eigenvalues is present can be arrived at by taking cases with finite boundaries, thus with discrete spectra, and considering the limiting situation when one or both of the boundaries becomes infinite. It is clear that, in general, we have

$$\lambda \geqq 0. \tag{19}$$

Further, even in the limiting cases $\lambda = 0$ must remain a discrete eigenvalue, since the corresponding eigenfunction $\varphi = 1$ is always square-integrable with respect to the density function $W(x)$. It follows, from the fact that $\lambda = 0$, $\varphi = 1$ is always a discrete solution, that

$$\int_{x_1}^{x_2} p(x|x_0, t)W(x_0)\,dx_0 = W(x). \tag{20}$$

Further, from the fact that $\lambda = 0$ is also the minimum eigenvalue, it follows that

$$\lim_{t\to\infty} p(x|x_0, t) = W(x). \tag{21}$$

The construction procedure is seen to consist of two parts. First, starting with a first-order probability density function $W(x)$ and a corresponding Pearson equation, we identify the functions $A(x)$ and $B(x)$ in (1) with the polynomials in the Pearson equation according to (10) and (11). Secondly, the density function $p(x|x_0, t)$ of the transitional probability is obtained as the principal solution to (1). (For a brief discussion along similar lines, see Kolmogorov [**13**].)

2. **Some specific processes.** If we consider the roots of the equation $B(x) = 0$, five distinct situations are possible, namely: (a) no root, in which case $B(x)$ is a constant, (b) a single real root, (c) two unequal real roots, (d) two equal real roots, and (e) a pair of complex-conjugate roots. In this section we shall consider six specific processes which, while by no means exhausting all the possibilities, include at least one example of each of the five situations corresponding to the roots of $B(x) = 0$. In every case except one, the choice of boundaries will be a natural one in that each boundary is either at a real root of "$B(x) = 0$" or is infinite. Without loss of generality we shall set $\beta = 1$, thus normalizing the time scale.

A. Consider the first-order density function

$$W(x) = e^{-x}, \qquad 0 \leqq x < \infty, \tag{22}$$

with a corresponding Pearson equation

$$\frac{dW(x)}{dx} = -\frac{1}{1} W(x).$$

The resulting Fokker–Planck equation is

$$\frac{\partial^2 p}{\partial x^2} + \frac{\partial p}{\partial x} = \frac{\partial p}{\partial t}$$

with boundary condition

$$\frac{d}{dx} p(x|x_0, t) = 0, \qquad x = 0.$$

The principal solution $p(x|x_0, t)$ is given by

$$p(x|x_0, t) = e^{-x}\left\{1 + e^{-t/4}\int_0^\infty e^{-\mu^2 t}\psi(\mu, x_0)\psi(\mu, x)\, d\mu\right\}, \tag{23}$$

where

$$\psi(\mu, x) = \sqrt{\frac{2}{\pi}}\,\frac{2\mu}{\sqrt{1 + 4\mu^2}}\left[\cos \mu x - \frac{1}{2\mu}\sin \mu x\right] e^{x/2}.$$

The function $p(x|x_0, t)$ can also be written as

$$\begin{aligned} p(x|x_0, t) = {} & \frac{1}{2\sqrt{\pi t}} \exp\left[-\tfrac{1}{2}(x - x_0)\right] \exp\left[-\tfrac{1}{4}t\right]\left\{\exp\left[-\frac{(x - x_0)^2}{4t}\right]\right. \\ & \left. + \exp\left[-\frac{(x + x_0)^2}{4t}\right]\right\} + \frac{1}{\sqrt{\pi}} e^{-x}\int_{(x+x_0-t)/2\sqrt{t}}^\infty e^{-z^2}\, dz. \end{aligned} \tag{24}$$

B. Let the first-order density function be given by

$$W(x) = \frac{1}{\sqrt{2\pi}} \exp\left[-\tfrac{1}{2}x^2\right], \qquad -\infty < x < \infty, \tag{25}$$

with an associated Pearson equation

$$\frac{dW(x)}{dx} = -\frac{x}{1} W(x).$$

The resulting Fokker–Planck equation can be written as

$$\frac{\partial^2 p}{\partial x^2} + \frac{\partial}{\partial x}(xp) = \frac{\partial p}{\partial t}.$$

The density function $p(x|x_0, t)$ is given by

$$p(x|x_0, t) = \frac{1}{\sqrt{2\pi}} e^{-x^2/2} \sum_{n=0}^{\infty} \frac{e^{-nt}}{n!} H_n(x_0) H_n(x), \tag{26}$$

where $H_n(x)$ are the Hermite polynomials **[14]**

$$H_n(x) = (-1)^n e^{-x^2/2} \frac{d^n}{dx^n}(e^{-x^2/2}).$$

By the use of Mehler's formula we can write $p(x|x_0, t)$ as

$$p(x|x_0, t) = \frac{1}{\sqrt{2\pi(1 - e^{-2t})}} \exp\left[-\frac{1}{2(1 - e^{-2t})}(x - x_0 e^{-t})^2\right]. \tag{27}$$

C. Consider the first-order density function

$$W(x) = \frac{x^\alpha}{\Gamma(\alpha + 1)} e^{-x}, \qquad \alpha > -1, 0 \leqq x < \infty \tag{28}$$

with corresponding Pearson equation

$$\frac{dW(x)}{dx} = \left(\frac{\alpha - x}{x}\right) W(x).$$

The associated Fokker–Planck equation is

$$\frac{\partial^2}{\partial x^2}(xp) - \frac{\partial}{\partial x}[(\alpha + 1 - x)p] = \frac{\partial p}{\partial t}.$$

The principal solution $p(x|x_0, t)$ is given by

$$p(x|x_0, t) = x^\alpha e^{-x} \sum_{n=0}^{\infty} \frac{n!}{\Gamma(n + \alpha + 1)} e^{-n\beta t} L_n^\alpha(x_0) L_n^\alpha(x), \tag{29}$$

where

$$L_n^\alpha(x) = \frac{1}{n!} x^{-\alpha} e^x \frac{d^n}{dx^n}(x^\alpha e^{-x}),$$

are the Laguerre polynomials [14]. The function $p(x|x_0, t)$ can also be written as

$$(30)\quad \begin{aligned} p(x|x_0, t) &= \frac{1}{1-e^{-t}}\left(\frac{x}{x_0 \exp[-t]}\right)^{\alpha/2} \\ &\quad \cdot \exp\left[-\frac{1}{(1-e^{-t})}(x + x_0 e^{-t})\right] I_\alpha\left(\frac{2\, e^{-t/2}\sqrt{x_0 x}}{1-\exp[-t]}\right), \end{aligned}$$

where $I_\alpha(z)$ is the modified Bessel function.

D. Corresponding to the situation when "$B(x) = 0$" has two unequal real roots, we take $W(x)$ to be

$$(31)\quad \begin{aligned} W(x) &= \frac{\Gamma(\alpha+\gamma+2)}{\Gamma(\alpha+1)\Gamma(\gamma+1)} \frac{(1+x)^\alpha(1-x)^\gamma}{2^{\alpha+\gamma+1}}, \\ &\alpha, \gamma \geqq -1, \; -1 \leqq x \leqq +1, \end{aligned}$$

with associated Pearson equation

$$\frac{dW(x)}{dx} = \frac{(\alpha-\gamma)-(\alpha+\gamma)x}{(1-x^2)} W(x).$$

The resulting Fokker–Planck equation becomes

$$\frac{\partial^2}{\partial x^2}[(1-x^2)p] + (\alpha+\gamma+2)\frac{\partial}{\partial x}[xp] - (\alpha-\gamma)\frac{\partial p}{\partial x} = \frac{\partial p}{\partial t}.$$

The solution $p(x|x_0, t)$ is given by

$$(32)\quad p(x|x_0, t) = \frac{(1+x)^\alpha(1-x)^\gamma}{2^{\alpha+\gamma+1}} \sum_{n=0}^{\infty} e^{-n(n+\alpha+\gamma+1)t} A_n P_n^{\alpha,\gamma}(x_0) P_n^{\alpha,\gamma}(x),$$

where $P_n^{\alpha,\gamma}(x)$ are the Jacobi polynomials[1] [14]

$$P_n^{\alpha,\gamma}(x) = \frac{(-1)^n}{2^n}(1+x)^\alpha(1-x)^\gamma \frac{d^n}{dx^n}[(1+x)^{\alpha+n}(1-x)^{\gamma+n}],$$

and

$$A_n = \frac{(2n+\alpha+\gamma+1)\Gamma(n+\alpha+\gamma+1)}{\Gamma(n+\alpha+1)\Gamma(n+\gamma+1)n!}.$$

E. Corresponding to a pair of complex conjugate-roots of "$B(x) = 0$," we take

$$(33)\quad W(x) = \frac{\Gamma(\alpha+\frac{1}{2})}{\Gamma(\frac{1}{2})\Gamma(\alpha)}(1+x^2)^{-(\alpha+1/2)}, \qquad \alpha > 0, \; -\infty < x < \infty,$$

and associate with it a Pearson equation

$$\frac{dW(x)}{dx} = -\frac{(2\alpha+1)x}{(1+x^2)} W(x).$$

---

[1] The normalization for $P_n^{\alpha,\gamma}$ here is not the conventional one.

The Fokker–Planck equation for this case becomes

$$\frac{d^2}{dx^2}[(1+x^2)p] + (2\alpha - 1)\frac{d}{dx}(xp) = \frac{\partial p}{\partial t}.$$

The Sturm–Liouville equation (12) in this case has $N+1$ discrete eigenvalues ($\alpha - 1 \leqq N < \alpha$), and a continuous range of eigenvalues. More precisely, we have

$$\lambda_n = n(2\alpha - n), \qquad n = 0, 1, 2, \cdots, N,$$

and

$$\lambda = \alpha^2 + \mu^2, \qquad \mu \geqq 0.$$

The solution $p(x|x_0, t)$ can be written as

$$\begin{aligned} p(x|x_0, t) = (1+x^2)^{-(\alpha+1/2)} \Bigg\{ & \frac{1}{\pi}\sum_{n=0}^{N} \frac{(\alpha - n)}{n!\,\Gamma(2\alpha + 1 - n)} e^{-n(2\alpha-n)t}\theta_n(x_0)\theta_n(x) \\ & + \frac{1}{2\pi}\int_0^\infty e^{-(\alpha^2+\mu^2)t}[\psi(\mu, x_0)\psi(-\mu, x) + \psi(-\mu, x_0)\psi(\mu, x)]\, d\mu \Bigg\}, \end{aligned} \tag{34}$$

where

$$\theta_n(x) = 2^{\alpha-n}\Gamma(\alpha - n + \tfrac{1}{2})(-1)^n(1+x^2)^{\alpha+1/2}\frac{d^n}{dx^n}[(1+x^2)^{n-\alpha-1/2}], \tag{35}$$

are polynomials of degree n, and $\psi(\mu, x)$ is given by

$$\psi(\mu, x) = (x + \sqrt{1+x^2})^{i\mu}(1+x^2)^{1/2}{}_2F_1\left(-\alpha, \alpha+1; 1+i\mu; \frac{1}{2} + \frac{1}{2}\frac{x}{\sqrt{1+x^2}}\right),$$

${}_2F_1$ being the Gauss hypergeometric series [7].

For $\alpha = K$, a positive integer, $p(x|x_0, t)$ can be written somewhat more explicitly as

$$\begin{aligned} p(x|x_0, t) = \frac{1}{(1+x^2)^{K+1/2}} \Bigg\{ & [(1+x_0^2)(1+x^2)]^{K/2}\frac{1}{2\sqrt{\pi t}} e^{-K^2 t} e^{-u^2} \\ & + \frac{1}{\pi}\sum_{n=0}^{K-1}\frac{(K-n)}{n!\,\Gamma(2K+1-n)} e^{-n(2K-n)t}\theta_n(x_0)\theta_n(x)f_n(x_0, x, t)\Bigg\}, \end{aligned} \tag{36}$$

where

$$u = u(x_0, x, t) = \frac{\text{arc sinh}\, x - \text{arc sinh}\, x_0}{2\sqrt{t}},$$

$$f_n(x_0, x, t) = \frac{1}{\sqrt{\pi}}\int_{u-(K-n)\sqrt{t}}^{u+(K-n)\sqrt{t}} e^{-z^2}\, dz,$$

and θ_n are polynomials defined by (35).

F. Corresponding to the situation where "$B(x) = 0$" has a double real root, we consider the first-order density function

$$W(x) = \frac{1}{\Gamma(2\alpha)} x^{-(2\alpha+1)} e^{-1/x}, \qquad \alpha > 0, 0 \leqq x < \infty, \tag{37}$$

with corresponding Pearson equation

$$\frac{dW(x)}{dx} = \frac{1 - (2\alpha + 1)x}{x^2} W(x).$$

The resulting Fokker–Planck equation is given by

$$\frac{\partial^2}{\partial x^2}[x^2 p] - \frac{\partial}{\partial x}\{[1 - (2\alpha - 1)x]p\} = \frac{\partial p}{\partial t}.$$

The solution of the Sturm–Liouville equation for this case consists of $N + 1$ discrete eigenvalues ($\alpha - 1 \leqq N < \alpha$), and a continuous range of eigenvalues:

$$\lambda_n = n(2\alpha - n), \qquad n = 0, 1, \cdots, N,$$
$$\lambda = \alpha^2 + \mu^2, \qquad \mu \geqq 0.$$

The transitional probability density function $p(x|x_0, t)$ is found to be

$$\begin{aligned} p(x|x_0, t) = x^{-(2\alpha+1)} e^{-1/x} \Bigg\{ & \sum_{n=0}^{N} \frac{2(\alpha - n)}{\Gamma(2\alpha + 1 - n)} \frac{1}{n!} e^{-n(2\alpha-n)t} \theta_n(x_0)\theta_n(x) \\ & + \frac{1}{2\pi} \int_0^\infty e^{-(\alpha^2+\mu^2)t} A(\mu)\psi(\mu, x_0)\psi(\mu, x)\, d\mu \Bigg\}. \end{aligned} \tag{38}$$

Here, $\theta_n(x)$ are orthogonal polynomials of degree n,

$$\theta_n(x) = (-1)^n x^{2\alpha+1} e^{1/x} \frac{d^n}{dx^n}(x^{2n-2\alpha-1} e^{-1/x}),$$

and

$$\psi(\mu, x) = {}_2F_0(-\alpha - i\mu, -\alpha + i\mu, -x),$$

${}_2F_0$ being the generalized hypergeometric series [7]. Alternative representations of $\psi(\mu, x)$ in terms of confluent hypergeometric functions follow from properties of ${}_2F_0$, e.g.,

$${}_2F_0(-\alpha - i\mu, -\alpha + i\mu, -x) = x^{(\alpha+i\mu)}\Psi\left(-\frac{\alpha}{2} - i\mu, 1 - 2i\mu, \frac{1}{x}\right),$$

where Ψ is the hypergeometric Ψ-function [7]. The quantity $A(\mu)$ is a normalization factor given by

$$A(\mu) = \frac{\Gamma(-\alpha + i\mu)\Gamma(-\alpha - i\mu)}{\Gamma(i\mu)\Gamma(-i\mu)}.$$

3. **Physical interpretation and properties.** The processes outlined in (A) through (D) of §2 are familiar processes with some well-known interpretations. The process of (2 A) represents Brownian motion in a constant force-field (e.g., a gravitational field) with a reflecting barrier [**3**; **11**]. The process of (2 B) is the Ornstein–Uhlenbeck process.

The process of (2 C) has been studied in connection with population growth [**8**]. For $\alpha = N/2 - 1$, $N = 1, 2, \cdots$, it can also be considered as the sum of the squares of N independent and identical Ornstein–Uhlenbeck processes, or alternatively as the square of the radial component of a Brownian motion in N dimensions with radial restoring force proportional to the distance from the origin [**12**].

The process of (2 D), whose transitional density function involves Jacobi polynomials, has been studied by Bochner, and Karlin and McGregor [**2**; **12**]. For special values of the parameters α and γ, $\alpha = \gamma = (N - 3)/2$, $N = 2, 3, \cdots$, a geometric interpretation of the Jacobi diffusion process in terms of Brownian motion on a unit sphere in N dimensions has been given by Karlin and McGregor. It has also been used in connection with biological applications (see Karlin and McGregor).

The process of (2 E) and (2 F) appear to be new. It is of some interest to note that the density function $W(x)$ in (2 E) and (2 F), for $\alpha = \frac{1}{2}$ and $\alpha = \frac{1}{4}$ respectively, become $1/\pi(1 + x^2)$ and $(1/\sqrt{\pi})x^{-3/2}\, e^{-1/x}$. Both of these are known to be density functions for stable distributions [**10**].

The process $X(t)$ of (2 E) can be interpreted in terms of a Langevin type stochastic differential equation. Specifically, if we make the transformation $Y(t) = \sinh X(t)$, then $Y(t)$ is the solution of a differential equation [**6**]

$$dY(t) + 2\alpha \tanh Y(t)\, dt = dU(t),$$

where $U(t)$ is a Brownian motion process. The term $2\alpha \tanh Y(t)$ is interesting from the point of view of application, since it approximates a saturating linear element (e.g., a saturating linear amplifier).

For $\alpha = K$ an integer, the form of $p(x|x_0, t)$ given by (36) suggests that a simple interpretation of the process (2 E) in terms of Brownian motion should be possible. However, no such interpretation has yet been found.

The process $X(t)$ of (2 F) can also be interpreted in terms of a differential equation

$$dY + [2\alpha - \exp(-Y)]\, dt = dU(t),$$

where $Y(t) = \ln X(t)$ and $U(t)$ is a Brownian motion process.

A feature of processes of this class is that the transitional probability density function can always be represented in terms of relatively simple classical orthogonal functions. This is due to the fact that $B(x)$ and $A(x)$ are chosen to be polynomials of second and first degrees, thus simplifying the resulting Sturm–Liouville equation. In particular, we note the presence of classical orthogonal polynomials. The transitional probability density function $p(x|x_0, t)$ given by (26), (29) and (32) have the following common form of representation:

$$p(x|x_0, t) = W(x) \sum_{n=0}^{\infty} e^{-\lambda_n t} \theta_n(x_0) \theta_n(x), \tag{39}$$

where $\theta_n(x)$ are normalized orthogonal polynomials. Representations of second-order probability density functions as a single sum of orthogonal polynomials were studied by Barrett and Lampard [**1**], where they discussed the properties and application of such density functions. It has been shown [**16**] that if $p(x|x_0, t)$ satisfies a Fokker–Planck equation of the form given by (1), and if

$$\lim_{t \to \infty} p(x|x_0, t) = W(x),$$

then $p(x|x_0, t)$ has the representation given by (39) if and only if

(1) $B(x) = ax^2 + bx + c$, $A(x) = dx + e$,
(2) $B(x_1)W(x_1) = B(x_2)W(x_2) = 0$,
(3) $\int_{x_1}^{x_2} W(x)x^n \, dx < \infty$, $x = 0, 1, 2, \cdots$.

In effect, (2 B), (2 C) and (2 D) exhaust all such possibilities.

A property, satisfied by most of the processes discussed in §2, is that the normalized covariance function is an exponential function of t, i.e.,

$$E\left(\frac{X(t+\tau) - m}{\sigma}\right)\left(\frac{X(\tau) - m}{\sigma}\right) = e^{-\beta t}; \qquad \beta > 0, t \geqq 0, \tag{40}$$

where m and σ^2 are the mean and variance respectively. This property has long been known for Ornstein–Uhlenbeck process, and is closely connected with the question of representing $p(x|x_0, t)$ in terms of orthogonal polynomials. It can be shown that if the transitional probability density function $p(x|x_0, t)$ of a Markoff process $X(t)$ satisfies (1) and if $\lim_{t \to \infty} p(x|x_0, t) = W(x)$, then (40) is satisfied if and only if

(1) $B(x) = ax^2 + bx + c$, $A(x) = dx + e$,
(2) $B(x_1)W(x_1) = B(x_2)W(x_2) = 0$,
(3) $\int_{x_1}^{x_2} W(x)x^n \, dx < \infty$, $n = 0, 1, 2$.

In addition to (2 B), (2 C) and (2 D), the process of (2 E) for $\alpha > 1$, and the process of (2 F) for $\alpha > 1$, also satisfy (40). In each of these two cases the representation of $p(x|x_0, t)$ is in part in terms of a sum of orthogonal polynomials.

4. The distribution of functionals of Markoff processes. We consider a functional of the form

$$Y(t) = \int_0^t f[X(\tau)] \, d\tau, \tag{41}$$

where $X(\tau)$ is a stationary Markoff process of the class being considered in this paper. Darling and Siegert [**5**] have defined a function

$$r(x|x_0, t, \eta) \equiv E\{e^{-\eta Y(t)} | X(0) = x_0, X(t) = x\} \cdot p(x|x_0, t),$$

which in our case is the principal solution of

$$\frac{\partial^2}{\partial x^2}[B(x)r] - \frac{\partial}{\partial x}[A(x)r] - \eta f(x)r = \frac{\partial r}{\partial t}. \tag{42}$$

The corresponding Sturm–Liouville equation becomes

$$\frac{d}{dx}\left[B(x)W(x)\frac{d\varphi(x)}{dx}\right] + W(x)[\lambda - \eta f(x)]\varphi(x) = 0. \tag{43}$$

A comparison of (43) and (12) shows that the only difference is the presence of a term $\eta f(x)$ in (43). If the addition of the term $\eta f(x)$ does not significantly complicate the Sturm–Liouville equation, then it is to be expected that the distribution of the corresponding functional is not too difficult to find.

With a standard transformation, (43) can be rewritten in the form

$$\frac{d^2\psi}{dz^2} + [\lambda - V(z) - \eta f]\psi = 0, \tag{44}$$

with

$$z = \int \frac{1}{\sqrt{B(x)}}\, dx,$$

$$q = [B(x)W^2(x)]^{1/4},$$

$$\psi = q\varphi,$$

$$V(z) = q^{-1}(z)\frac{d^2}{dz^2}q(z)$$

and

$$f = f(x(z)).$$

If the kernel f of the functional is such that

$$V(z) + \eta f(x(z)) = a^2 V(az + b) + c, \tag{45}$$

where a, b, c are constants (i.e., independent of z), then (44) can be rewritten as

$$\frac{d^2\psi}{d\zeta^2} + \left[\left(\frac{\lambda - c}{a^2}\right) - V(\zeta)\right]\psi = 0, \tag{46}$$

with

$$\zeta = az + b.$$

In that case the solutions of (43) follow immediately from the solution of (12).

As an example, consider the functional

$$Y(t) = \int_0^t X(\tau)\, d\tau, \tag{47}$$

where $X(\tau)$ is the process of (2 C) with first-order probability density function

$$W(x) = \frac{1}{\Gamma(\alpha + 1)} x^\alpha e^{-x}.$$

For this case (43) becomes

$$\frac{d}{dx}\left[x^{\alpha+1}e^{-x}\frac{d\varphi}{dx}\right] + x^{\alpha}e^{-x}[\lambda - \eta x]\varphi(x) = 0. \tag{48}$$

It can be verified that $f(x) = x$ for this case satisfies (45) with

$$\begin{aligned} a &= (1 + 4\eta)^{1/4}, \\ b &= c = 0. \end{aligned} \tag{49}$$

The solutions of (48) are

$$\lambda_n = a^2(n + \alpha + 1) - (\alpha + 1) \tag{50}$$

and

$$\varphi_n(x) = e^{(1-a^2)x/2}L_n^{\alpha}(a^2x), \tag{51}$$

with

$$L_n^{\alpha}(x) = \frac{1}{n!}x^{-\alpha}e^{x}\frac{d^n}{dx^n}(x^{n+\alpha}e^{-x}).$$

The function $r(x|x_0, t; \eta)$ can be written as

$$r(x|x_0, t; \eta) = a^2(a^2x)^{\alpha}e^{-x}\sum_{n=0}^{\infty}\frac{n!}{\Gamma(n + \alpha + 1)}\varphi_n(x_0)\varphi_n(x). \tag{52}$$

From (52) we find

$$\begin{aligned} F(\eta, t) = E(e^{-\eta Y(t)}) &= \int_0^{\infty}\int_0^{\infty} W(x_0)r(x|x_0, t, \eta)\,dx_0\,dx \\ &= \left[\frac{4a^2e^{-(a^2-1)t/2}}{(a^2+1)^2 - (a^2-1)e^{-a^2t}}\right]^{\alpha+1}. \end{aligned} \tag{53}$$

Finally, the probability density function for $Y(t)$ can be found from (53) using the inversion integral of Laplace transform. Specifically, let $W(y, t)$ be the density function. Then

$$W(y, t) = \frac{1}{2\pi i}\int_{c-i\infty}^{c+i\infty} e^{\eta y}F(\eta, t)\,d\eta, \qquad c > -\tfrac{1}{4}. \tag{54}$$

References

1. J. F. Barrett and D. G. Lampard, *An expansion for some second-order probability distributions and its application to noise problems*, IRE Trans. **IT–1** (1955), 10–15.

2. S. Bochner, *Sturm-Liouville and heat equations whose eigenfunctions and ultraspherical polynomials or associated Bessel functions*, Proc. Conf. Differential Equations, pp. 23–48, University of Maryland Book Store, College Park, Md., 1955.

3. S. Chandrasekhar, *Stochastic problems in physics and astronomy*, Rev. Modern Phys. **15** (1943), 1–89.

4. H. Cramer, *Mathematical methods of statistics*, Princeton Univ. Press, Princeton, N. J., 1946.

5. D. A. Darling and A. J. F. Siegert, *A systematic approach to a class of problems in the theory of noise and other random phenomena.* I, IRE Trans. **IT–3** (1957), 32–37.

6. J. L. Doob, *The Brownian movement and stochastic equations*, Ann. of Math. (2) **43** (1942), 351–369.

7. A. Erdelyi, ed., *Higher transcendental functions*, Vol. I, McGraw-Hill, New York, 1953.

8. W. Feller, *Diffusion processes in genetics*, Proc. 2nd Berkeley Sympos. Math. Statist. and Prob., pp. 227–246, Univ. of California Press, Berkeley, Calif., 1951.

9. ———, *Diffusion processes in one dimension*, Trans. Amer. Math. Soc. **77** (1954), 1–31.

10. B. V. Gnedenko and A. N. Kolmogorov, *Limit distributions for sums of independent random variables*, Addison-Wesley, Cambridge, 1954.

11. M. Kac, *Random walk and the theory of Brownian motion*, Amer. Math. Monthly **54** (1947), 369–391.

12. S. Karlin and J. McGregor, *Classical diffusion processes and total positivity*, J. Math. Anal. Appl. **1** (1960), 163–183.

13. A. N. Kolmogorov, *Über die analytische Methoden in der Wahrscheinlichkeitsrechrung*, Math. Ann. **104** (1931), 415–458.

14. G. Szegö, *Orthogonal polynomials*, Amer. Math. Soc. Colloq. Publ. Vol. 23, Amer. Math. Soc., Providence, R. I., 1939.

15. M. C. Wang and G. E. Uhlenbeck, *On the theory of the Brownian motion*. II, Rev. Modern Phys. **17** (1945), 323–342.

16. E. Wong and J. B. Thomas, *On polynomial expansions of second-order distributions*, J. Soc. Indust. Appl. Math. **10** (1962), 507–516.

UNIVERSITY OF CALIFORNIA,
BERKELEY, CALIFORNIA

PROBABILITY BOUNDS VIA DYNAMIC PROGRAMMING

BY

DAVID BLACKWELL

1. A general theorem. Let M be any set of probability measures m on the Borel sets of n-space. A sequence $X_1, X_2, \cdots$ of n-dimensional random variables will be called an M-sequence if (a) the distribution of X_1 is an element of M and (b) the conditional distribution of X_{k+1} given $X_1, \cdots, X_k$ is an element of M, with probability 1, for $k = 1, 2, \cdots$. Thus if M consists of the single element m, the M-sequences are independent with common distribution m; if M consists of all distributions with mean 0, the M-sequences are those for which $\{S_k = X_1 + \cdots + X_k\}$ is a martingale with mean 0.

Fix a subset R of n-space, and a point $r \in R$. For any M-sequence $\{X_k\}$, define $S_k = r + X_1 + \cdots + X_k$, $k = 0, 1, \cdots$. Define N as the smallest k for which $S_k \notin R$. The value $+\infty$ is not excluded. As $\{X_k\}$ varies over all M-sequences, the least upper bound of EN is, for fixed M, R, a function of r. We denote this function by v and define $v = 0$ for $r \notin R$. Our problem is to find interesting upper bounds for v.

This problem can be considered as a dynamic programming or gambling problem, in which we start in state r, and choose any displacement distribution m from M. An x_1 is selected from m and we move to $r + x_1$. We continue as long as the state remains in R, receiving one unit of income per play. Play stops as soon as a state not in R is reached. $v(s)$ is then our maximum expected income, starting from s. Indeed the main purpose of this paper is to show how a dynamic programming idea can be applied. The idea is described in the following theorem.

THEOREM. *For any non-negative f on n-space and any probability measure m on n-space, let $T_m f$ be the function defined by*

$$T_m f(r) = \begin{cases} 1 + \int f(r + x)\, dm(x) & \text{for } r \in R, \\ 0 & \text{for } r \notin R, \end{cases}$$

and define $Tf = \sup_{m \in M} T_m f$. If $Tf \leqq f$, then $v \leqq f$.

A very general form of this theorem appears in Dubins and Savage [4]. See also Blackwell [7].

We sketch the proof. For $f_0 \equiv 0$, we show by induction on j that, for every

D-sequence $\{X_k\}$, $E \min(N, j) \leqq T^j f_0$. This is true for $j = 1$. If true for j_0, we have, starting from $r \in R$

$$(1) \qquad E \min(N, j_0 + 1 | X_1) = 1 + E \min(N', j_0),$$

where N' is the N for the M-sequence $X_2, X_3, \cdots$ conditioned by X_1 and with starting point $S_1 = r + X_1$. The inductive hypothesis implies

$$E \min(N', j_0) \leqq T^{j_0} f_0(r + x_1).$$

Taking expectation in (1) yields $E \min(N, j_0 + 1) \leqq 1 + ET^{j_0} f_0(r + X_1) \leqq T^{j_0+1} f_0(r)$.

The operator T is monotone in the sense that $f_1 \leqq f_2$ for all r implies $Tf_1 \leqq Tf_2$ for all r. Thus $f \geqq 0 = f_0$ implies $T^j f \geqq T^j f_0$ for all j. If in addition $Tf \leqq f$, then $T^j f \leqq f$ for all j, so that $f \geqq E \min(N, j)$ for all j. Letting $j \to \infty$ yields $f \geqq v$.

We remark that, as will be familiar to workers in dynamic programming, $T^j f(r)$ is the maximal income, starting from r when play is truncated after j moves even if the state r' is still inside R, and you receive a final payment $f(r')$.

2. **Applications.** (A) $n = 1$, $R = \{|r| \leqq H\}$, M consists of all distributions concentrated on $|x| \leqq 1$, with mean 0 and second moment $s > 0$. Take any quadratic function $q = A - Cr^2$ which is $\geqq 0$ for $|r| \leqq H + 1$, and take $f = \max(q, 0)$. We have, for $|r| \leqq H$, $Tf(r) = 1 + A - C(r^2 + s)$, so that $Tf \leqq f$ if $C \geqq 1/s$. For $C_0 = 1/s$, the smallest A which makes $q \geqq 0$ for $|r| \leqq H + 1$ is $C_0(H + 1)^2$. We conclude that

$$(2) \qquad v(r) \leqq \frac{(H + 1)^2 - r^2}{s}.$$

This bound is in fact sharp for integral r, H, and is achieved for the M-sequence with X_k independent, $\Pr\{X_k = 1\} = \Pr\{X_k = -1\} = s/2$, $\Pr\{X_k = 0\} = 1 - s$. For independent identically distributed M-sequences, the bound (2) is known as a consequence of Wald's identity (see Doob [**2**] or Wolfowitz [**6**]). The arguments given to obtain this consequence actually use only the present hypotheses so could also be used to obtain (2).

(B) $n = 1$, $R = \{r \leqq 0\}$, M consists of all distributions concentrated on $|x| \leqq 1$ with mean $m > 0$. Take any linear function $q = A - Bt$ with $q \geqq 0$ for $t \leqq 1$, and take $f = \max(q, 0)$. For $r \leqq 0$,

$$Tf(r) = 1 + A - Br - Bm = f(r) + 1 - Bm,$$

so that $Tf \leqq f$ if $B \geqq 1/m$. For $B = 1/m$, the smallest A which makes $q \geqq 0$ for $t \leqq 1$ is $A = 1/m$. We conclude

$$(3) \qquad v(r) \leqq \frac{1 - r}{m}.$$

Again the bound is exact for integral r, and is attained, for example, for $\{X_k\}$ independent with $\Pr\{X_k = \pm 1\} = (1 \pm m)/2$. The bound (3) can be obtained directly from the fact that $\{S_k - mk\}$, stopped when $S_k > 0$, is a martingale bounded above (by 1).

(C) $n = 1$, $R = \{|r| \leqq H\}$, M consists of all distributions concentrated on $|x| \leqq 1$ with non-negative mean and second moment at least $s_0 > 0$. For a quadratic function $q = A - Bt - Ct^2$ with $q \geqq 0$ for $|t| \leqq H + 1$, and $f = \max(q, 0)$, the condition $Tf \leqq f$ becomes $1 - Bm - 2Ctm - Cs \leqq 0$ for $m \geqq 0$, $s \geqq s_0$, $|t| \leqq H$. For $m = 0$, $s = s_0$ we obtain $C \geqq 1/s_0$. For $t = -H$, $s = s_0$, $C = 1/s_0$, $M = 1$, we obtain $B \geqq 2H/s_0$. The values $C_0 = 1/s_0$, $B_0 = 2H/s_0$ satisfy the conditions, and the smallest A which makes $q \geqq 0$ for $|t| \leqq H + 1$ is $B_0(H + 1) + C_0(H + 1)^2$. We conclude

$$v(r) \leqq \frac{(H + 1)^2 - r^2 + 2H(H + 1 - r)}{s_0}. \tag{4}$$

For $r = 0$, H integral, the bound $(H + 1)(3H + 1)/s_0$ is exact, and is achieved by the random walk with displacements $-1, 0, 1$ with probabilities $s_0/2$, $1 - s_0$, $s_0/2$ except when position $-H$ is reached, when the displacements are 0, 1 with probabilities $1 - s_0$, s_0. The expected income is clearly equivalent to that in the random walk with boundaries $-2H$, $2H$ with starting point H and displacements $-1, 0, 1$ with probabilities $s_0/2$, $1 - s_0$, $s_0/2$. As noted in (A), the exact expected income is $((2H + 1)^2 - H^2)/s_0 = (H + 1)(3H + 1)/s_0$.

(D) For any positive integer n, let M be the set of distributions concentrated within the unit sphere $|x| \leqq 1$, with mean 0 and covariance matrix $\sigma^2 I$, σ^2 fixed and positive. Let $R = \{|r| \leqq \rho\}$. Take $q(t) = A((\rho + 1)^2 - \sum_1^n t_i^2)$, $f = \max(q, 0)$. $Tf \leqq f$ reduces to $A \geqq 1/n\sigma^2$. We conclude

$$v(r) \leqq \frac{(\rho + 1)^2 - |r|^2}{n\sigma^2}. \tag{5}$$

I do not know how sharp (5) is.

(E) Even in problems where v is infinite, the method can be used to obtain bounds on the distribution of N, by introducing a discount factor $\beta < 1$. If the state is still inside R at time k, we receive an income increment β^k, so that the total expected reward is bounded above by $1/(1 - \beta)$. The operator T becomes

$$Tf(r) = \begin{cases} 1 + \beta \sup\limits_{m \in M} \displaystyle\int f(r + x)\, dm(x) & \text{for } r \in R, \\ 0 & \text{for } r \notin R, \end{cases}$$

and the theorem and proof are as before, with

$$v = \sup \sum_{k=0}^{\infty} \beta^k \Pr N \geqq k,$$

where the sup is over all M-sequences $\{X_k\}$. We illustrate with $n = 1$, M consisting of the single distribution on ± 1 with equal probabilities, and $R = \{r \geqq 0\}$.

It is known that N is finite with probability 1, but EN is infinite. For any $f \geqq 0$ on $t \geqq -1$, $Tf \leqq f$ becomes

$$2 + \beta[f(t+1) + f(t-1)] \leqq 2f(t) \quad \text{for } t \geqq 0.$$

For

$$f(t) = A(1 - e^{-C(t+1)}), \quad \text{where } A > 0,\ C > 0,$$

the required inequality becomes

$$2 + 2\beta A(1 - (\cosh C)\, e^{-C(t+1)}) \leqq 2A(1 - e^{-C(t+1)}).$$

We get equality for $A = 1/(1-\beta)$, $\cosh C = 1/\beta$, and conclude:

$$(6) \qquad v(r) \leqq \frac{1 - e^{-C(r+1)}}{1-\beta}, \quad \text{where } C > 0,\ \cosh C = 1/\beta.$$

For integral r, the bound is exact. For β near 1, $C \simeq (1-\beta)^{1/2}$, so that, for integral r, as noted in **[5]**,

$$v(r) \simeq \frac{r+1}{(1-\beta)^{1/2}}.$$

The same approach can be used to bound the probability that $\{S_n\}$ ever escapes from R **[1]**. The operator T becomes

$$TF(r) = \begin{cases} \sup_{m \in M} EF(r+x) & \text{for } r \in R, \\ 1 & \text{for } r \notin R. \end{cases}$$

For another application of the same approach, see Dubins **[3]**.

References

1. D. Blackwell, *On optimal systems*, Ann. Math. Statist. **25** (1954), 394–397.

2. J. L. Doob, *Stochastic processes*, pp. 350–352, Wiley, New York, 1953.

3. L. E. Dubins, *Rises and upcrossings of non-negative martingales*, Illinois J. Math. **6** (1962), 226–241.

4. L. E. Dubins and L. J. Savage, *How to gamble if you must* (to appear).

5. W. Feller, *An introduction to probability theory and its applications*, 2nd ed., p. 87, Wiley, New York, 1957.

6. J. Wolfowitz, *The efficiency of sequential estimates and Wald's equation for sequential processes*, Ann. Math. Statist. **18** (1947), 215–230.

7. D. Blackwell, *On the functional equation of dynamic programming*, J. Math. Anal. Appl. **2** (1961), 273–276.

University of California,
Berkeley, California

MARKOVIAN SEQUENTIAL DECISION PROCESSES[1]

BY

CYRUS DERMAN

1. **Introduction.** We are concerned with a dynamic stochastic system which is observed at times $t = 0, 1, \cdots$, and classified into one of a finite number of states $0, 1, \cdots, L$. After each observation the system is "controlled" by making one of a finite number of decisions $1, \cdots, K$. Let $\{Y_t\}$, $t = 0, 1, \cdots$, denote the sequence of observations and $\{\Delta_t\}$, $t = 0, 1, \cdots$, the sequence of decisions. We assume that

$$P(Y_{t+1} = j \mid Y_0, \Delta_0, \cdots, Y_t = i, \Delta_t = k) = q_{ij}(k),$$

for $t = 0, 1, \cdots$; $i, j = 0, \cdots, L$; $k = 1, \cdots, K$, where the $q_{ij}(k)$'s are given non-negative numbers such that

$$\sum_{j=0}^{L} q_{ij}(k) = 1, \qquad i = 0, \cdots, L;\ k = 1, \cdots, K.$$

We shall say a rule R is a collection of functions

$$D_k(Y_0, \Delta_0, \cdots, \Delta_{t-1}, Y_t), \qquad t = 0, 1, \cdots;\ k = 1, \cdots, K$$

of the observations and decisions such that

$$D_k(\cdot) \geqq 0, \qquad k = 1, \cdots, K$$

and

$$\sum_{k=1}^{K} D_k(\cdot) = 1.$$

A rule R is used to control the system by setting

$$P(\Delta_k = k \mid Y_0, \Delta_0, \cdots, \Delta_{t-1}, Y_t) = D_k(Y_0, \Delta_0, \cdots, Y_t), \qquad k = 1, \cdots, K$$

for every possible set of observations and decisions $Y_0, \Delta_0, \cdots, Y_t$, $t = 0, 1, \cdots$. Once the initial probabilities $P(Y_0 = i)$, $i = 0, \cdots, L$ are given and a rule R is designated we may speak of the sequence $\{Y_t\}$, $t = 0, 1, \cdots$ as being a stochastic process with state space $0, 1, \cdots, L$.

Processes of this sort were first discussed by Bellman [**1**; **2**]. The monograph by Howard [**17**] and papers by d'Epenoux [**13**], Manne [**19**], and Dantzig and Wolfe [**6**], providing computational methods, have stimulated recent activity in this area [**4**; **8**; **9**; **10**; **15**; **16**; **18**; **20**].

[1] Work sponsored in part by the Office of Naval Research under contract NR–042–099.

The problems of interest center around determining optimal rules. In a number of problems the criterion to be optimized is expressible in terms of $\Phi_T(i)$, as $T \to \infty$, where $\Phi_T(i)$ is the vector of components

$$\phi_{Tjk}(i) = \frac{1}{T+1}\sum_{t=0}^{T} P(Y_t = j, \Delta_t = k \mid Y_0 = i), \qquad j = 0, \cdots, L;\ k = 1, \cdots, K,$$

for a given i.

We give several examples.

EXAMPLE 1. Suppose $Y_0 = i$ with probability 1. Let

$$Z_t = w_{jk}, \quad \text{if } Y_t = j,\ \Delta_t = k,$$

for $j = 0, \cdots, L$; $k = 1, \cdots, K$; $t = 0, 1, \cdots$. We can think of Z_t as being the cost or conditional expected cost ascribed to the system at time t given it is in state j and decision k is made. The expected average cost up to time T is

$$Q_T(i) = E\frac{1}{T+1}\sum_{t=0}^{T} Z_t = \sum_{j=0}^{L}\sum_{k=1}^{K} w_{jk}\phi_{Tjk}(i).$$

A problem of interest is to find that rule R which minimizes $\lim\sup_{T\to\infty} Q_T(i)$.

EXAMPLE 2. Let $Q_T(i)$ be as in Example 1. A second problem is to find the rule R which maximizes $\lim\sup_{T\to\infty} Q_T(i)$. This problem may arise when the $q_{ij}(k)$'s represent the parameters associated with a given system design or statistical procedure; e.g. a continuous sampling plan, and the rule R denotes the behavior of "Nature." In these cases it is of interest to evaluate a procedure in terms of the maximum possible expected cost it may incur.

EXAMPLE 3. Suppose again $Y_0 = i$ with probability 1. Let

$$\tau = \min\{t \mid Y_t = i,\ t \geqq 1\}.$$

Then $\sum_{t=1}^{\tau} Z_t$, where Z_t is defined as in Example 1, is the cost associated with $\{Y_t\}$, $1 \leqq t \leqq \tau$. Consider the problem of choosing R, of all possible R such that $E\tau < \infty$, which minimizes

$$S(i) = E\sum_{t=1}^{\tau} Z_t.$$

Eaton and Zadeh **[12]**, except for slight differences, have referred to such problems as "pursuit" problems; the idea being that at time τ (a random variable) a certain target state is reached for the first time. The aim is to reach the target state in the most efficient manner.

In order to express $S(i)$ as a function of $\Phi_T(i)$, as $T \to \infty$ we first notice that

$$S(i) = \sum_{k=1}^{K}\sum_{j=0}^{L} w_{jk}\eta_{jk}$$

where η_{jk}, $j = 0, \cdots, L$; $k = 1, \cdots, K$, is the expected number of t, $1 \leqq t \leqq \tau$, such that $Y_t = j$, $\Delta_t = k$. For the purposes of this problem it is clear that we may restrict ourselves to rules which repeat themselves whenever the system returns to state i; i.e., the process $\{Y_t\}$, $t = 0, 1, \cdots$, under such a rule is a recurrent event process (see Feller [**14**]) with the recurrent event identified as "entrance of the system into state i." When this is the case, standard recurrent event type arguments lead to

$$\lim_{T\to\infty} \phi_{Tjk}(i) = \frac{\eta_{ik}}{E\tau}, \qquad j = 0, \cdots, L;\ k = 1, \cdots, K.$$

However, by definition of τ,

$$\sum_{k=1}^{K} \eta_{ik} = 1,$$

from which it follows that

$$E\tau = \frac{1}{\lim\limits_{T\to\infty} \sum\limits_{k=1}^{K} \phi_{Tik}(i)}.$$

On substitution we get

$$S(i) = \frac{\sum\limits_{j=0}^{L} \sum\limits_{k=1}^{K} w_{jk} \lim\limits_{T\to\infty} \phi_{Tjk}(i)}{\lim\limits_{T\to\infty} \sum\limits^{K} \phi_{Tik}(i)}.$$

EXAMPLE 4. Suppose $Y_0 = i$ with probability 1 and τ is defined as in Example 3. Further, suppose there are states $j_1, \cdots, j_r$ different from i such that for every rule R

$$P(Y_{t+1} = i \mid Y_t = j_v) = 1, \qquad v = 1, \cdots, r;\ t = 1, 2, \cdots.$$

That is, whenever the system enters state j_v, $v = 1, \cdots, r$, its next state is i. Let

$$\alpha_{j_v} = P(Y_t \neq j_v,\ 1 \leqq t \leqq \tau \mid Y_0 = i), \qquad v = 1, \cdots, r.$$

α_{j_v} is the probability of avoiding state j_v within the first recurrence cycle of i. Consider the problem of finding that R, of all considered in Example 3, such that $E\tau$ is maximized subject to the constraints

$$\alpha_{j_v} \geqq c_v, \qquad v = 1, \cdots, r,$$

where c_v, $v = 1, \cdots, r$ are given constants. This problem may arise in replacement type situations where τ is the length of time until a certain component, say, is replaced and states $j_1, \cdots, j_r$ stand for events of possible catastrophic proportions.

$E\tau$ is as in Example 3. Since $Y_t = j_v$ for at most one t, $1 \leqq t \leqq \tau$, it follows that

$$1 - \alpha_{j_v} = \sum_{k=1}^{K} \eta_{j_v k}, \qquad v = 1, \cdots, r.$$

Hence, using the relationships from Example 3, the problem is of the form: minimize

$$\lim_{T\to\infty} \sum_{k=1}^{K} \phi_{Tik}(i),$$

subject to the constraints

$$\lim_{T\to\infty} \sum_{k=1}^{K} \phi_{Tj_v k}(i) \leqq (1 - c_v) \lim_{T\to\infty} \sum_{k=1}^{K} \phi_{Tik}(i), \qquad v = 1, \cdots, r.$$

Before proceeding it is helpful to classify the possible rules. Let C denote the class of *all* rules and let C' denote the sub-class of rules for which

$$D_k(Y_0, \Delta_0, \cdots, Y_t = i) = D_{ik}, \qquad i = 0, \cdots, L; \; k = 1, \cdots, K; \; t = 0, 1, \cdots,$$

where $\{D_{ik}\}$, $i = 0, \cdots, L$; $k = 1, \cdots, K$, are non-negative numbers such that

$$\sum_{k=1}^{K} D_{ik} = 1, \qquad i = 0, \cdots, L.$$

Let C'' be the sub-class of C' for which $D_{ik} = 0$ or 1.

When $R \in C'$, the stochastic process $\{Y_t\}$, $t = 0, 1, \cdots$, is a Markov chain with stationary transition probabilities

$$P_{ij} = \sum_{k=1}^{K} D_{ik} q_{ij}(k), \qquad i, j = 0, \cdots, L.$$

In seeking optimal rules in problems such as described above, a question presents itself. Namely, is it necessary to consider rules outside the class C' (or sometimes C'')? If not, the problems are more manageable, for then we can bring to bear techniques of dynamic programming, linear programming, and Markov chain theory (see [**6**; **7**; **8**; **10**; **12**; **13**; **15**; **16**; **17**; **18**; **19**; **20**]).

This question has been treated for various separate cases (see [**13**; **4**; **8**; **10**; **11**]). The results presented in the next section are more generally relevant to this question for problems of the above type.

2. **Limit theorems.** Let $H_R(i)$ denote the set of limit points of $\{\Phi_T^R(i)\}$ as $T \to \infty$. If $R \in C'$ it is well known from Markov chain theory (see [**5**, p. 32]) that $\lim_{T\to\infty} \Phi_T^R(i)$ exists. However, in general, $\{\Phi_T^R(i)\}$, $T = 0, 1, \cdots$ may have more than one limit point. Let

$$H(i) = \bigcup_{R\in C} H_R(i),$$

$$H'(i) = \bigcup_{R\in C'} H_R(i),$$

and

$$H''(i) = \bigcup_{R\in C''} H_R(i).$$

In keeping with the terminology employed by Feller [**14**], we call a Markov chain with stationary transition probabilities *irreducible* if for every ordered pair of states (i, j) there exists a t such that

$$P(Y_t = j \mid Y_0 = i) > 0.$$

The following theorem in a slightly different form was proved in [**9**].

THEOREM 1. *If the Markov chain* $\{Y_t\}$ *is irreducible for every* $R \in C''$, *then* $H(i) = H'(i)$.

The proof makes use of the fact that under the irreducibility assumption $H'(i)$ is a closed convex set. This, and the result obtained in [8] that $\limsup_{T\to\infty} Q_t(i)$ of Example 1 is minimized over all $R \in C$ by a rule $R^* \in C''$, combine to imply Theorem 1.

Theorem 1 applies to Examples 3 and 4 for most cases of interest. However, the irreducibility assumption is too strong to be of general use in Example 2. The following theorem applies.

THEOREM 2. *Let* $\bar{H}'(i)$ *and* $\bar{H}''(i)$ *denote the convex hulls of* $H'(i)$ *and* $H''(i)$, *then we always have*

$$\bar{H}''(i) = \bar{H}'(i) \supset H(i).$$

The proof of Theorem 2 is suggested, with certain modifications, by that of Theorem 1 and will appear elsewhere.

Since all the extreme points of $\bar{H}''(i)$ are points of $H''(i)$, this theorem asserts that every point of $H(i)$ can be achieved by an appropriate initial random selection of rules $R \in C''$. With respect to Example 2, since $\limsup_{T\to\infty} Q_T(i)$ is maximized at the extreme points of $\bar{H}''(i)$ it follows that there exists a rule $R^{**} \in C''$ such that $\limsup_{T\to\infty} Q_T(i)$ is maximized over all $R \in C$ at R^{**}.

Though we shall not go into its possible applications we can state a strong law counterpart to Theorem 2. Suppose $P(Y_0 = i) = 1$. Let

$$Z_{tjk} = \begin{cases} 1, & \text{if } Y_t = j,\ \Delta_t = k, \\ 0, & \text{otherwise,} \end{cases}$$

for $j = 0, \cdots, L$; $k = 1, \cdots, K$; $t = 0, 1, \cdots$. For any rule R let $\hat{\Phi}_T^R(i)$ be the vector of components

$$\hat{\phi}_{Tjk}(i) = \frac{1}{T+1} \sum_{t=0}^{T} Z_{tjk}, \qquad j = 0, \cdots, L;\ k = 1, \cdots, K.$$

Let $U^R(i)$ denote the set of limit points of $\{\hat{\Phi}_T^R(i)\}$, as $T \to \infty$; $U^R(i)$ is a random set dependent upon the sample sequence $\{Y_t, \Delta_t\}$, $t = 0, 1, \cdots$ we can state

THEOREM 3. *For each* $R \in C$,

$$P(U^R(i) \subset \bar{H}'') = 1,$$

where $\bar{H}''$ *is the convex hull of* $\bigcup_{j=0}^{L} H''(j)$.

The proof of this theorem will also appear elsewhere.

3. **A counter-example.** A simple counter-example given in [9] shows that the irreducibility condition of Theorem 1 is relevant. Suppose $L = 1$, $K = 2$ with

$$q_{00}(1) = 0, \quad q_{01}(1) = 1, \quad q_{10}(1) = 0, \quad q_{11}(1) = 1, \quad q_{00}(2) = 1,$$
$$q_{00}(2) = 1, \quad q_{01}(2) = 0, \quad q_{10}(2) = 0, \quad q_{11}(2) = 1.$$

In words, decision 2 permits the system to remain in state 0; decision 1 carries the system to state 1 from state 0; once the system enters state 1 it remains there.

From elementary Markov chain considerations, if $R \in C'$ we have that

$$\lim_{T\to\infty} \frac{1}{T} \sum_{t=1}^{T} P(Y_t = 0 \mid Y_0 = 0) = \lim_{T\to\infty} \sum_{k=1}^{2} \phi_{T0k}(0) = 1 \text{ or } 0;$$

no intermediate value is possible. However, consider R as follows:

$$D_2(Y_0, \Delta_0, \cdots, Y_t = 0) = e^{-(1/2)^t}, \qquad t = 0, 1, \cdots,$$

$$D_2(Y_0, \Delta_0, \cdots, Y_t = 1) = 1, \qquad t = 0, 1, \cdots;$$

i.e., make decision 1 with probability $1 - e^{-(1/2)^t}$ if the system is in state 0 at time t and make decision 2 whenever the system is in state 1. Under this rule it follows that

$$P(Y_t = 0 \mid Y_0 = 0) = \exp\left[-\sum_{v=0}^{t-1} (1/2)^v\right], \qquad t = 1, 2, \cdots,$$

from which we have

$$\lim_{T\to\infty} \sum_{k=1}^{2} \phi_{T0k}(0) = e^{-2},$$

a value unattainable with a rule $R \in C'$.

This counter-example makes use of the fact that there is no $R \in C'$ for which the Markov chain $\{Y_t\}$, $t = 0, 1, \cdots$, is irreducible. However, this is not crucial; it is possible to construct a similar example for which there are some rules $R \in C'$ which result in irreducible chains.

With this counter-example we can formulate an optimization problem where the optimal rule is not a member of C'. Namely, find that rule $R \in C$ such that

$$\limsup_{T\to\infty} \sum_{k=1}^{2} \phi_{T0k}(0)$$

is minimized subject to the constraint that

$$\limsup_{T\to\infty} \sum_{k=1}^{2} \phi_{T0k}(0) \geqq e^{-2}.$$

Clearly the above rule is optimal for this problem.

4. **Linear programming formulations.** We can easily show how the linear programming formulation of Manne **[19]** and Dantzig and Wolfe **[6]** applies to the four examples. We assume that the irreducibility condition of Theorem 1 holds. From Theorem 1 it then follows that we can restrict our attention to rules in C' for which we can assert that

$$\lim_{T\to\infty} \phi_{Tjk}(i) = \pi_j D_{jk}, \qquad j = 0, \cdots, L;\ k = 1, \cdots, K,$$

where $\{\pi_j\}$, $j = 0, \cdots, L$ are all positive and uniquely satisfy the system of inequalities and equalities

$$\pi_j \geqq 0 \qquad j = 0, \cdots, L,$$

(*)
$$\pi_j = \sum_{i=0}^{L} \pi_i p_{ij}, \qquad j = 0, \cdots, L,$$

$$\sum_{j=0}^{L} \pi_j = 1.$$

Letting $x_{jk} = \pi_j P_{jk}$, $j = 0, \cdots, L$; $k = 1, \cdots, K$, Example 1 (Example 2) becomes: minimize (maximize)

$$\sum_{j=0}^{L} \sum_{k=1}^{K} w_{jk} x_{jk}$$

subject to

$$x_{jk} \geqq 0, \qquad j = 0, \cdots, L;\ k = 1, \cdots, K,$$

(**)
$$\sum_{k=1}^{K} x_{jk} = \sum_{i=0}^{L} \sum_{k=1}^{K} x_{ik} q_{ij}(k), \qquad j = 0, \cdots, L,$$

$$\sum_{j=0}^{L} \sum_{k=1}^{K} x_{jk} = 1.$$

Example 4 becomes: minimize

$$\sum_{k=1}^{K} x_{ik}$$

subject to (**) and

$$\sum_{k=1}^{K} x_{j_v k} \leqq (1 - C_v) \sum_{k=1}^{K} x_{ik}, \qquad v = 1, \cdots, r.$$

Example 3 is of the form: minimize

$$\frac{\sum_{j=0}^{L} \sum_{k=1}^{K} w_{jk} x_{jk}}{\sum_{k=1}^{K} x_{ik}}$$

subject to (**). The transformation

$$Z_0 = \frac{1}{\sum_{k=1}^{K} x_{ik}}$$

and

$$Z_{jk} = \frac{x_{jk}}{\sum_{k=1}^{K} x_{ik}}, \qquad j = 0, \cdots, L;\ k = 1, \cdots, K,$$

yields the linear programming problem: minimize

$$\sum_{j=0}^{K} \sum_{k=1}^{K} w_{jk} Z_{jk}$$

subject to

$$Z_0 \geqq 0, \quad Z_{jk} \geqq 0, \quad j = 0, \cdots, L; \ k = 1, \cdots, K,$$

$$\sum_{k=1}^{K} Z_{jk} = \sum_{i=0}^{L} \sum_{k=1}^{K} Z_{ik} q_{ij}(k), \qquad j = 0, \cdots, L,$$

$$\sum_{j=0}^{L} \sum_{k=1}^{K} Z_{jk} = Z_0,$$

$$\sum_{k=1}^{K} Z_{ik} = 1.$$

The optimal rule is obtained from the linear programming solutions by setting for each j and k

$$D_{jk} = \frac{x_{jk}}{\sum_{k=1}^{K} x_{jk}} \quad \text{(for Examples 1, 2, and 4)}$$

$$= \frac{Z_{jk}}{\sum_{k=1}^{K} Z_{jk}} \quad \text{(for Example 3).}$$

Because of the irreducibility assumption the denominators in the above are always positive so that D_{jk} is well defined for every j and k (see [8] for the details).

References

1. R. Bellman, *Dynamic programming*, Princeton Univ. Press, Princeton, N. J., 1957.

2. ———, *A Markovian decision process*, J. Math. Mech. **6** (1957), 679–684.

3. D. Blackwell, *On the functional equation of dynamic programming*, J. Math. Anal. Appl. **2** (1961), 273–276.

4. ———, *Discrete dynamic programming*, Ann. Math. Statist. **33** (1962), 719–726.

5. Kai Lai Chung, *Markov chains with stationary transition probabilities*, Springer, Berlin, 1960.

6. G. Dantzig and P. Wolfe, *Linear programming in a Markov chain*, Operations Res. **10** (1962), 702–710.

7. C. Derman, *On optimal replacement rules when changes of state are Markovian*, Mathematical optimization techniques, pp. 201–210, Univ. of California Press, Berkeley, Calif., 1963.

8. ———, *On sequential decisions and Markov chains*, Management Sci. **9** (1962), 16–24.

9. ———, *Stable sequential control rules and Markov chains*, J. Math. Anal. Appl. **6** (1963), 257–265.

10. ———, *Optimal replacement and maintenance under Markovian deterioration with probability bounds on failure*, Management Sci. **9** (1963), 478–481.

11. C. Derman, M. V. Johns and G. J. Lieberman, *Continuous sampling procedures without control*, Ann. Math. Statist. (1959), 1175–1191.

12. J. H. Eaton and L. A. Zadeh, *Optimal pursuit strategies in discrete state probabilistic systems*, Trans. ASME Ser. D, J. Basic Engrg. **84** (1962), 23–29.

13. F. d'Epenoux, *Sur un problème de production et de stockage dans l'aléatoire*, Revue Française de Recherche Opérationnelle **4** (1960), 13–15.

14. W. Feller, *An introduction to probability theory and its applications*, 2nd ed., Wiley, New York, 1957.

15. M. Freimer, *On solving a Markovian decision problem by linear programming*, Institute for Defense Analyses, Cambridge, Mass., December 1961, rev. March 1962 (unpublished).

16. Guy de Ghellink, *Solving a multistage decision problem*, Carnegie Institute of Technology, Pittsburgh, Pa., November, 1959 (unpublished).

17. R. A. Howard, *Dynamic programming and Markov processes*, Wiley, New York, 1960.

18. M. Klein, *Inspection-maintenance replacement schedules under Markovian deterioration*, Management Sci. **9** (1962), 25–32.

19. A. S. Manne, *Linear programming and sequential decisions*, Management Sci. **6** (1960), 259–267.

20. H. M. Wagner, *On the optimality of pure strategies*, Management Sci. **6** (1960), 304–318.

Columbia University,
New York, New York

THE APPLICATION OF TRUNCATED HIERARCHY TECHNIQUES IN THE SOLUTION OF A STOCHASTIC LINEAR DIFFERENTIAL EQUATION

BY

J. M. RICHARDSON

1. **Introduction.** Stochastic linear operators, in particular linear equations with stochastic coefficients, constitute a topic receiving rapidly increasing attention in recent years.[1] In spite of the work devoted to the general properties of such equations (see, for example, [**1**]) and to the derivation of exact solutions to special problems [**2**], it is the writer's conviction that there exists a paucity of effective approximation techniques of general applicability. It is the purpose of the present paper to present several truncated hierarchy methods that appear to have promise.

In general, a hierarchy of the type considered here is obtained from a stochastic linear differential equation by multiplication by the stochastic coefficient an arbitrary number of times with each factor involving a different value of its argument. The hierarchy can either be averaged or left as is. The hierarchy can be truncated at a given member by a suitable approximation yielding a finite sequence of equations with a consistent number of dependent variables. Truncated hierarchy methods apparently are not well known in most areas of mathematical research although in theoretical physics they are used extensively: for example, the Tamm–Dancoff method [**3**], the Green's function method of Martin and Schwinger [**4**], and the BBGKY hierarchy with various truncation approximations [**5**].

In the succeeding paragraphs we develop three related truncated hierarchy methods and apply them to a very elementary stochastic linear differential equation chosen for purposes of illustration. However, it is clear that the same methods with rather trivial extensions can be applied to equations involving general stochastic linear operators. The present investigation has a somewhat exploratory character and is pursued at a rather low level of rigor.

2. **Formulation of the problem.** Specifically, it is desired to apply various truncated hierarchy methods to the simple stochastic differential equation for the t-dependent scalar variable x:

$$\frac{d^2x}{dt^2} + (1 + u)x = 0, \qquad x(0) = c_1, \qquad \frac{dx}{dt}(0) = c_2, \tag{2.1}$$

[1] See, for example, the contribution of A. T. Bharucha-Reid to this volume.

where c_1 and c_2 are nonrandom constants, and where $u = u(t)$ is a stationary random process with zero mean whose further properties will be defined later. It follows that $x = x(t)$ is also a random process but not necessarily with zero mean. The general problem is then the determination of the statistical properties of $x(t)$ given those of $u(t)$. For the sake of brevity this paper will treat only the problem of determining the mean value of $x(t)$. The considerably more complicated problem of calculating the further statistical properties of $x(t)$ (e.g., the second and higher order correlation functions) will be treated in a future communication.

3. **Perturbation theory.** It is instructive to review the application of the usual perturbation method to the solution of the above problem and the deficiencies of this method will provide a motivation for the search for more sophisticated procedures. By the term perturbation method we simply mean the following. Let u in (2.1) be replaced by εu, where ε is a parameter of smallness, with the result

$$\frac{d^2x}{dt^2} + (1 + \varepsilon u)x = 0 \tag{3.1}$$

where the initial conditions of (2.1) are retained. Now, the solution of (3.1) depends[2] also upon the parameter ε, namely $x = x(t, \varepsilon)$. The solution of the original problem defined by (2.1) is of course regained by setting $\varepsilon = 1$. The perturbation method then consists in expanding x in a power series in ε and then solving the sequence of equations obtained by substituting the series in (3.1) and setting to zero the resultant coefficient of each power of ε.

Before going further into the application of the perturbation method it is illustrative to consider the properties of the exact solution for the special case in which u is independent of t. The exact solution of (3.1) is then

$$x = \text{Re}\{[c_1 - ic_2(1 + \varepsilon u)^{-1/2}] \exp [it(1 + \varepsilon u)^{1/2}]\}. \tag{3.2}$$

Writing x in the power series

$$x(t, \varepsilon) = \sum_{n=0} x_n(t)\varepsilon^n, \tag{3.3}$$

we find that the first two orders of $x_n(t)$ are given by

$$\begin{aligned} x_0(t) &= \text{Re}\,[(c_1 - ic_2)\, e^{it}], \\ x_1(t) &= \tfrac{1}{2}\,\text{Re}\,\{[c_1uit + ic_2u(1 - it)]\, e^{it}\}. \end{aligned} \tag{3.4}$$

It is to be noted that the second of (3.4) oscillates with increasing amplitude as $t \to \infty$ because of the linear dependence on t in the coefficient of e^{it}. This is the well-known secular term difficulty. The expression for $x_n(t)$ will involve a factor

[2] It is tacitly understood that x is also a function of c_1 and c_2, and a functional of $u(t)$.

of t^n multiplied into e^{it}. Thus we see that the asymptotic behavior of x_n (as $t \to \infty$) becomes progressively worse as n increases. Taking the mean values of x_n does not improve the asymptotic behavior (except for $n = 1$, in which case the mean of x_1 vanishes).

Consider now the case in which u is dependent upon t. The perturbation method gives the following sequence of coupled equations

$$\left(\frac{d^2}{dt^2} + 1\right) x_0 = 0, \tag{3.5}$$
$$\left(\frac{d^2}{dt^2} + 1\right) x_n = -ux_{n-1}, \qquad n = 1, 2, \cdots,$$

with the initial conditions

$$x_0(0) = c_1, \qquad \frac{dx_0}{dt}(0) = c_2, \tag{3.6}$$
$$x_n(0) = 0, \qquad \frac{dx_n}{dt}(0) = 0, \qquad n = 1, 2, \cdots.$$

The zeroth order solution is

$$x_0 = A \sin(t + \theta), \tag{3.7}$$

where

$$A^2 = c_1^2 + c_2^2, \tag{3.8}$$
$$\tan \theta = c_1/c_2.$$

The higher order solutions are obtained by repeated application of the recursion relation

$$x_n(t) = -\int_0^t dt' \sin(t - t')u(t')x_{n-1}(t') \tag{3.9}$$

with the results

$$x_1 = -\int_0^t dt' \sin(t - t')u(t')x_0(t'), \tag{3.10}$$
$$x_2 = \int_0^t dt' \int_0^{t'} dt'' \sin(t - t') \sin(t' - t'')u(t')u(t'')x_0(t''), \text{ etc.}$$

Denoting the mean value of a quantity by surrounding it by the angular brackets $\langle\,\rangle$, we obtain finally

$$\langle x_0(t)\rangle = x_0(t) = A \sin(t + \theta),$$
$$\langle x_1(t)\rangle = 0, \tag{3.11}$$
$$\langle x_2(t)\rangle = A \int_0^t dt' \int_0^{t'} dt'' \sin(t - t') \sin(t' - t'')C(t' - t'') \sin(t'' + \theta), \text{ etc.,}$$

where $C(\tau)$ is the second order correlation function of $u(t)$ given by

$$C(\tau) = \langle u(t)u(t+\tau)\rangle. \tag{3.12}$$

Since $u(t)$ is assumed to be a stationary process, the r.h. side of (3.12) is independent of t. Integration of the third equation of (3.11) on t' gives

$$\begin{aligned}\langle x_2(t)\rangle = \tfrac{1}{4}A\int_0^t ds\, C(s)\sin s \\ \cdot [\cos(t-s+\theta) - \cos(t-s-\theta) - 2(t-s)\cos(t-s-\theta)].\end{aligned} \tag{3.13}$$

If $C(s)$ is constant, corresponding to the case previously considered in which $u(t)$ is independent of t, the asymptotic behavior of (3.13) is the same as previously stated, namely $\langle x_2(t)\rangle$ oscillates with an amplitude that increases as t^2. Consider now the case in which

$$\int_0^\infty ds\, C(s) \quad \text{and} \quad \int_0^\infty ds\, sC(s)$$

exist.[3] Now, it can be shown that $\langle x_2(t)\rangle$ oscillates with an amplitude that increases as t. In either case, the asymptotic behavior of $\langle x_2(t)\rangle$ is an unsatisfactory representation of the actual behavior of $\langle x(t)\rangle$ and one is obliged to consider other methods of solution.

4. **Hierarchies.** In developing various truncated hierarchy methods (at least as applied to (2.1)), we first define several types of hierarchies. The first type is obtained by multiplying (2.1) by factors of the form $u(t_1)$, $u(t_1)u(t_2)$, $\cdots$, $u(t_1)\cdots u(t_n)$ with the result

$$\begin{aligned}\left[\frac{d^2}{dt^2} + 1 + u(t)\right] x(t) = 0, \\ \left[\frac{d^2}{dt^2} + 1 + u(t)\right] u(t_1)x(t) = 0, \\ \left[\frac{d^2}{dt^2} + 1 + u(t)\right] u(t_1)u(t_2)x(t) = 0, \text{ etc.}\end{aligned} \tag{4.1}$$

It should be noted that the number of independent variables increases with the order of the member of the hierarchy. In subsequent work (4.1) will be called the *unaveraged hierarchy*.

[3] We exclude the uninteresting case of "white noise" in which $\int_0^\infty ds\, s^m C(s)$, $m = 1, 2, \cdots$, all vanish.

The second type of hierarchy is obtained from the first type (see (4.1)) by averaging. We obtain

$$\left(\frac{d^2}{dt^2}+1\right)\langle x(t)\rangle + \langle u(t)x(t)\rangle = 0,$$

$$\left(\frac{d^2}{dt^2}+1\right)\langle u(t_1)x(t)\rangle + \langle u(t_1)u(t)x(t)\rangle = 0, \tag{4.2}$$

$$\left(\frac{d^2}{dt^2}+1\right)\langle u(t_1)u(t_2)x(t)\rangle + \langle u(t_1)u(t_2)u(t)x(t)\rangle = 0, \text{ etc.}$$

The above mean values are well defined by virtue of the fact that $x(t)$ is a functional of $u(t)$ and the statistical properties of $u(t)$ are assumed to be completely specified. It is not in general possible to compute the above mean values directly, but it is possible to infer them indirectly from the hierarchy. (4.2) are subject to the initial conditions

$$\langle x(t)\rangle|_{t=0} = c_1, \qquad \frac{d}{dt}\langle x(t)\rangle|_{t=0} = c_2,$$

$$\langle u(t_1)x(t)\rangle|_{t=0} = 0, \qquad \frac{d}{dt}\langle u(t_1)x(t)\rangle|_{t=0} = 0, \tag{4.3}$$

$$\langle u(t_1)u(t_2)x(t)\rangle|_{t=0} = \langle u(t_1)u(t_2)\rangle c_1,$$

$$\frac{d}{dt}\langle u(t_1)u(t_2)x(t)\rangle = \langle u(t_1)u(t_2)\rangle c_2, \text{ etc.}$$

Henceforth we will call (4.3) the *averaged hierarchy*.

The above equations ((4.2) and (4.3)) suffice for the determination of the mean value of $\langle x(t)\rangle$ and all correlation functions that are linear in $x(t)$. In order to determine $\langle x(t)x(t')\rangle$ and all correlation functions linear in $x(t)x(t')$ (a task beyond the scope of the present paper) it would be necessary to consider a somewhat more complex hierarchy obtained by multiplying every member of (4.1) by $x(t')$ and then averaging. The still higher order statistical properties of $x(t)$ would involve the derivation of still more complex hierarchies by analogous procedures.

5. **Truncation approximations.** Since it is not possible in the general case to solve the averaged hierarchy (4.2) with the associated initial conditions (4.3), it is necessary to terminate or truncate the sequence at some finite (preferably low) order. Clearly, it is possible in principle to achieve an *exact* truncation at the nth order member by solving for $\langle u(t_1)\cdots u(t_n)x(t)\rangle$ in the infinite hierarchy starting with the $(n+1)$st member, thus obtaining a closed set of n equations with a compatible set of dependent variables. This finite hierarchy is precisely equivalent to the original infinite one and unfortunately the difficulties in deriving and solving the former are also precisely equivalent to the difficulties in solving the latter.

Thus, in order to obtain truncated hierarchy methods with any degree of tractability it is necessary to consider various approximate truncation procedures. We discuss three such procedures in the following paragraphs.

(a) *Correlation discard.* In the nth member of the averaged hierarchy we neglect the correlation $\langle u(t_1) \cdots u(t_{n-1})u(t)\,\Delta x(t)\rangle$, where $\Delta x(t) = x(t) - \langle x(t)\rangle$. This is equivalent to the approximation

$$\langle u(t_1) \cdots u(t_{n-1})u(t)x(t)\rangle \simeq \langle u(t_1) \cdots u(t_{n-1})u(t)\rangle\langle x(t)\rangle. \tag{5.1}$$

This approximation is equivalent to the "local independence" assumption of Bourret [6], employed in other examples.

(b) *Cumulant discard.* This approximation involves the neglect in the nth member of the averaged hierarchy of the $(n + 1)$st order cumulant (Thiele semi-invariant) corresponding to the variables $u(t), \cdots, u(t_{n-1}), u(t)$, and $\Delta x(t)$. More specifically, we neglect the quantity

$$i^{-n-1}\left[\frac{\partial^{n+1}}{\partial\lambda_1 \cdots \partial\lambda_{n-1}\partial\lambda\,\partial\mu} \log\left\langle \exp\left[i\sum_{j=1}^{n-1}\lambda_j u(t_j) + i\lambda u(t) + i\mu\Delta x(t)\right]\right\rangle\right]^0, \tag{5.2}$$

where the super zero on the square bracket implies that the auxiliary variables $\lambda_1, \cdots, \lambda_{n-1}, \lambda$, and μ are all set equal to zero after the differentiations have been performed. The neglect of (5.2) implies that the unwanted quantity in the nth member of the hierarchy, namely $\langle u(t_1) \cdots u(t_{n-1})u(t)x(t)\rangle$, is approximated by a linear combination of the lower order quantities $\langle x(t)\rangle, \langle u(t_1)x(t)\rangle, \cdots, \langle u(t_1) \cdots u(t_{n-1})x(t)\rangle$ with coefficients composed of combinations of various correlation functions of the $u(t_1)$, $u(t_2)$, etc. It is known that the second and third order cumulants are equal to the corresponding order correlation functions, namely

$$i^{-2}\left[\frac{\partial^2}{\partial\lambda\,\partial\mu}\log\langle\exp(i\lambda u(t) + i\mu\,\Delta x(t))\rangle\right]^0 = \langle u(t)\,\Delta x(t)\rangle, \tag{5.3a}$$

$$\begin{aligned} &i^{-3}\left[\frac{\partial^3}{\partial\lambda_1\,\partial\lambda\,\partial\mu}\log\langle\exp(i\lambda_1 u(t_1) + i\lambda u(t) + i\mu\,\Delta x(t))\rangle\right]^0 \\ &\qquad = \langle u(t_1)u(t)\,\Delta x(t)\rangle. \end{aligned} \tag{5.3b}$$

Thus, when applied to the first and second members of the hierarchy the correlation discard and cumulant discard procedures are identical. A difference occurs in the next order. Where one considers the fourth order cumulant

$$\begin{aligned} &i^{-4}\left[\frac{\partial^4}{\partial\lambda_1\,\partial\lambda_2\,\partial\lambda\,\partial\mu}\log\langle\exp(i\lambda_1 u(t_1) + i\lambda_2 u(t_2) + i\lambda u(t) + i\mu\,\Delta x(t))\rangle\right]^0 \\ &\qquad = \langle u(t_1)u(t_2)u(t)\,\Delta x(t)\rangle - \langle u(t_1)u(t_2)\rangle\langle u(t)\,\Delta x(t)\rangle \\ &\qquad\quad - \langle u(t_1)u(t)\rangle\langle u(t_2)\,\Delta x(t)\rangle - \langle u(t_2)u(t)\rangle\langle u(t_1)\,\Delta x(t)\rangle. \end{aligned} \tag{5.3c}$$

(c) *Least mean square error.* The third truncation procedure is substantially different from the previous two in several respects, a basic one being the fact that the procedure is applied to the *unaveraged* hierarchy. We will not define the procedure in a general way to the nth member of the hierarchy. Instead, we will illustrate the procedure for the first member of the unaveraged hierarchy (4.1), namely, the original stochastic differential equation

$$\left(\frac{d^2}{dt^2} + 1\right) x(t) + u(t)x(t) = 0. \tag{5.4}$$

To obtain an approximating linear *nonstochastic* differential equation with x as the dependent variable we proceed as follows. We approximate the troublesome term $u(t)x(t)$ as a linear functional of $x(t')$ in the range $(0, t)$, namely,

$$u(t)x(t) = w(t) + \int_0^t dt' K(t, t')x(t') + \eta(t), \tag{5.5}$$

where functions $w(t)$ and $K(t, t')$ are to be determined in such a way as to minimize the error $\eta(t)$ in the mean square sense. More specifically, we wish to minimize $\langle\eta^2(t)\rangle'$ with respect to the choice of the functions $w(t)$ and $K(t, t')$. The averaging process denoted by $\langle\,\rangle'$ need not be the same as that previously denoted by $\langle\,\rangle$. It should involve the correct statistical properties for $u(t)$ but it may differ otherwise in that $x(t)$ will not necessarily be the correct functional of $u(t)$ and the initial conditions may possibly be temporarily regarded as stochastic. It must be emphasized that the divergence of $\langle\,\rangle'$ from $\langle\,\rangle$ is not critical since if the error is small according to the criterion $\langle\eta^2 t\rangle'$ it is likely to be small also according to $\langle\eta^2(t)\rangle$ as long as $\langle\,\rangle'$ does not involve strong biases compared with $\langle\,\rangle$. In §8 a specific example of $\langle\,\rangle'$ will be treated. The procedure just outlined, when generalized to the nth order, involves the approximation of $u(t_1) \cdots u(t_{n-1})u(t)x(t)$ by a linear combination of linear functionals of $x(t)$, $u(t_1)x(t), \cdots, u(t_1) \cdots u(t_{n-1})x(t)$. These linear functionals involve integrations on t; t_1, t; t_1, t_2, t; etc.

6. **Application of correlation discard truncation.** In the present section we give a detailed discussion of the truncation procedure of paragraph (a) of the last section to the averaged hierarchy (4.2) with the initial conditions (4.3). The explicit expressions for the truncated hierarchies containing one, two, and three members will be discussed. Using the approximation (5.1) with $n = 1, 2$, and 3, respectively, we obtain the following results.

$n = 1$:

$$\left(\frac{d^2}{dt^2} + 1\right) \langle x(t)\rangle = 0, \tag{6.1a}$$

$$\langle x(0)\rangle = c_1, \qquad \frac{d}{dt}\langle x(t)\rangle\big|_{t=0} = c_2; \tag{6.1b}$$

$n = 2$:

$$\left(\frac{d^2}{dt^2} + 1\right) \langle x(t)\rangle + \langle u(t)x(t)\rangle = 0,$$

(6.2a)
$$\left(\frac{d^2}{dt^2} + 1\right) \langle u(t_1)x(t)\rangle + \langle u(t_1)u(t)\rangle\langle x(t)\rangle = 0,$$

$$\langle x(0)\rangle = c_1, \quad \frac{d}{dt}\langle x(t)\rangle|_{t=0} = c_2,$$

(6.2b)
$$\langle u(t_1)x(0)\rangle = 0, \quad \frac{d}{dt}\langle u(t_1)x(t)\rangle|_{t=0} = 0;$$

$n = 3$:

$$\left(\frac{d^2}{dt^2} + 1\right) \langle x(t)\rangle + \langle u(t)x(t)\rangle = 0,$$

(6.3a)
$$\left(\frac{d^2}{dt^2} + 1\right) \langle u(t_1)x(t)\rangle + \langle u(t_1)u(t)x(t)\rangle = 0,$$

$$\left(\frac{d^2}{dt^2} + 1\right) \langle u(t_2)u(t_1)x(t)\rangle + \langle u(t_2)u(t_1)u(t)\rangle\langle x(t)\rangle = 0,$$

$$\langle x(0)\rangle = c_1, \quad \frac{d}{dt}\langle x(t)\rangle| = c_2,$$

$$\langle u(t_1)x(0)\rangle = 0, \quad \frac{d}{dt}\langle u(t_1)x(t)\rangle|_{t=0} = 0,$$

(6.3b)
$$\langle u(t_2)u(t_1)x(0)\rangle = C(t_2 - t_1)c_1,$$

$$\frac{d}{dt}\langle u(t_2)u(t_1)x(t)\rangle|_{t=0} = C(t_2 - t_1)c_2.$$

The case of $n = 1$ is trivial since it corresponds to the neglect of u altogether and it is consequently identical to the zeroth order perturbation equation (the first of (3.5)).

The $n = 2$ case is nontrivial and will be given a detailed discussion. Let us first eliminate $\langle u(t_1)x(t)\rangle$ from the two equations in (6.2a) with the result

$$\left(\frac{d^2}{dt^2} + 1\right) \langle x(t)\rangle = \int_0^t dt' \sin(t - t')C(t - t')\langle x(t')\rangle, \tag{6.4}$$

where $C(t - t')$ is the second order correlation function of $u(t)$ given by (3.12). In lieu of a rigorous analysis of the properties of (6.4), we shall discuss several limiting cases.

If $t << C(0)$, (6.4) can be solved by iteration with the result

(6.5)
$$\langle x(t)\rangle = A \sin(t + \theta) + A\int_0^t dt' \int_0^{t'} dt'' \sin(t - t') \sin(t' - t'')\, C(t' - t'') \sin(t'' + \theta) + \cdots.$$

This expression, as far as it goes, is in exact agreement with the results of the perturbation method presented in (3.11). As might be expected, the higher order terms, not shown in (6.5), will disagree with the corresponding higher order terms of the perturbation series.

Another interesting limiting case is one in which the correlation time is short. More specifically it is assumed that

$$\int_0^\infty ds\, C(s) >> \left|\int_0^\infty s\, ds\, C(s)\right| >> \left|\int_0^\infty s^2\, ds\, C(s)\right| >> \cdots. \tag{6.6}$$

On this basis, we can with acceptable accuracy reduce (6.7) to the form

$$\frac{d^2}{dt^2}\langle x(t)\rangle + C_2\frac{d}{dt}\langle x(t)\rangle + (1 - C_1)\langle x(t)\rangle = 0, \tag{6.7}$$

where

$$C_n = \int_0^\infty s^n\, ds\, C(s). \tag{6.8}$$

It can thus be seen that if $C_2 \geqq 0$, the solution of (6.7) is bounded for all positive values of t, and in particular if $C_2 > 0$ the solution is dominated by an exponentially damped function. On the other hand if $C_2 < 0$ the solution is dominated by an exponentially growing function.

Another interesting limiting case is the one in which u is a random variable independent of t having zero mean and variance σ. It follows immediately that $C(t) = \sigma^2 =$ constant. (6.4) reduces to

$$\left(\frac{d^2}{dt^2} + 1\right)\langle x(t)\rangle - \sigma^2\int_0^t dt' \sin(t - t')\langle x(t')\rangle = 0. \tag{6.9}$$

Solution of the above integro-differential equation by use of the Laplace transform gives

$$\begin{aligned} x(t) &= \tfrac{1}{2}c_1[\cos(1 + \sigma)^{1/2}t + \cos(1 - \sigma)^{1/2}t] \\ &\quad + \tfrac{1}{2}c_2[(1 + \sigma)^{-1/2}\sin(1 + \sigma)^{1/2}t + (1 - \sigma)^{-1/2}\sin(1 - \sigma)^{1/2}t], \end{aligned} \tag{6.10}$$

where $c_1 = x(0)$ and $c_2 = (dx/dt)(0)$. This result is remarkable in that it is the *exact* solution for a particular distribution of u, namely, one in which u assumes the two values $\pm\sigma$ with equal probability.

In the case of $n = 3$, the elimination of $\langle u(t_1)x(t)\rangle$ and $\langle u(t_1)u(t_2)x(t)\rangle$ from (6.3a) with the help of the initial conditions (6.3b) yields

$$\left(\frac{d^2}{dt^2} + 1\right)\langle x(t)\rangle - \int_0^t dt'\, L(t, t')\langle x(t')\rangle = g(t), \tag{6.11}$$

where

$$L(t, t') = -\int_{t'}^t dt'' \sin(t - t'')\sin(t'' - t')\langle u(t)u(t')u(t'')\rangle, \tag{6.12}$$

$$g(t) = -\int_0^t dt' \sin(t - t')C(t - t')A\sin(t' + \theta). \tag{6.13}$$

In (6.13) the quantities A and θ are defined by (3.8). It is to be noted that the integro-differential equation of the third approximation (see (6.11)) possesses a substantially different structure from that of the corresponding equation of the second approximation. It also involves rather surprisingly the zeroth order solution (the factor $A \sin(t' + \theta)$ in (6.13)).

7. **Application of cumulant discard truncation.** As stated in paragraph (b) of §5, the cumulant discard truncation procedure is identical to the correlation discard procedure in the first and second orders ($n = 1, 2$). It is only in the next order that significant differences appear. For the case of $n = 3$ we obtain

$$\left(\frac{d^2}{dt^2} + 1\right) \langle x(t)\rangle + \langle u(t)x(t)\rangle = 0,$$

$$\left(\frac{d^2}{dt^2} + 1\right) \langle u(t_1)x(t)\rangle + \langle u(t_1)u(t)x(t)\rangle = 0,$$

(7.1)

$$\left(\frac{d^2}{dt^2} + 1\right) \langle u(t_2)u(t_1)x(t)\rangle + \langle u(t_2)u(t_1)u(t)\rangle\langle x(t)\rangle$$
$$+ \langle u(t_1)u(t_2)\rangle\langle u(t)x(t)\rangle + \langle u(t_1)u(t)\rangle\langle u(t_2)x(t)\rangle$$
$$+ \langle u(t_2)u(t)\rangle\langle u(t_1)x(t)\rangle = 0$$

subject, of course, to the initial conditions (4.3). The elimination of quantities of the type $\langle u(t')x(t)\rangle$ and $\langle u(t')u(t'')x(t)\rangle$ from the above set of equations is not elementary. It can be seen, however, that the integro-differential equation for $\langle x(t)\rangle$ obtained by the above elimination will be substantially more complicated than (6.11) resulting from the third order correlation discard approximation.

8. **Application of the least mean square error procedure.** In the present section we discuss the use of the procedure of paragraph (c) of §5, in the first order case ($n = 1$). To review our earlier statements, we consider the first member of the unaveraged hierarchy (4.1), namely,

(8.1) $$\left(\frac{d^2}{dt^2} + 1\right) x(t) + u(t)x(t) = 0$$

and approximate $u(t)x(t)$ by the least mean square error procedure discussed previously. This procedure involves the minimization of the mean square error $\langle \eta^2(t)\rangle'$ where according to (5.5) the error is given by

(8.2) $$\eta(t) = u(t)x(t) - w(t) - \int_0^t dt'\, K(t, t')x(t').$$

The next step is to minimize $\langle \eta^2(t)\rangle'$ with respect to $w(t)$ and $K(t, t')$. However, before taking this step we must make more precise the meaning of $\langle\,\rangle'$ (as contrasted with $\langle\,\rangle$). As stated before, we will retain the given statistical properties of $u(t)$.

However, we will use the perturbation method of §3 to determine $x(t)$ as an approximate functional of $u(t)$. We will also regard for the moment that c_1 and c_2 are not constant but are random in such a way that A given by (3.8) is a constant and θ also given by (3.8) is random with a uniform probability distribution in the interval $(0, 2\pi)$.

In applying the perturbation method of §3, we proceed in an unrigorous and experimental way. As a first step, let us apply the perturbation method to the zeroth order. We then obtain to this order

$$\eta(t) = u(t)x_0(t) - w(t) - \int_0^t dt' K(t, t')x_0(t'), \tag{8.3}$$

whereupon the minimization of $\langle \eta^2(t) \rangle'$ with respect to $w(t)$ and $K(t, t')$ gives $w(t) = 0$ and $\int_0^t dt' K(t, t') \cos (t' - t'') = 0$. A sufficient condition for the vanishing of the last integral is the vanishing of $K(t, t')$; however, if we require that $K(t, t') = K(t - t')$, the vanishing of $K(t - t')$ is a necessary *and* sufficient condition.

Thus, the use of the zeroth order perturbation approximation for $x(t)$ in $\eta(t)$ leads to trivial results and it is clear that this situation arises from the fact that, due to the low order of approximation, the term $u(t)x(t)$ of $\eta(t)$ disappeared from the variational problem. To rectify this, we replace the zeroth order approximation into $u(t)x(t)$ by the first order obtaining

$$\eta(t) = u(t)[x_0(t) + x_1(t)] - w(t) - \int_0^t dt' K(t, t')x_0(t'), \tag{8.4}$$

where $x_1(t)$ is given by (3.10) of §3. Minimization of $\langle \eta^2(t) \rangle'$ with the new approximate expression yields $w(t) = 0$ and

$$\int_0^t dt' \, [K(t, t') + \sin (t - t')C(t - t')] \cos (t' - t'') = 0. \tag{8.5}$$

It is clear that a sufficient condition for the vanishing of (8.5) is that

$$K(t, t') = - \sin (t - t')C(t - t'). \tag{8.6}$$

However, if we require in advance that $K(t, t') = K(t - t')$ then it follows that (8.6) is a necessary *and* sufficient condition. It is to be remarked that (8.4) does not represent a consistent perturbation expansion of $\eta(t)$. The rationale behind the above procedure is that every term in $\eta(t)$ involving $x(t)$ is treated in the lowest order that will insure its survival in the minimization of the mean square error.

Proceeding further, it follows that according to the last least mean square error procedure, the term $u(t)x(t)$ of (8.1) is to be approximated in the manner below:

$$u(t)x(t) \cong - \int_0^t dt' \sin (t - t')C(t - t')x(t') \tag{8.7}$$

and consequently (8.1) reduces to

$$\left(\frac{d^2}{dt^2} + 1\right) x(t) - \int_0^t dt' \sin (t - t')C(t - t')x(t') = 0. \tag{8.8}$$

The mean value of (8.8) is identical to the second order approximation resulting from both the correlation and cumulant discard procedures.

The same type of truncation procedure could be applied to later members of the unaveraged hierarchy. However, in the interest of brevity such considerations are excluded from this paper.

9. **Discussion.** In the preceding paragraphs, the derivation of the average solution of the simple stochastic differential equation (2.1) was treated by three different methods, all involving truncated hierarchies. Two kinds of hierarchies have been considered: the unaveraged hierarchy (see (4.1)) and the averaged hierarchy (see (4.2)). Two types of truncation procedures have been applied to the averaged hierarchy, namely, correlation discard and cumulant discard. The unaveraged hierarchy has been truncated by means of the least mean square error method. We now compare the results of these procedures.

When the averaged hierarchy is truncated at the first member by either correlation or cumulant discard, the result is identical to the solution of the original differential equation with the stochastic coefficient set equal to zero. In the truncation of the first member of the unaveraged hierarchy by the least mean square error procedure the same result is obtained if in the computation of the mean square error the dependence of $x(t)$ on $u(t)$ is treated by zeroth order perturbation theory.

However, if the averaged hierarchy is truncated at the second member by either correlation or cumulant discard, the result is more interesting. After appropriate eliminations of variables, we find that the average $x(t)$ approximately satisfies the integro-differential equation

$$(9.1) \qquad \left(\frac{d^2}{dt^2} + 1\right) \langle x(t)\rangle - \int_0^t dt' \sin(t - t')C(t - t')\langle x(t')\rangle = 0,$$

where $C(t - t') = \langle u(t)u(t')\rangle$. In the case of the *first* member of the unaveraged hierarchy an identical result (after averaging) is obtained if in the least mean square error procedure a higher order perturbation approximation is used for the relation between $x(t)$ and $u(t)$ as discussed at the end of §8. This result suggests that the mean least square error truncation procedure may be basically more powerful since when it is applied with suitable refinement to the first member of the unaveraged hierarchy, it gives (after a final averaging) the same result as the other truncation procedures applied to the second member of the averaged hierarchy.

The integro-differential equation (9.1) was investigated to a limited extent and the following properties were established:

(a) For $t << C(0)$ the solution of (9.1) is identical to the result of the perturbation method carried to the second order.

(b) If u is time-independent, that is, the correlation function $C(t) = \sigma^2 =$ const., the solution of (9.1) is exact if it is assumed to take the values $\pm\sigma$ with equal probability.

(c) The solution of (9.1) is in some cases bounded as $t \to \infty$, depending upon the correlation function $C(t)$, while the perturbation method never yields bounded solutions (except in the trivial case where $\int_0^\infty dt\, t^n C(t) = 0,\ n \geqq 1$).

Although much remains to be done in the study of (9.1), the above properties suggest that truncated hierarchy techniques have promise, at least as applied in the above manner.

The correlation discard and cumulant discard procedures yield quite different results when applied to the third member of the averaged hierarchy. Further study is required in order to understand the nature of these results.

In this paper only one statistical property of $x(t)$, namely $\langle x(t) \rangle$, has been considered. The extension of the methods discussed here to the calculation of higher order statistical properties (e.g., $\langle \Delta x(t)\, \Delta(t') \rangle$, etc.) will be treated in a future communication.

References

1. A. T. Bharucha-Reid, *On random operator equations in Banach spaces*, Bull. Acad. Polon. Sci. Sér. Sci. Math. Astronom. Phys. **1** (1959), 561–564.
2. F. Dyson, *The dynamics of a disordered linear chain*, Phys. Rev. **92** (1953), 1331–1338.
3. I. Tamm, *Relativistic interaction of elementary particles*, J. Phys. (USSR) **9** (1945), 449.
4. P. C. Martin and J. Schwinger, *Theory of many-particle systems*. I, Phys. Rev. (2) **115** (1959), 1342–1373.
5. N. N. Bogoliubov, *Problems of a dynamical theory in statistical physics*, Studies in statistical mechanics, de Boer and G. E. Uhlenbeck, eds., pp. 5–116, North-Holland, Amsterdam, 1962.
6. R. C. Bourret, *Stochastically perturbed fields, with applications to wave propagation in random media*, Nuovo Cimento (10) **26** (1962), 1–31.

Hughes Research Laboratories,
Malibu, California

AUTHOR INDEX

Italic numbers refer to pages on which a complete reference to a work by the author is given.

Roman numbers refer to pages on which a reference is made to a work of the author. For example, under Minkowski would be the page on which a statement like the following occurs: "This theorem was proved earlier by Minkowski [7, §2] in the following manner . . ."

Boldface numbers indicate the first page of articles in this volume.

SUBJECT INDEX